GLOSSARY *of* MARITIME TECHNOLOGY

Edited By
N S Swindells
CEng FIMarE

Published by the Institute of Marine Engineers

GLOSSARY *of* MARITIME TECHNOLOGY

Edited By
N S Swindells
CEng FIMarE

Published by the Institute of Marine Engineers

Published by the Institute of Marine Engineers
The Memorial Building
76 Mark Lane
London
EC3R 7JN

Copyright © 1997 The Institute of Marine Engineers

A Charity Registered in England and Wales
Reg. No 212992

A CIP catalogue record for this book is available from the
British Library.

ISBN 0 907206 90 5

Typeset in Palatino

General Editor: J R. Harris
Cover Design: B. Carew

Printed by Arrowhead Books Ltd, 14 Portman Road, Reading, Berkshire, RG30 1LZ

CONTENTS

Greek Alphabet

The letters of the Greek alphabet are frequently used in technical terms.
They are given here to provide a convenient form of reference.

A	α	alpha	a	N	ν	nu	n
B	β	beta	b	Ξ	ξ	xi	x
Γ	γ	gamma	g	O	o	omicron	o
Δ	δ	delta	d	Π	π	pi	p
E	ε	epsilon	e	P	ρ	rho	r
Z	ζ	zeta	z	Σ	σ	sigma	s
H	η	eta	e	T	τ	tau	t
Θ	θ	theta	t	Y	υ	upsilon	u
I	ι	iota	i	Φ	φ	phi	p
K	κ	kappa	k	X	χ	chi	k
Λ	λ	lambda	l	Ψ	ψ	psi	p
M	μ	mu	m	Ω	ω	omega	o

GLOSSARY OF MARITIME TECHNOLOGY TERMS

Introduction

Fully updated and revised to reflect the many changes and developments within the Marine Industry, this update of the 1980 *Glossary of Marine Technology Terms* takes into consideration the Institute's ever expanding involvement in all things maritime. This new edition, in addition to expanding the range of existing marine technology terms, includes specialist terms relating to shipping management, nautical activities, offshore exploration, naval architecture, marine electrical, marine petroleum technology and the Royal Navy. Covering all these individual subjects in depth would require several volumes, therefore, this selection aims to focus on those terms most likely to be encountered every day within our industry.

There are over 30 explanatory diagrams contributing to a better understanding of the meaning of individual terms.

This edition also contains many of the definitions and formulae which are part of the Marine Safety Agency examinations for Certificates of Competency and will be useful to those taking these examinations, whether they be deck or engineering officers. SI units have been widely used but other metric or imperial units have been included where appropriate.

Much of the information contained in the glossary has been gleaned from various books and papers available within the Institute of Marine Engineer's, Marine Information Centre and anyone seeking a more in-depth knowledge of any particular entry in this glossary, should have no hesitation in using this facility.

Using this Glossary

The illustrations have been inserted in the text at the point where they are first mentioned and may be referred to later under other related entries. For general convenience the illustrations are listed in full at the end of the glossary. **Bold** within the text has been used to denote where additional information is available under another heading.

There are three appendices, Conversion Factors, Elemental Symbols and Atomic Weights, and Lubricant and Grease Classifications.

Norman S Swindells

A

Abaft
Position on a ship near the **stern**.

Abeam
Another ship or object, on either side of and in line with a ship.

Abaft the beam
Term referring to another ship or shore location to the rear of a line drawn across the **beam** of a ship.

Abandon ship
To leave a ship in an emergency such as sinking.

Abandonment
The right of a marine assured to abandon property to establish a **constructive total loss.** Underwriters are not obliged to accept abandonment, however, if they do, they accept responsibility for the property and liabilities attached thereto, in addition to liability for the full sum insured.

Able seaman
Experienced seaman competent to perform customary duties on deck.

Abort
Halt or abandon a course of action.

A-bracket
Bracket resembling the letter A lying on its side. Certain multiple-screw merchant ships and many warships have **propeller shafts** extending outside the hull, forward of the **stern post.** Such shafts are supported by a bearing in an A-bracket attached to the hull.

Abrasive wear
The **scraping** or **scoring** of gear teeth caused by solid particles supported in lubricating oil, combined with the sliding effect of one tooth over another. Particles cut furrows in the engaging surfaces in the direction of sliding. Abrasion, as a common wear mechanism, relates to foreign particles within machinery of such size and hardness as to promote the removal of metal. In diesel engines this is characterised by the appearance of fine scratches or fairly regularly spaced grooves in the direction of movement on the contact surfaces of the mating components.

Abrasives
Materials such as sandstone, quartz, emery, corundum, silicon carbide, aluminium oxide and diamonds used for grinding, honing and polishing.

Abscissa
The x co-ordinate of a graph. This is the quantity represented by a point on a curve measured horizontally from the axis of the graph. Distances to the right of the axis are positive; to the left negative.

ABS
American Bureau of Shipping. Premier American classification society founded in 1862.

Absolute humidity
Mass of vapour present in a volume of dry air, expressed in g/cm^3.

Absolute temperature
Temperature above absolute zero where heat is entirely absent. Absolute zero is - 273.16°C. The **SI unit** is the **kelvin (K)**. To convert kelvin to Celsius, add 273.16.

Absolute viscosity
Also known as dynamic viscosity. Force required to move 1 sq cm of plane surface at a speed of 1 cm/sec relative to another parallel plane surface from which it is separated by a layer of liquid 1cm thick. This viscosity is expressed in $dynes/cm^2$, its unit being the poise which is 1 $dyne\text{-}sec/cm^2$. The centipoise (cP) is a more convenient unit in common use. The **SI unit** of absolute viscosity is the pascal second (Pa/s). The corresponding numerically equal **SI unit** to the centipoise (cP) is the millipascal second (mPa/s).

Absorber
In the oil industry, an apparatus where gases or vapours are brought into contact with the fluid in which they are to be dissolved. In the nuclear industry, a term for material used to remove **radiation** either wholly or in part, or to cause it to lose **energy.**

Absorption
Process by which one substance draws into itself another substance, such as a sponge absorbing moisture or a liquid absorbing another liquid or gas.

Abyssalbenthic zone
Area of the sea deeper than 1000 metres.

ACAF
Alternating Current Anti Fouling. Technology that claims to prevent barnacle larvae from settling and growing by deploying an alternating current on

the submerged surface of a ship's hull.

Acceleration
Rate of change of **velocity** (speed) or the average increase of velocity in a unit of time, usually expressed in m/s^2. Angular acceleration is the rate of increase of rotational velocity expressed in radians per second per second.

Accelerometer
Instrument for measuring **acceleration.** Can also be used to obtain readings of **displacement** and **velocity** and to measure shock and **vibration.**

Acception tests
Tests carried out on a ship, its machinery and equipment to check quality and performance. Must be carried out in the presence of the owners representative, a government inspector, a **classification society** and other interested parties. May also be performed on machinery or equipment prior to installation.

Accommodation (Crew)
Space in a ship for sleeping, mess rooms, wash rooms and recreation.

Accommodation ladder
Portable ladder that can be attached to a platform at either side of the ship and positioned to give access to the ship from water or shore.

Accommodation platform
Platform or **semi-submersible rig** adapted as a hotel for offshore personnel.

Accumulated pitch error
Algebraic sum of all pitch errors in any arc or number of **gear teeth.**

Accumulation test
Test on boilers to ensure **safety valves** can release steam fast enough to prevent pressure rising by 10 per cent. The main steam valve must be closed while testing takes place.

Accumulator
(1) Electric storage battery. British Standards apply for lead-acid and alkaline types. (2) Kierselbach accumulator of thermal storage enables a boiler to cope with heavy demands for steam. (3) Accumulators can be used to store liquid and gases at constant pressure, acting as a reservoir such as a liquid refrigerant in the low pressure side of a **refrigeration system.**

Acidisation
Stimulation technique used in oil well production where acid (generally some form of hydrochloric) is injected into the reservoir rock, thereby enlarging the pore spaces and increasing the flow of oil.

Acidity
Amount of free acid in a substance. In lubricating oils acidity may be due to weak (**organic**) or strong (**inorganic**) acids. Measurement is by the **neutralisation number.**

Acoustics
Science of sound dealing with its **propagation, transmission** and effects.

Acrid
Sharp or harsh to the taste or smell.

Active gear oil
The terms *active* and *mild* as applied to gear oils refer to the chemical nature of the compounding agents added to the **mineral** or **synthetic** base, and to the chemical reaction which takes place on the surface of the gear teeth designed to prevent scuffing. *Active* is the more severe reaction.

Actuator
Motor providing rotary or linear motion.

ACV
Air Cushion Vehicle. Craft riding on a cushion of air over water and land. Air pressure is maintained beneath the vehicle by power driven rotors or fans. *See also* **hovercraft.**

Added Mass
Total hydrodynamic force per unit **acceleration** exerted on a ship or other body proportional to the acceleration.

Addendum
Part of the working surface of a **gear tooth** which is towards the tip of the tooth above the pitch line. *See* Figure 1.

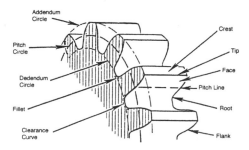

Figure 1 Gear Teeth Nomenclature

Addendum angle
Difference between the tip angle and the pitch angle of a **bevel gear.**

Additives
Chemical substance added to a petroleum product to impart or improve certain properties. May be used in fuel oil to improve **combustion** and prevent the formation of deposits such as corrosive oxides of vanadium which may collect on **superheater tubes.** In the case of lubricating oils, chemicals may be added to affect either the chemical or physical characteristics. Anti-oxidants, wear-reducing agents, **detergent/dispersants, alkali** and anti-bacterial additives are used to improve the chemical characteristics. To improve the physical characteristics chemicals may be added to prevent **foaming,** reduce the **pour point,** improve the **viscosity index,** and to prevent **emulsification.**

Adhesion
Frictional grip between two surfaces in contact.

Adhesives
Used to unite materials so they adhere permanently. An adhesive should wet the surfaces being bonded and, on solidification, should not disrupt the bond. There are many kinds of adhesives, both organic and inorganic.

Adiabatic Expansion
Change of volume and pressure of a gas under such conditions that no heat is added or subtracted from it and no losses occur from friction or eddies. The law of expansion is PV^n = a constant.

$n = 1 4$ for air at normal temperature.

Admiralty coefficient
For comparing a ships performance based on displacement, speed and horsepower defined by the formula:

$$\frac{speed^3 \times displacement^{2/3}}{ships\ power}$$

Should be used on similar ships of about the same speed. Large variations in its value occur depending on the length and speed of a vessel. Ship's power is usually given as shaft **horse power** or brake horse power. Values for merchant ships usually range between 400 and 600. High coefficients indicate economical propulsion, that is speed with relatively low power.

Admittance
Ratio of the **root-mean-square (rms)** values of current and voltage in a circuit. The reciprocal of **impedance.**

Adrift
To float at random, such as a ship broken away from its moorings left at the mercy of the wind and waves.

Adsorption
Process involving the taking up of one substance at the surface of another. A solid removes a substance from a gas or liquid by holding an extremely thin layer of the substance on its surface.

Advance
Distance travelled by centre of gravity of a ship, after the instant the **rudder** is put over, in a direction parallel to the original course.

Adze
Shipwrights tool for shaping wood.

Aerobic bacteria
Microbes that live and grow only in the presence of oxygen.

AFR
*A*ir *F*uel *R*atio.

AFRA
*A*verage *F*reight *R*ate *A*ssessment. Published monthly, an assessment of tanker freight, time charter rates and other useful information relating to the tanker business.

Aft
Near or towards the **stern**.

After Body
Portion of a ship's hull **abaft** the midship point.

After burning
(1) Combustion continued in **internal combustion engines** after exhaust ports or valves are opened. The resulting flame in the exhaust system can ignite carbon or oil deposits, or result in high temperature corrosion of the **exhaust valves**. Can cause **knocking** after burning due to faulty injectors or a lack of compression, however, is deliberately promoted in petrol engines to reduce harmful exhaust emissions. **(2)** Combustion in uptake from a boiler caused by burner faults. **(3)** Fuel injected into jet engine exhaust to give additional **thrust** on take off.

Aftercooler
Heat exchanger fitted between **turbo-charger** and engine air-inlet manifold to cool the incoming air. Also called intercooler.

After peak
A **watertight** compartment between rear watertight bulkhead and stern.

After perpendicular
Line drawn perpendicular to the waterline where the after edge of the **rudder post** meets the summer **load line**. In cases where no **rudder post** is fitted, the centreline of the **rudder stock** is taken. *See* Figure 2.

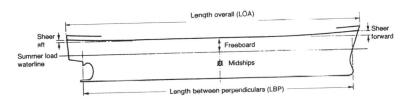

Figure 2 Ship Terms, Longitudinal

Age hardening
See **precipitation hardening.**

Agitators
Mixing devices used to bring about intimate contact between liquids or solutions of dissolved solids, or to keep solids suspended in liquids.

AGMA
American Gear Manufacturers Association.

AHR
Antwerp-Hamburg Range of ports.

AIMU
American Institute of Marine Underwriters.

Air compressor
Machine compressing air from low pressure at the intake valve to high pressure at discharge. Can be reciprocating or rotary.

Air conditioning
Treatment of air to suit climatic conditions that involve machinery used to raise or lower temperature and in some cases to control dust, odours and bacteria.

Air cooler
Consists of battery of finned tubes, the material depending on the cooling medium. When warm humid air is exposed to the chilled surfaces of the

cooler, coming into contact with the finned tubes, the air is cooled to a mean surface temperature. If this is below its **dew-point**, moisture is deposited.

Air ejectors
Used to extract air from surface condensing plants. Air and vapour from the **condenser** is sucked out and cooled by a steam jet ejector. The water condensate is returned to the system and the air is returned to the atmosphere.

Air gap
Distance between sea surface and underside of rig; must be larger in bad weather.

Air heaters
Air is heated through the medium of steam, water, electricity or gas. Steam or water heaters consisting of tube banks that contain a heating medium around which air passes. The steam is at a relatively low pressure and electric air heaters are convenient for small systems while gas air heaters have considerable industrial application.

Air lock
(1) Compartment with air-tight door at each end. **(2)** Bubble of air in a pipe stopping flow of liquid.

Air pipe
Ventilation pipe fitted to liquid storage tanks allowing filling or emptying to take place without significant pressure changes within the tank.

Air receiver
Vessel for storing compressed air.

Aldis lamp
Hand held electric lamp fitted with a finger operated mirror; used for sending signals at sea.

Algae
Group of marine plants ranging from single cell varieties to large **kelps**.

Algorithm
Defined sequence of operations to be taken to solve a problem.

Align
In **electronics**, to adjust two or more **resonant** circuits.

Alignment gauge
Instrument used to check the alignment of an engine **crankshaft**.

Aliphatic hydrocarbons
Comprised of **hydrocarbons** with carbon atoms joined in open chains rather than rings. Examples would be **ethane, propane,** and **butane.**

Alkali
Hydroxide or carbonate of an alkali metal such as calcium, lithium, sodium, or potassium. Used as an additive to neutralise acids.

Alkalinity
Extent to which a solution is alkaline. *See also* **pH value.**

Alkane
General name for unsaturated **hydrocarbons** of the methane series, of general formula C_nH_{2n+2}.

Alkyd resins
Tough, hard, durable products with excellent adhesion to most surfaces. Paints based on alkyd media are quick drying, more durable and of improved appearance. Used extensively in **primers** and undercoats.

Allen key
Cranked hexagonal bar for turning socket head screws.

Allotropes
Elements such as **iron** and **carbon** that can exist in two or more states, each stable within certain limits of temperature and pressure, with widely different properties.

Alloy
Mixture of metals. Bearing metals are almost invariably alloys.

Alpha brass
Copper-zinc alloy containing up to 36 per cent zinc, consisting of a homogeneous solid solution of zinc in copper. Alpha brasses are suitable for cold working.

Alpha iron
An **allotropic** modification of pure iron that crystallises in the body-centred cubic system and is stable below 910°C. The crystallographic change is not instantaneous and consequently there is some difference between the transition temperatures on heating and cooling. In cast iron and steels the transition temperature varies with the carbon content. This phase is commonly known as **ferrite**.

Alphanumeric
Set of characters including letters, numbers and some punctuation marks.

Altar
Step in a **graving dock**.

Alternating current (ac)
Current that reverses at regular intervals of time and has alternatively positive and negative values in res‚ ⬚ ‚e to alternating voltage. Each complete reversal is termed a cycle. The number of cycles per second is the **frequency**.

Alternator
Machine that generates alternating voltage when its rotating **conductor** cuts a **magnetic field**.

Altimeter
Instrument measuring the height above sea level.

Altitude
Height of an object above sea level or the horizon.

Aluminising
Process for impregnating the surface of steel with aluminium in order to obtain protection from oxidation and corrosion. The aluminium is applied by metal spraying or dipping in molten aluminium with a suitable flux.

Aluminium (Al)
Light metal with good resistance to atmospheric corrosion. Widely used as a base metal for light alloys.

Aluminium brass
Alpha brass with aluminium added for increased resistance to **corrosion.** Mainly used as tubes for heat exchangers and pipes for sea water services. Nominal composition would be: copper 78 per cent; zinc 20 per cent; aluminium 2 per cent.

Aluminium bronze
Copper-rich alloys with aluminium as the main alloying element; often with added iron, nickel and manganese. Single phase alloys (alpha) usually contain 5–8 per cent aluminium and are used in sheet form for their tarnish resistant properties. Two phase alloys (duplex) are more widely used, and in wrought or cast form are suitable for applications where strength and resistance to marine **corrosion** are required. Nominal composition would be: 10 per cent aluminium; 5 per cent iron; 5 per cent nickel with 1–3 per cent manganese.

Ambient
Pertains to any localised condition such as temperature, humidity or atmospheric pressure.

AMD
*A*dvanced *M*ulti-hull *D*esigns.

Amidships
(1) Point midway between forward and after perpendiculars, also known as midships. The special symbol   is used to represent this point, see Figure 2. (2) Term used when **rudder** is in the fore and aft or central position.

Ammeter
Instrument for measuring electric current in amperes.

Ammonia (NH_3)
Noxious, pungent gas, extremely soluble in water and alcohol.

Amorphous
Without definite form, noncrystalline.

Ampere (A)
The **SI unit** of electrical current.

Ampere-hour
Unit of charge equal to 3600 coulombs, or 1 ampere flowing for 1 hour. Multiplying current in amperes by time of flow in hours gives ampere-hours.

Amplification
Ratio of output to input **magnitude** in a device designed to produce an increased value output.

Amplifier
Device capable of increasing the **magnitude** or power level of a physical quantity. Most amplifiers are electronic, however, pneumatic or hydraulic units may be used.

Amplitude
(1) Angle between the point at which the sun rises and sets and the true east and west points of the horizon. (2) Maximum displacement of a varying quantity, measured from some datum.

Anaerobic bacteria
Microbes that thrive in the absence of oxygen. Of particular concern are sulphate reducing bacteria (SRB) that are highly corrosive and will penetrate steel plate.

Analogue
(1) A computer using data in the form of continuously variable physical quantities. Data represents, for example, a pressure or temperature transduced into an electrical quantity, which is an analogue of the data. (2) Any

form of signal where **amplitude** or **frequency** are varied in continuously direct proportion to intensity, brightness and volume.

Analysis

Literally means 'a breaking down process', however, is now applied to any process which has the determination of the nature of the constituents of a substance (qualitative analysis) or the estimation of the quantity of one or more of the constituents (quantitative analysis) as its object.

Anchor

Device to moor a ship rendering it stationary. The main anchors carried aboard ship are of two types, stock anchors and stockless anchors as shown in Figure 3. Anchors and cables are inspected at the annual docking survey. Offshore rigs and **support vessels** often have multi anchoring systems.

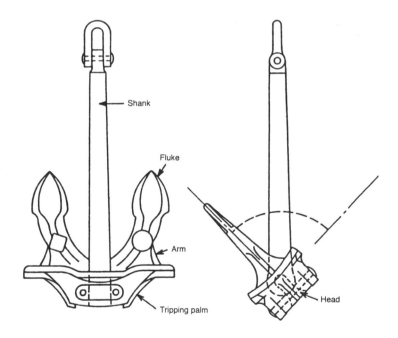

Figure 3 Stockless Anchor

Anchorage
Area off the coast where the ground is suitable for ships to lay at anchor. Often marked on charts with an anchor symbol.

Anchor handling vessel (AHV)
Ship designed to lay and retrieve rig moorings; can double as a supply ship and/or tug.

Andrew
Sailors slang name for the British Royal Navy, said to derive from an 18th century press-gang officer named Andrew Miller.

Anemometer
Instrument for measuring the speed of wind. May also indicate direction.

Andrew
Sailors slang name for the British Royal Navy, said to derive from an 18th century press-gang officer named Andrew Miller.

Anemometer
Instrument for measuring the speed of wind. May also indicate direction.

Angle of obliquity
Deviation of the direction of force between two gear teeth in contact from that of their common tangent.

Angle of repose
Angle at which a cargo settles in the hold.

Anhydrous
Substance containing no water.

Aniline point
Minimum temperature for complete mixing of equal volumes of aniline and oil under specified test conditions. An empirical measure of the solvent power of a hydrocarbon, the lower the aniline point the greater the solvency. Aromatics have low aniline points hence their desirability as fuel oil blending components.

Annealing
Process of heating metals to sufficiently high temperatures for recrystallising of the structure to occur, then cooling gradually, increasing the ductility of the material and relieving internal stresses.

Annular gears

Internal **gears** with parallel teeth similar to the **spur gear**, except they are cut on the inside rim or inner surface of a cylinder or ring. The companion pinion of an annular gear must be a standard gear.

Annulus

Name given to the annular space between **drill string** and well bore.

Anode

Positive **electrode** of an **electrolytic** cell. In electronics, the principal electrode for the collection of electrons or ions. In a system of cathodic protection sacrificial anodes, attached to a material such as steel, corrode preferentially to the steel therefore protecting it from corrosion. Sacrificial anodes mounted on the hull are made of zinc or aluminium alloy with strictly controlled composition.

Anomalous viscosity

Property exhibited by certain liquids showing a decrease of apparent viscosity as the rate of shear increases.

ANSI

American National Standards Institute.

Anti-fouling

Paint or other coating system applied to the wetted surface of a ship to prevent the adherence and growth of biological organisms such as slime, weed and shell. Such growth leads to increased resistance so that additional power and fuel are needed to maintain the same speed. The composition may include tin containing poisons (TBT) causing damage to plant life and sea animals. TBT paints are now being phased out and replacement technology includes low surface energy coatings such as teflon, silicon and electric fields combined with special coatings. *See* **ACAF** and **TBT coatings.**

Anti friction bearings

Refers to **ball and roller bearings** and thinwall type metal bearings.

Aperiodic

System that does not vibrate when subjected to impulses if sufficiently damped.

Aperture

Space between **rudder post** and **propeller post** for propeller.

Apex

Common intersection of the axes of a pair of **bevel gears** and instantaneous axis of relative motion of either gear with respect to the other, called the pitch element, that all lie in the axial plane.

API
American Petroleum Institute.

API gravity
Measure of **density** used in the American petroleum industry.

Apparent viscosity
Ratio of shear stress to rate of shear of a non-Newtonian fluid, calculated from the poiseuille equation and measured in poises. Varies with temperature and **shear** rate. Must be reported at a given shear rate and temperature.

Appraisal drilling
Wells drilled to determine both the physical extent and likely production rate of a field.

Aqueous
Watery. Usually refers to solutions where water is present.

ARA
Antwerp, Rotterdam and Amsterdam range of ports.

Arbitration
Settlement of a dispute by the appointment of an arbitrator.

Arbitrator
Person appointed by two parties to settle a dispute. Shipping contracts, which in the event of a dispute call for arbitration rather than litigation, often stipulate that the arbitrator appointed has experience in shipping.

Archibenthic zone
Area of sea 200–1000 metres in depth.

Archimedes principle
When a body is totally or partially immersed in a fluid, the apparent loss in weight is equal to the weight of the displaced fluid.

Arc blow
Deflection of the **welding** arc by the **magnetic fields** produced by the passage of direct welding currents, one of the disadvantages of dc welding.

Arc of contact
Arc on the pitch circle of a gear wheel over which two teeth are in contact. *See* Figure 1.

Arc welding
Joining metals by striking an electric arc between the parts to be joined, causing melting and fusion. The most common welding processes are the manual metal arc (MMA), submerged arc and metal inert gas (MIG).

Argon (Ar)
Inert gas present in small quantities in the earth's atmosphere. Used in electric light bulbs to prevent oxidation of the tungsten element, and in (MIG) argon arc welding to shield the molten metal from oxidation.

Armature
Part of an electrical machine, whether rotating or stationary, which carries the winding connected to the external supply and in which the principal **electro motive force (emf)** is induced. The term is usually limited to the rotating part of a dc machine, however, can also apply to an ac machine, commonly known as the stator.

Arming
Lump of grease placed on the end of a sounding lead. By examining the particles adhering to it, an indication of the character of the seabed is provided.

Aromatic hydrocarbons
Unsaturated hydrocarbons identified by one or more benzene rings and a chemical behaviour similar to **benzene**. Widely used as blending components for marine fuels due to their excellent solvency and ability to improve the compatibility of a blended product.

ARPA
*A*utomatic *R*adar *P*lotting *A*id.

Arrest
Seizure of a ship by the authority of a court of law, either as security for a debt or to prevent a ship from leaving until a dispute is settled.

Arrived ship
All voyage charters require a ship to arrive before lay time can commence. The charterer must nominate an arrival point such as a port, berth or dock.

Articulation
System of components, such as **gears** or levers, where the sharing or equalisation of a load is effected by proportioning the leverages in relation to the fulcrum. Typical is an **epicyclic** train of gears in which the input **torque** is applied via the planet carrier, and the planet wheel gears act as articulated levers sharing tooth loads between sun wheel and annulus ring. In principle, the basis of a differential gear train.

Artificial intelligence
Design of computer program or system that attempts to imitate human intelligence and decision making functions.

Asbestos
Fibrous mineral of calcium and magnesium silicates that can be woven into incombustible fabrics. Once widely used as thermal insulation for compartments and pipes, it is now illegal and a dangerous health hazard. Operators removing lagging must wear breathing apparatus and protective clothing.

ASCII
American Standard Code for Information Interchange. Eight bit computer code using seven bits to represent character data such as letters, punctuation, symbols and control characters. The eighth bit can be used for parity.

ASDIC
Anti Submarine Detection Investigation Committee. Echo sounding device for detecting underwater objects. Modern word is **sonar**.

Ash content
Non combustible residue of a lubricant or fuel. Ash normally comprises lubricant metallic additives such as calcium, phosphorus and crude oil, elements like vanadium and sodium, and catalytic fines such as aluminium and silicon.

ASME
American Society of Mechanical Engineers.

Aspect ratio
Ratio of the span to the mean chord line of an aerofoil section. For a ship's **rudder** this is the mean span or depth divided by the mean chord or width.

Asperity
(1) In **tribology**, a protuberance in the small scale topographical irregularities of a solid surface. (2) Applied to the surface of steel after blast cleaning where the use of coarse grit may produce peaks which penetrate the subsequently applied paint coating.

Asphaltenes
High molecular weight hydrocarbon components of asphalt and heavy residual stock, which may adversely affect the combustion, residue formation and **compatibility** of fuel oils.

Assemble
Preparation of a machine language programme from a programme written in symbolic language such as **BASIC** or **FORTRAN**.

Associated gas
Natural gas found in association with oil, either dissolved in the oil or as a cap of free gas above the oil.

Astern power

Power available for driving a ship astern. In direct drive diesel machinery the power available is 100 per cent of that available for ahead movement. In turbine driven ships only a proportion of ahead power is provided by separate astern stages of turbine blades, therefore, **propeller efficiency** is considerably lower when a ship is going astern. Non-direct drive ships may provide astern power through a **reversing gearbox**, electrically (diesel or turbo electric machinery), or a **controllable pitch propeller** that is able to vary the pitch to provide astern power.

ASTM

American Society for Testing Materials.

ASTM grain size (E112)

Specification defining the methods of determining grain size of metal by comparing the microstructure with standard charts.

Astronavigation

Astronomical navigation, or navigation involving observation of astronomical bodies.

Athwartship

In a direction across the ship, at right angles to the fore and aft centreline.

Atmosphere (atm)

The generally gaseous envelope surrounding a body.

Atmospheric distillation

Primary crude oil refinery distillation process carried out at normal **atmospheric pressure.**

Atmospheric plant

Tank in the feed system of a steam drain tank to which condensed water from auxiliaries heating coils, for example, are led. The tank is at atmospheric pressure.

Atmospheric pressure

Pressure equal to the downward thrust of a column of mercury 760 mm in height at $0^{\circ}C$, which is the average pressure of the earth's atmosphere at sea level. Standard atmosphere is 101325 Pa. Varies with density and altitude. The standard value is 1.01325 bar or 14.7 $lbfin^{-2}$.

Atmospheric valve

(1) Valve in a closed exhaust steam line opening to the atmosphere when pressure exceeds a certain limit. **(2)** Pressure/vacuum valve (Blundell Atmos

Valve) fitted to tank top to maintain atmospheric pressure in tank. The valve vents excessive pressure allowing air to enter tank under vacuum conditions.

Atom
Smallest chemically indivisible **particle** of an **element**.

Atomic number
Number of **electrons** or **protons** in the **atom** of an **element**.

Atomic weight
Relative weight of the average **atom** of an **element**. *See* **Appendix I**.

Atomisation
Subdivision of a material into its smallest parts, such as liquids reduced to a fine spray by diesel engine or boiler fuel injectors.

Attapulgite
Clay used in offshore salt water **drilling muds** to improve the mud's carrying capacity. Also called salt gel.

Attemporator
Heat exchanger used in the control of the final superheat temperature of steam to the main engine.

Attenuation
Reduction in current, voltage or power due to **transmission** losses; opposite of **amplification**.

Augmentor
(1) Device increasing or improving the operation or performance of a piece of equipment already in a system. (2) Steam ejector fitted to a steam reciprocating engine assisting the reciprocating air pump when the main engine is stopped.

Austenite
Allotropic form of iron (**gamma iron**). Not stable at ordinary temperatures, however, **stability** can be increased by alloying.

Austenitic
Non magnetic state of iron or iron alloy, in contrast to **ferritic**.

Auto ignition temperature
Test to determine the minimum temperature a mixture of petroleum or similar vapour and air must be raised to before **ignition** or active **combustion** will occur.

Auto start valve

Fitted in the main air line to the starting air valves of a diesel engine. Operation of the starting lever causes the valve to open and air is then supplied to the air distributor and individual cylinder starting air valves. The valve will close once the starting lever is released.

Automatic control

Control system where the value of a controlled or related condition gets compared with a desired value. A corrective action, depending on the deviation, can be taken without the intervention of a human element. The automatic-control system includes a measuring unit, controlling unit, correcting unit, and the plant being controlled. Contains a mechanism measuring the value of a process variable operating to limit the deviation of such variable from a desired value. The theory of an automatic control system is complex and has been the subject of extensive mathematical analysis. BS 1523 gives a Glossary of terms used in Automatic Controlling and Regulating Systems. Also known as Predictive Control.

Automatic pilot

Automatic control system. Many ships travel for long periods of time on a fixed course, the only deviations being those created by variations in tide, waves or wind. In such circumstances the automatic control system (automatic pilot) is most valuable. The system can sense the difference between the ordered course and the actual course and will cause the rudder to move to an angle proportional to this error. May also be described as Auto-heading or Auto-track.

Automation

Equipment incorporating monitoring and alarm surveillance. Computerised facilities for alarm recording, trend recording, automatic log keeping, performance monitoring, and automatic plant protection may also be provided.

Auto transformer

A **transformer** consisting of one electrically continuous winding with one or more fixed movable taps, so that part of the winding is common to both primary and secondary circuits.

Average adjuster

Skilled person apportioning loss and expenditure between interested parties involved in a maritime adventure or claim under a **general average** act. An expert on all aspects of marine insurance law and loss adjustments.

Average sample

Sample representing the contents of a compartment, container or sump.

AVR
*A*utomatic *V*oltage *R*egulator. Device operating to maintain the output voltage of a **generator** within predetermined limits, usually by controlling the excitation in response to load changes.

Awash
When the seas wash over a wreck or shoal, or a ship lies so low in the water that the seas wash over her.

Awning
Canvas canopy spread over the deck for protection from the sun.

Axial
In line with, or pertaining to, an axis.

Axial flow pump
A pump that is effectively a propeller in a casing that produces a large volume flow of liquid at low pressure.

Azimuth thruster
A **thruster** that can rotate through 360 degrees, fixed or retractable.

B

Babbit's metal
Non-ferrous anti-friction bearing alloy consisting of tin, copper, and antimony. Originated by Isaac Babbit. Typical composition (according to BSS 3332/2): 87 per cent tin; 9 per cent antimony; 4 per cent copper.

Backlash
Lost angular motion in a mechanical transmission system due to the working clearance between components. Excessive backlash in a geared system is generally caused by wear to the gear teeth and/or bearings.

Back pressure
Pressure on the exhaust side of an engine or system. The system's output or efficiency can be reduced if the back pressure exceeds the designed value.

Back spring
Mooring line led from a shoulder pipe aft to a **bollard** ashore or from a quarter pipe in a forward direction.

Backup
(1) Process of saving all computer data to an alternative medium such as a

floppy disc, magnetic tape or file server. (2) Term to describe the process where one section of a drill pipe is held stationary using tongs while another section is screwed into or out of it.

Bailer
Long cylindrical container fitted with a valve at its lower end; used to remove water, sand, oil or mud from a well.

Bainite
Acicular constituent of steel formed when **austenite** is **isothermally** transformed at a temperature between that which forms **pearlite** and **martensite**.

Balance weight
Weight used to counterbalance an out of balance force in a machine.

Balanced rudder
A **rudder** type in which a proportion of the rudder area, 25–30 per cent, is forward of the axis of turning. This is to reduce the operating **torque** required at the **rudder stock,** as the effective centre of pressure acting on a balanced rudder is closer to the rudder stock axis. *See* Figure 4.

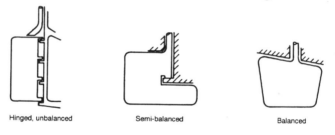

Hinged, unbalanced   Semi-balanced   Balanced

Figure 4 Types Of Rudder

Balancing
Means of reducing **vibration** in a reciprocating engine, by balancing forces.

Ball and roller bearings
Ball and roller bearings have low **friction** losses as the relative movement between two surfaces is accommodated by the rolling motion of intermediary case hardened spheres or cylinders. Such bearings are extensively used as journal or thrust bearings in shafting systems where cleanliness of the lubrication can be guaranteed. Roller bearing should be employed at higher load factors.

Ballast
Any solid mass or liquid positioned in a ship to change its trim, increase draught or improve seaworthiness.

Ballast line
Piping system used to fill and empty **ballast** tanks.

Baltic Exchange
The full name is Baltic Mercantile & Shipping Exchange. Located in London its main function is to provide facilities for the chartering of ships. Other activities include air chartering, futures trading, ship sale, and purchase.

Bandwidth
Range of frequency required for radio transmission.

Bar(b)
(1) Meteorological unit of atmospheric pressure. Absolute cgs unit of pressure equal to 1 dyne/sq cm. One bar = 1.02 kg/sq cm = 14.50 psi. The **SI unit** of pressure is the Pascal and 1 bar = 100 kPa (SI). (2) Bank across a river mouth or harbour entrance. Depth of water at the bar varies with the tide, imposing a limitation on the draught of ships that can cross.

Bareboat charter
Type of charter where the entire responsibility for maintaining a ship in good repair and the manning falls upon the **charterer**. The charterer must carry out all repairs necessary to maintain the vessel's class during the charter. This type of charter is infrequent as **shipowners** will not readily agree to the temporary transfer of management and control to charterers.

Barge rig
Drilling rig on non-propelled barge, used in the shallow waters of coastal regions

Barite
Barium Sulphate ($BaSo_4$). Mineral used to increase the weight of drilling mud; specific gravity 4.2.

Barnacle
Crustacean adhering to underwater objects and to ships hulls; have a hard shell and long fleshy parts that adhere firmly and are not easy to remove. Will have a noticeable effect on a ship's speed.

Barometer
Instrument for determining **atmospheric pressure**. Aneroid and mercury types are most commonly used at sea.

Barratry
Wrongful act willingly performed by the master and/or crew against the ship without the prior knowledge of the owners or **charterers**.

Barrel

(1) Revolving cylinder on a machine. (2) Standard petroleum unit of measurement. One barrel contains 42 US gallons, equal to approximately 35 Imperial gallons and approximately159 litres.

Base

Number from which a numeration or logarithm system begins.

Baseline

(1) On flush shell plated vessels, the fore and aft reference line on the upper surface of a flat plate keel at the centreline. (2) Thickness of **garboard strake** above the level for ships having lap seam **shell plating**. Vertical dimensions are measured from a horizontal plane through the baseline, often called moulded baseline.

Base number (BN)

Measure of a lubricants **alkalinity** expressed in mgKOH/g. Amount of perchloric acid required to neutralise one gram of oil under specified test conditions. Formerly known as TBN (Total Base Number).

BASIC

Computer symbolic language. *B*eginners *A*ll-purpose *S*ymbolic *I*nstruction *C*ode. *See also* **assemble**.

Bathymetry

Study and measurement of water's depth, salinity, and temperature.

Baud

Unit of transmission speed for computer telecommunications of one bit per second. Often used in computing to indicate the rate a modem will receive or transmit information. To convert a baud rate into an approximate number of characters per second, divide by 10.

Bauer Wach turbine

German designed exhaust steam turbine fitted to many **compound reciprocating steam engines** utilising energy remaining in the exhaust from the low pressure cylinder.

Beam ends

When a ship has heeled over to such an extent that there is no righting moment left to bring it back to the normal upright position.

Beam

The maximum breadth of a ship.

Beams

Steel rolled sections **athwartship** supporting the deck

Bearing

(1) An item common to two members of a mechanism so they can move relative to each other and transmit force from one to the other. There are three main categories of bearing; journal, thrust and special. A journal bearing supports a rotating shaft and a thrust bearing is designed to withstand force along the axis of a shaft. Special bearings include ball, roller and universal joints. (2) Horizontal angle between the direction of true north or true south and that of the object of which the bearing is being taken.

Beaufort scale

Wind force expressed numerically on a scale from 0 to 12. A reading of 0 indicates calm (under 1 knot); 5 indicates a fresh breeze (17 to 21 knots), 8 indicates a fresh gale (34 to 40 knots);12 indicates a hurricane (64 knots or over).

Beaume density

Formula expressing the density of fuel oil in degrees.

Beetle

Heavy mallet used by shipwrights to drive reeming irons into the seems of wooden planked decks to facilitate caulking with oakum and pitch.

Bedplate

Structure forming the base of a machine. In a marine engine, in addition to supporting the engine columns and crankshaft bearings, it also helps to distribute the engine weight and stress to the ship's structure.

Belay

Make fast or secure.

Belfast bow

Name given to raked stem introduced by Harland and Wolff of Belfast. Gives large forecastle deck.

Bell, Henry (1767–1830)

While a number of British engineers, notably Hulls, Miller and Symington, did a great deal of pioneering work on steamship propulsion it was Henry Bell who made the first successful UK commercial breakthrough in 1812. His paddle steamer *Comet* was the first practical steamship in the UK and although only 42 ft in length, drawing just 4 ft of water and driven by a 4 nominal hp engine, it operated a regular service on the Clyde between Glasgow, Greenock and Helensburgh. The Clyde's later dominance in building steamers has been attributed to Bell's early success with *Comet*.

Bellmouth

Suction pipe arrangement used in a tank. The inlet area is increased to approximately 1.5 times the pipe area.

Bending moment
Sum of all the moments of force acting at a point in a body.

Bends
Dangerous condition suffered by divers surfacing quickly after working at a considerable depth. *See also* **Caisson disease**.

Bend test
Test for the **ductility** of a material, revealing defects by bending a bar over a former of specified radius related to the thickness of the bar.

Beneficial owner
Person who has no legal title to the ship but has a tangible interest in it as he is acting as a trustee.

Benthic division
Primary division of the sea, including its floor. Subdivisions are: **(a)** Littoral System, including waters between high water and depths of 200 metre or the continental shelf edge. **(b)** Deep-sea System, including all other waters.

Benzene (C_6H_6.)
Simplest of the aromatic hydrocarbons and one of the most important petroleum derived raw materials used in the chemical industries.

Bessemer process
Process of steel production where air is blown through molten pig iron in a pear shaped Bessemer converter.

Beta brass
Copper-zinc alloy with 36–45 per cent zinc, not resistant to sea water corrosion.

Bevel gear
Gear with teeth cut on an angular surface such as a truncated cone. Used for the transmission of motion between shafts with intersecting centre lines which form an angle between each other, usually 90 degrees. *See* Figure 5.

Big end
Bearing at the end of a connecting rod engaging with the crank pin. *See also* **bottom end bearing**.

Bilge
(1) Curved portion, often circular, between bottom and side shell plating as shown in Figure 6. **(2)** Lower parts of holds, tanks and machinery spaces.

Bilge cleaning
Washing down the bilge area of a ship to remove any pungent, unhygienic or dirty substances present. Bilges act as collecting points for any free liquids

in holds and machinery space. If not properly cleaned, corrosion will occur rapidly. Cleaning is essential to avoid microbiological attack and can be carried out manually or by Tank Cleaning Vessels.

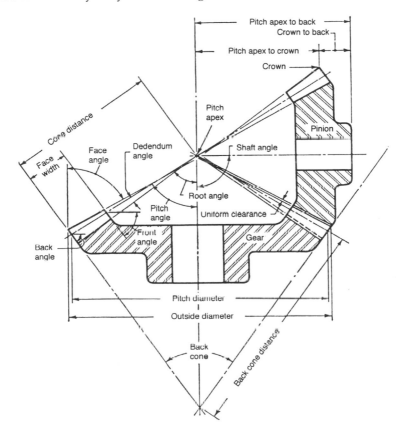

Figure 5 Bevel Gears

Bilge ejector

Means of removing water from tank tops, holds and other areas where water gathers. Pressurised water is passed through a nozzle, or venturi. The resulting jet entrains the water from the bilges, discharging it into a holding tank.

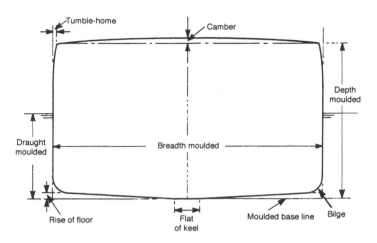

Figure 6 Ship Terms, Transverse

Bilge keel
External fin at round of bilge to reduce rolling. May extend outwards perpendicular to the ship's shell for, in some cases, up to 1 metre. Also extends in the fore and aft direction for about two thirds of the length of the ship.

Bilge pump
Must be self-priming unless an efficient means of priming is provided. Usually of the centrifugal type with in-built self priming. Ships must have an emergency bilge pump of the submersible type that can function when the compartment is flooded. The electric motor is located in an air bell with dimensions that create air compression in the bell preventing water from reaching the motor in case of flooding. The power source and controls must be situated above the bulkhead deck.

Bilge radius
Radius of the plating that joins the side shell to the bottom shell, measured at **midships**.

Bilge strake
Continuous horizontal fore and aft strip of plating from **stem** to **stern** in way of the bilge.

Bill of lading
Ship Master's detailed receipt for cargo received on board, evidence of the contract between the shipper and the shipowner.

BIMCO

Baltic and International Maritime Council. International association based in Copenhagen whose main objective is to promote and defend the interests of shipowners.

Bimetal

Metal strip composed of two layers of dissimilar metals laminated together, each having a different co-efficient of expansion. Controls operations such as the opening and closing of electrical contacts and the opening of valves in response to temperature changes.

Binnacle

Stand of wood or metal in which a **compass** is suspended. Top of binnacle protects compass from weather and reduces glare from lighting.

Bipod mast

Mast structure strong enough to dispense with supporting rigging. Suitable for use with heavy derricks and special derrick systems as shown in Figure 7.

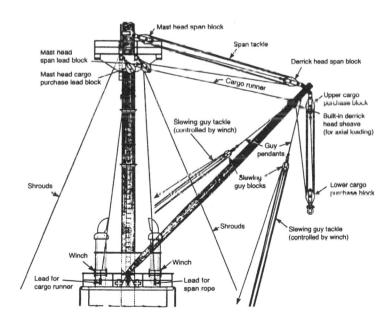

Figure 7 Heavy Derrick Rig

Bit

(1) Cutting device at the bottom of the **drill string,** shown in Figure 8. **(2)** The smallest unit of data in binary notation

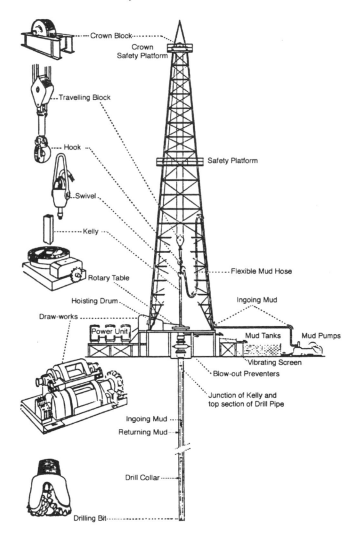

Figure 8 Drilling Rig and Associated Equipment
(Courtesy of the Institute of Petroleum)

Bit breaker
Heavy metal plate that fits in the drilling table to hold the drill bit while it is being unscrewed from the drill collar.

Bitt
Strong part of ships structure, generally based on the keel and attached firmly to a main deck, to which a hawser or warp can be hitched when exceptionally heavy loads are applied such as when the vessel is towed. In small vessels this is often termed the **samson post** and the mooring chain or anchor cable is normally made fast to it particularly when mooring in a tideway.

Bitter end
End of anchor cable secured in the **chain locker** by a **clench** pin.

Bitumen
Mineral pitch or **asphalt**. Viscous **hydrocarbon** that can be mixed with solvents to reduce softening temperature. Used for roadbuilding, weatherproofing and protecting steel from corrosion. When carried as cargo, ships are constructed with heated tanks isolated from the hull by double bottoms.

Blade, propeller
Screw propellers have two or more blades projecting from a **boss**. The surface of each blade viewed from aft is called the face, and the alternate surface is the back. Individual blades may be cast with or screwed to the boss, or variable pitch.

Blade area
Area enclosed by the developed propeller blade outline, shown in Figure 9.

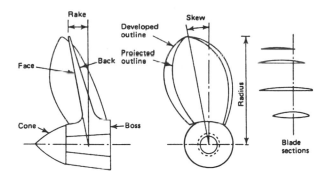

Figure 9 Propeller Blade

Blading, impulse
Each steam turbine stage pressure drop occurs in a row of fixed nozzles converting the internal energy of steam to **kinetic energy**. The high speed steam jet impinges on a moving row of blades, reducing the velocity of the steam with no change in pressure.

Blading, reaction
Type of blading fitted in **steam turbines** progressively expanding steam as it passes through each row of fixed and moving blades. Excess **kinetic energy** is used up driving the moving blades. Reaction blading gives a series of small pressure drops over the whole length of the turbine whereas with **impulse blading** pressure drops occur in the nozzles only.

Blading, turbine
Radial projections on turbine rotors converting pressure and/or kinetic energy in steam, water or combustion gas into mechanical work.

Blanketing
Replacing air in or around process equipment with an inert gas, such as nitrogen, to reduce oxidation, explosion or fire hazards.

Blast cleaning
Process for cleaning steel. Grit, sand or shot is projected onto the surface at high velocity. Best method for removal of mill-scale and rust prior to the application of a coating to preserve the metal.

Blast injection
In diesel engines, when fuel is blasted into the engine combustion chamber with compressed air. Common practice with early diesel engines.

Bleeding
Process of purging air from a system.

Blending
Mixing selected components in the preparation of a product with specified properties. In fuel oils, refers to the mixing of fuels of differing viscosities to obtain a product of the required viscosity and density. In lubricating oils, refers to the mixing of base oils and additive packages.

Block coefficient (Cb)
Ratio of the volume of **displacement** of a ship to a given waterline and the volume of the circumscribing block having the same length, breadth and draught as the ship.

Blocking diode
Solid state device to split charge two separate batteries of similar voltage.

Blocks
Device made of wood or metal forming part of lifting tackle equipment, typically used with **derricks**. Two blocks are fitted to each derrick, one at the head known as the head block, gin block or cargo block, the other at the bottom known as a heel block. *See also* **sheave blocks.**

Bloom
(1) Colour of an oil as reflected from its surface, different to the colour of the oil by transmitted light. (2) Semi-finished metal product of rectangular cross-section, produced by rolling or forging an ingot.

Blow-by
Unburned fuel, lubricant and combustion residues that escape from the combustion chamber past the piston rings, or piston rod glands in crosshead engines, into the crankcase of an internal combustion engine. Excessive amounts will causes rapid deterioration of the engine system oil.

Blow-down
Method of reducing dissolved solids in boiler water by opening blow-down cocks at the bottom of the boiler while maintaining correct water level in boiler gauge glasses by introducing additional feed water to the boiler. The Same method is used for reducing brine density in distillers.

Blower
Fitted to internal combustion engines to increase the weight of air supplied to the cylinders, each cycle increasing the available power output per cylinder. Excess air may be provided to assist the cylinder exhaust process. Driven either mechanically, electrically or by exhaust gas turbine. *See also* **supercharging** and **turbo-blower.**

Blower, lp
Low pressure air compressor.

Blower, soot
Unit using steam jet for externally cleaning boiler tubes when steaming. Retractable when located in or close to the boiler furnace to avoid heat damage when not in use.

Blow-out
When gas, oil or salt water escapes in an uncontrolled manner from a well. Can be due to a release of pressure in the **reservoir** rock due to the failure of the containment systems during production.

Blow out preventer (BOP)

Unit fitted at the wellhead or on the deck of a **jack-up rig** to seal off the well in the event of a **blow-out**. Usually consists of a number of devices arranged vertically in a stack or **christmas tree**. *See* Figure 8.

Blue Peter

Rectangular flag, blue with a white square in the centre, displayed to indicate that a ship is ready to proceed.

Blue Riband

Denotes the fastest passage across the North Atlantic by a passenger liner. Exact origins are unknown, however, it is thought to have been introduced around 1865 with records backdated to the first steamer to cross the North Atlantic under its own power for the entire journey, notably the *Sirius* in 1838 with an average speed of 6.7 knots. The holder is permitted to fly a long blue pennant from the foremast and in 1933 the British MP, Harold K. Hales donated the Hales Trophy as a further honour. The last large passenger ship to hold the Blue Riband is the *United States* which crossed in 1953 at an average speed of 35.59 knots. In June 1990 the Sea Container group's *Sea Cat*, although not a large passenger liner, averaged 36.99 knot. Currently the Hales trophy is held at the group's London headquarters.

BMEA

British Maritime Equipment Association. Trade association of the British manufacturers of marine equipment.

BMEC

British Marine Equipment Council. Trade association of British manufacturers of marine equipment.

BMT

British Maritime Technology. National research organisation with foundations in traditional fields of marine research and development.

Boat compass

Small magnetic **compass** mounted in a box for use in small marine craft.

Boatswains chair

Wooden seat on which a man may be hoisted aloft or lowered over the ship's side safely to carry out repairs or painting.

Body

(1) Any definite portion of matter. (2) Appearance of a solid or liquid given by its consistency, density, or opacity.

Body plan
Shows the shape of transverse sections of the ship as shown in Figure 10.

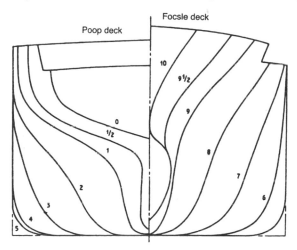

Figure 10 Body Plan of Cargo Ship

Boiler
Closed vessel for boiling liquid to create steam. There are numerous examples of fire tube, water tube and compound types. The majority of steamers have large, high pressure, high temperature, water tube boilers. Diesel vessels will have smaller, lower pressure water tube or fire tube types, usually able to operate with exhaust gas or fuel oil as the heating medium.

Boiler, closed feed
System where water leaving the condenser is in a closed system until it reaches the boiler so that air is not absorbed. Essential for water tube boilers and high boiler pressures.

Boiler, combustion
Process of burning fuel in a furnace to produce steam. Good combustion is important to avoid atmospheric pollution and fouling of boiler tubes.

Boiler efficiency
Ratio of heat energy in steam delivered by boiler to heat energy supplied to boiler. As it is difficult to measure the steam and oil fuel quantities accurately, efficiency is usually computed by the method of losses. This subtracts heat loss from heat supplied and divides by the latter. Heat supplied is obtained from fuel characteristics and heat loss from flue gas conditions plus

assumed radiation and other unaccountable losses (usually between 1 and 1.5 of the fuel Gross Combustion Value). Modern boilers with air preheaters can achieve efficiencies in excess of 95 per cent.

Boiler scale
Hard deposit on the interior of a boiler plate or tube of varying composition. The scale generally contains magnesium and calcium carbonates as well as calcium sulphate derived from the water used.

Boiler water treatment
Provided to reduce corrosion and scale formation in boilers. Boiler water must be maintained in slightly alkaline conditions by the carefully controlled addition of chemicals.

Boiling point
Temperature of a liquid when its vapour pressure equals external pressure. Boiling liquids are normally quoted for standard atmospheric pressure. At a fixed pressure, a liquid will not exceed its boiling point and further heating merely converts more liquid to vapour. Standard is 100°C or 212°F.

Boiling range
Temperature spread between the initial boiling point and final boiling point of a petroleum fraction.

Boil-off
Liquid evaporation due to heat transfer into the cargo or containment. Mainly applicable to **LNG** and **LPG** which are transported near their boiling points. Would not occur if perfect insulation was available. In **LNG** ships the boil off is used as fuel for the boiler.

Bollard
Large and firmly secured post of circular section for securing **hawsers** and mooring ropes. Often fitted in pairs on the same **base plate**.

Bollard pull
Tractive effort produced by a tug when pulling against a static object such as a bollard. Expressed in tons (imperial) or tonnes (metric).

Bond
The chemical bond joining **atoms** together in a **molecule**.

Bonding
Electrical connection between the armouring or sheath of adjacent lengths of cable or across a joint to ensure continuity.

Bonjean curves
Curves of transverse sectional areas of the ship drawn against a vertical scale

or draught. Use of Bonjean curves enables immersed volume to be obtained for waterlines not parallel to base.

Boom
(1) Woodspar or steel tube for discharging or loading cargo. (2) Spar for extending foot of sail. (3) Floating or moored obstruction to restrict oil spillage or defend a harbour entrance during wartime. (4) Structure used to support an **offshore** pipeline during laying.

Booster
Electric **generator** or **transformer** interposed in series in a circuit to increase or decrease voltage acting in the circuit. The former is a positive booster and the latter a negative booster.

Booster platform
Platform built part of the way along an oil or gas underwater pipeline to boost the pumping process.

Boot topping
Area of a ship's side immediately above and below the deep **load line**. Particularly susceptible to marine weed growth and often coated with specially formulated anti-fouling paint. Term not usually applicable to cargo vessels with a large distance between deep and light **load lines**.

Borehole
Exploratory hole drilled in search of oil or gas.

Boss
Central portion of **propeller** to which blades are attached and through which the **tailshaft** passes and is connected.

Bossings
Curved portion of a ship's shell plating surrounding and supporting the **propeller** shaft of a twin screw ship. Offers less resistance than an **A- bracket**.

Bottle screw
Adjustable screw for tightening up stays and wires. Left-hand and right-hand threaded screws led into outer ends of a shroud and fitted with locknut or preventer.

Bottom dead centre (BDC)
Position of a **piston** in its cylinder when it is at the bottom of its stroke. The **crank** of the **crankshaft** will then be vertical.

Bottom end bearing
Bearing located at the end of the **connecting rod** engaging with the **crankpin** of the **crankshaft**.

Bottom hole assembly (BHA)
Collection of tools and weights at the lower end of the drill string, such as bits, drill collars, stabilisers, and weights. *See* Figure 8.

Bottoms
Oil refining term for the high boiling point residual liquid or residuum that collects at the bottom of a distillation tower. Includes residual fuel and asphaltic substances.

Boundary layer
Narrow layer of moving water adjacent to the hull of a ship as it moves through the water.

Boundary lubrication
Form of lubrication between two rubbing surfaces without a full-fluid lubricating film developing. Evident at high loading or slow speed.

Bourdon gauge
Instrument for measuring the pressure of steam or other gases.

Bow
Forward end of a ship.

Bow door
Hinged door in the fore end of a ship opened in dock to allow vehicles and cargo to be loaded or discharged via the bow ramp. Mostly used on **RO/RO** ships and ferries. Due to accidents involving such doors stringent safety regulations have now been introduced.

Bow wing doors
Doors at the forward end of a ferry opening to port and starboard to allow the bow ramp to connect with the quay so vehicles can be driven on and off.

Bower anchors
The two largest anchors in a ship carried permanently attached to their **cables**, one on either side of the bow. The cables run through their **hawse pipes** so the anchors are always ready in an emergency. *See* Figure 3.

Bow thruster
Manoeuvring propeller installed at or near the bow for docking assistance, or maintaining vessel heading, often in association with a **dynamic positioning system**. *See also* **thruster**. In offshore vessels requiring a high degree of accuracy in position-keeping, such as a diving support vessel, two or even three bow thrusters may be fitted adjacent to each other to provide sufficient athwartships thrust and system redundancy in the event of a unit failure.

Boyle's law
When temperature is constant the volume of a quantity of gas varies inversely with the pressure.

Bracket
Plate used to rigidly connect a number of structural parts, often triangular.

Brackish
Mixture of sea water and fresh water.

Brake horse power (bhp)
See **horse power.**

Brake thermal efficiency
Ratio between energy developed at the brake (output shaft) of an engine and the energy supplied.

Brass
Alloy of copper and zinc. Can also contain tin, aluminium or lead.

Brazing
Process of joining metals using a copper based filler metal with a melting range just below that of either of the parent metals. The gap between the metals to be joined allows molten filler metal to be drawn in by capillary attraction. Capillary brazing is used in the manufacture of important pressure pipe systems, such as in warships. The parts to be brazed in special jigs must be located to ensure a constant thickness of filler metal and achieve the maximum strength of joint.

Breadth, moulded
Measured at amidships and is maximum breadth over frames. *See* Figure 6.

Break
Point where a side shell plating section drops to the deck below, such as the **poop** or **forecastle.**

Break bulk cargo
Miscellaneous goods packed in boxes, bales, cases, barrels or drums.

Breaking capacity
Ability of a **circuit breaker** or similar device to break or open an electric circuit under specified conditions.

Breakout
Process where one section of a **drill pipe** is unscrewed from another.

Breakwater
(1) Protective wall built from the sea bed to provide shelter from sea waves

for an anchorage or harbour. **(2)** Barrier across **forecastle** head to check the force of water breaking over it during bad weather.

Breast hook
Triangular plate bracket joining port and starboard side stringers at the stem, holding both sides of ship together.

Breast plate
Horizontal plate that connects shell plating at the stem.

Breeches buoy
Device for transferring people from ship to ship or ship to shore.

Bridge
Superstructure **erection** above the **freeboard deck,** generally extending to the ship's side, giving a clear view from which the ship can be manoeuvred and navigated. The bridge structure is located amidships or towards the stern. On specialist ships, such as an offshore craft, it may be situated nearer the bow.

Bridge gauge
Gauge measuring wear-down on the journal bearing with the shaft in place. Arch or bridge fitted over journal after top half bearing is removed and clearance between bridge gauge and journal measured.

Bridge wings
Open portion of **bridge** extending from wheelhouse to the side of a vessel.

Bridle
Two short lengths of steel wire rope or chain cable, assembled to form a Y, used to connect a vessel being towed and a tug's towline.

Bridle gear
Metal **cross-piece** with a chain attached at either side on end of accommodation ladder tackle, the chains are then shackled to ladder. The main function of bridle gear is to take the weight of the ladder.

Bright stock
High viscosity lubricant base oil, highly refined and dewaxed, produced from residual stock or bottoms. Used for blending with lower viscosity base oils in the manufacture of finished lubricants.

Brine
(1) As a refrigerant, made by dissolving calcium chloride in fresh water. Has a freezing point well below the desired temperatures of the refrigerated compartments. **(2)** When seawater is evaporated in a distiller, the brine formed must be maintained at a specified density. An overly high density

causes the coils to scale up quickly and an overly low density wastes heat by discharging excessive brine overboard.

Brine trap
Cylindrical chamber or pot fitted with inlet and outlet cocks or valves to enable samples of brine to be removed from distillers and refrigerator systems to test the density.

Brinell hardness test
Indentation hardness test applying a standard load to a standard size steel ball placed on the prepared surface of an article. The diameter of the resulting impression is measured and the hardness number is calculated by dividing the load applied (kg) by the surface area (mm^2) of the indentation, or in practice, by referring to tables. The result of the test is the metals HB number.

Brinelling
Damage produced by the repeated local hammering of hardened steel balls in contact with another metal. Usually caused by continuous vibration of a static ball bearing, resulting in indentations on the bearing surface.

Brittle fracture
Fracture of metal with very little plastic deformation. Ductile **fracture** implies a slow fracture undergoing **elongation** prior to fracture. Propagation of brittle fracture is rapid, characterised by chevron shaped markings at the fracture zone.

Broaching
Involuntary and dangerous change in heading produced by a severe following or quartering sea.

Bronze
Alloy of copper and tin. Specialist bronzes can contain other metals.

Brow
(1) Gangway between ship and shore. (2) Small curved angle or flanged plate fitted on the outside of a ship's hull over an air port, preventing water running down the ship's side entering the open port.

Brunel, Isambard Kingdom (1806-1859)
In 1833 at the age of 27 Brunel was appointed Engineer in Charge of the projected British Great Western Railway and was subsequently responsible for the construction of many tunnels, bridges, and harbours. In 1837 when the railway decided to build their first steamer the *Great Western*, Brunel decided to oversee the whole project which would allow them to offer their passengers a through ticket to the United States. This ship, the subsequent *Great*

Britain (now in Bristol) and the *Great Eastern,* were all innovative ships in their day and bore the unmistakable mark of Brunel.

Brush gear

General term used for the equipment associated with the brushes of commutating or slip-ring electrical machinery.

BSI

British Standards Institute. National organisation which prepares and issues standard specifications.

BS&W

Bottom Sediment And Water. Test determining the percentage of water and other extraneous material present in crude and fuel oil. This content must be quite low before crude oil is accepted for pipeline delivery to the refinery.

BTN

Brussels Tariff Nomenclature. International tariff system classifying all commodities carried from one country to another. Each commodity has a unique code known as the **BTN** number.

BTU

British Thermal Unit. Quantity of heat required to raise the temperature of one pound of water, at its maximum density, by one degree fahrenheit.

Bubble cap

Covered hole in the tray of an oil refinery fractionating column. The vapour bubbles move upwards through the liquid in the tray.

Bucket valve

Suction and discharge valves on the pump end of a reciprocating pump, normally consisting of sets of spring loaded plate valves.

Buckler

Sliding plate covering the anchor hawse pipe when the ship is at sea.

Buckling

To crumple under longitudinal pressure.

Buffer

Part of a computers memory allocated for use as a temporary storage area while the stored data is waiting to be used for a specific task.

Bulbous bow

Protruding bow below waterline intended to reduce a vessel's resistance to motion under certain circumstances. Once considered favourable only for moderate to high speed ships, however, has now been beneficial in relatively low speed ships such as **tankers** and **bulk carriers**. Research shows that the bulb has a greater effect when situated some distance forward of the stem. This has led to adoption of the ram bulb.

Bulk carrier

Specialised dry cargo in bulk carrier with large cargo hold volume. Well suited for cargoes such as coal, grain, bauxite and sugar. Can be loaded without having to trim cargo. This is attained by sloping plating extending from hatch side to ship's side and from ship's side to tank top. This permits easy unloading as cargo will fall down below the hatch way as unloading proceeds allowing use of grabs. *See* Figure 11.

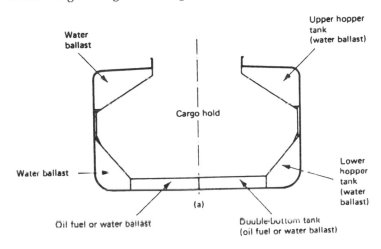

Figure 11 Bulk Carrier, Transverse Section

Bulkhead

Vertical partition subdividing a ship's interior into compartments.

Bulkhead, aft peak

First major transverse **watertight bulkhead** forward of the **stern frame**.

Bulkhead, collision or forepeak

Foremost major **watertight bulkhead.**

Bulkhead door

Door cut into a **bulkhead** to provide access from one cargo compartment or deck to another. Bulkhead doors must be watertight.

Bullet perforator
Tubular device that, when lowered to a selected depth within an oil well, fires bullets through the casing to provide holes through which well fluids can enter.

Bulwarks
Vertical plating erected at the **gunwales** of a ship to prevent people being washed overboard and to reduce the water breaking onto the deck in a seaway.

Bundwall
Concrete or earth wall surrounding a crude oil or refined product storage tank. Designed to hold entire contents if tank ruptures or springs a leak.

Bunker
Compartment where fuel oil or coal for ship's engines or boilers is stored.

Bunker fuel oil
Residual fuel remaining after the maximum amount of petroleum gases and lighter fuels have been distilled off; the primary source of heat for ships often blended with other fuels and products to attain the required viscosity, density and stability needed. In most marine diesel engines and boilers the fuel oil should have a kinematic viscosity of 30–450 centistokes (cSt) at 50°C.

Buoy
Floating object, other than a lightship, anchored at an assigned location to serve as an aid to navigation or mark a position (known as a marker buoy).

Buoyancy
Support given to a ship by the water the vessel floats in. Ship must have sufficient buoyancy to support the load it intends to carry.

$$buoyancy\ per\ unit\ length = \frac{A}{density\ of\ water}$$

Where A = immersed cross sectional area of a ship.

Bureau Veritas (BV)
Leading French **classification society** founded in 1828.

Burner
Oil fired boiler fuel injector.

Burgee
Rectangular flag with a swallow tail indentation at edge furthest from the mast. In the Merchant Navy it is customary for the **Commodores** of shipping companies to fly the house flag in the form of a burgee.

Bus
In computers, an electrical conductor transmitting power or data.

Busbars
Non-insulated copper bars at the back of main switchboard to which feeders from main **alternator** or **generator** main breakers are attached.

Bush
Cylindrical sleeve forming a bearing surface for a shaft or pin.

Butane (C_4H_{10})
Paraffin hydrocarbon obtained from casing head gases in crude petroleum refining. Supplied in pressurised containers (bottle gas) for cooking and heating. Known as **liquid petroleum gas (LPG)**. Previously transported in pressurised tanks, now refrigerated and carried in liquefied gas ships.

Butterfly valve
(1) Hinged flap connected to a throttle used to close off the air inlet manifold on gasoline engines and some diesel engines. (2) Pair of semi-circular plates hinged axially to a common diametral spindle in a pipe so the plates permit flow in one direction only.

Buttock
Breadth of a ship where the hull rounds down to the stern.

Butt strap
Connecting metal strap covering butt joint which adds strength to joint.

Butt weld
Weld made between two plates placed side by side without overlapping.

Butterworth system
System for cleaning cargo oil tanks with seawater heated to about 80°C. Water jets of approximately 12 bar are directed to all parts of the cargo tank to remove oil deposits remaining from previous cargo. Resultant oil/water mixture is then pumped to a slop tank for separation.

Butyl rubber
Copolymer of isobutylene and isoprene exhibiting good chemical and ozone resistance and low permeability to gases. Resistant to many phosphate-ester fluids but not petroleum-based fluids. Used for electric cable insulation as it can withstand higher temperatures than vulcanised rubber.

By-pass
Pipe used to control and divert circulation of a fluid or gas.

By-product
Material other than primary product obtained in a manufacturing process.

Byte
Group of adjacent bits forming a storage unit in a computer memory.

C

Cable
(1) Rope or chain used primarily for mooring a ship. The use of cables for mooring led to the cable length becoming a convenient unit of distance measurement, particularly in relation to manoeuvring ships close to shore or harbour works. One cable is equivalent to one tenth of a nautical mile, almost 184 metres. (2) Insulated, protected or armoured electrical conductor. (3) Frequently used to describe a telegraphic message transmitted over long distances such as between continents.

Cable lifter
A **windlass barrel** with specially shaped snugs into which the links of the anchor cable fit as they move round and drop into the chain locker.

Cable stopper
Device to secure cable when riding at anchor, reducing load on **windlass**.

Cable tool drilling
String of tools used in cable tool drilling. Consists of a bit fastened to a drilling jar, rope socket and the rope. The bore is made by percussion such as the drill being picked up and dropped to the bottom of the hole by the cable. Used only where the rock is hard and firm.

Cabotage
(1) French name for coastal trade, in universal use. (2) Reservation of the coasting trade of a country to ships operating under the flag of that country.

CAD/CAM
Computer Aided Design/Computer Aided Manufacturing.

Caisson
(1) Vertical column or leg supporting the deck of a semi-submersible or submersible rig. (2) Large watertight compartment open at the bottom. Water is kept out by air pressure in order to give access to underwater areas for engineering works such as construction of piers. (3) Gate or moveable structure closing the entrance to a dock or dry-dock.

Caisson disease
Colloquial name for compression sickness or **bends,** the painful condition where bubbles of nitrogen form in the body tissues of a diver making a rapid return to normal **atmospheric pressure** after subjection to greater than normal pressure. Workers returning from a **Caisson,** where air pressure is kept high to exclude water, must take the same precautionary measures as deep sea divers. It is essential to return slowly to atmospheric pressure, often using a decompression chamber, in order to avoid the bends.

Caisson rig
Type of submersible rig used in shallow water (usually Arctic waters) where the unit sits on a single short leg designed to withstand ice pressure.

Calcium chloride ($CaCl_2$)
Constituent of brine used in refrigeration process. Readily absorbs moisture from the atmosphere and so is a useful medium for drying gases.

Calibration
Where instrument readings are compared with a standard or known value.

Call sign
Sequence of letters and numbers unique to each ship for identification purposes when contacted.

CALM
Catenary Anchor Leg Mooring.

Calorie (cal)
Unit of heat. Quantity of heat required to raise the temperature of one gram of water at 15°C, by one degree centigrade, at a constant pressure of 101.325 kPa. One calorie = 4.1868 joule (SI).

Calorific Value
Heat content used mainly in connection with the combustion of gaseous or liquid fuels. Largely replaced by **specific energy.**

Calorifier
Apparatus for heating water in a tank, frequently taking the form of a coil of heated tubes immersed in the water.

Calorimeter
Apparatus used to determine **calorific value.**

Cam
Projection on a revolving shaft, or collar mounted on a shaft, shaped to impart the desired linear motion to the follower in contact with it. Used in machines, valve gear and fuel pumps for converting a rotary motion into a

desired reciprocating motion. During each revolution of a cam it is necessary to take up the movement in a controlled manner. Cam design takes various forms. Harmonic cams are the mathematically simplest form of cam profile made up from simple arcs and tangents. Non-geometric cams are not very suitable for high speed operation.

CAMS
Centre for Advanced Maritime Studies. Edinburgh based study centre.

Camber
Curvature of the deck in a longitudinal direction. Camber is measured between the **deck height** at the centre and the deck height at the side. Also called round of beam as shown in Figure 6.

Camshaft
Shaft carrying cam(s) operating the valves of an internal combustion engine.

Candela (cd)
Unit of luminous intensity.

Candle power
Light radiating capacity in terms of luminous intensity, expressed in candelas.

Cant
Inclination of an object from the perpendicular.

Cant frames
Frame not square to centre line at stern. Not required with a **transom stern** as flat stern plating can be stiffened with vertical stiffeners.

Cantilever-type rig
Jack-up unit allowing the drilling derrick to be moved on beams to overhang the water on one side, allowing a greater choice of well location without having to move the rig.

Capacitance (C)
The property of a capacitor allowing the storage of electrical energy when a potential difference exists across conductors. The unit of measurement is a farad (F).

Capacitor
Another term for an electrical condenser. Device consisting of two electrodes separated by an insulant, such as air, for introducing capacitance into an electric circuit. Has the capability of storing electrical energy. Fitted across the ignition make-and-break to produce a hot spark at the plug in an internal combustion engine.

Capacity plan
Document detailing the capacities of all cargo spaces in a ship and all tanks used for fuel, lubricating oil, fresh water and water ballast.

Capesize vessel
Description given to large vessels too wide to negotiate the Panama canal.

Capillary action
Elevation or depression of liquids in narrow tubes.

Capstan
Barrel device, or rolling drum, on vertical axis used for heaving-in mooring lines or anchor cable.

Captain
In the Royal and Merchant Navies, the senior officer on board in command of a ship. Denotes a specific military rank in the Royal Navy.

Carbon dioxide (CO_2)
Inert gas present in products of fuel combustion. Also used as a refrigerant gas and for firefighting, especially electrical fires.

Carbon monoxide (CO)
Colourless, odourless, highly poisonous gas produced by the combustion of organic compounds with a limited amount of oxygen.

Carbon residue
Laboratory test to determine the percentage of coked material remaining after a sample of fuel or lubricating oil has been exposed to high tempera ture under controlled conditions. It is a measure of the coke forming tendencies of an oil, however, should be interpreted cautiously as there may be little similarity between the test conditions and the actual service conditions.

Carbon-tetrachloride
Non-inflammable solvent used for cleaning the windings of electrical machines. Also a pressurised liquid found in fire extinguishers to combat fires in electrical equipment.

Carburettor
Device where a liquid fuel is atomised and mixed with air in the correct proportions for good combustion.

Carburising
Steel hardening process giving an increased carbon content surface layer.

Cardan shaft or joint
Flexible mechanical arrangement for taking up the limited misalignment between a diesel engine and propeller shaft.

Cardinal points
The four points of north, south, east and west on a magnetic **compass**; north east, south east, north west and south west are known as half cardinal points.

Careening
Process of imparting a list so that a large part of one side of the underwater part of the hull is exposed for cleaning or repair.

Cargo clusters
Group of lights fitted in a circular reflector, used for illumination purposes when working cargo at night.

Cargo heating coil
Tanks for heavy oils, molasses or other viscous fluids are fitted with heating coils so that the fluid is sufficiently liquefied to run freely to pump suctions.

Cargo manifold
Pipe branching into two or more flanged open ends. Usually fitted at the ends of the deck crossover pipes on tankers.

Cargo plan
Plan indicating the position of different cargoes in a ship.

Cargo port or door
Opening in a ship's side for loading and unloading cargo.

Cargo segregation
Separation of liquid cargoes to avoid cross contamination. Double shut off valves will be used in common pumping systems, otherwise a completely separate pump will be used for each tank.

Carnot cycle
The ideal heat engine cycle of **isothermal** expansion, **adiabatic** expansion, adiabatic compression, and isothermal compression. Would give maximum thermal efficiency.

Carrier wave
Waveform used in a signal transmission system that can have its **frequency, amplitude** or **phase** varied by **modulation.**

Carry-over
Water passing from the boiler into steam range and machinery, possibly causing **water hammer.**

Carvel built
Type of ship's plating made flush by **vee butt** welding or **butt strap** rivetting.

Carving note
Form completed by owner of ship under construction giving details such as tonnage, name and **port of registry.**

Cascade control system
Control system where one controller (the master) provides the command signal to one or more other controllers (slaves).

Case exfoliation
Allied to **pitting,** however, with **exfoliation** appreciable areas of surface, hardened teeth flake away from the parent metal of heavily loaded gears.

Case hardened steel
Low carbon steel with an enriched carbon content at the surface due to being heated in a carbon rich environment at about $900^{\circ}C$.

Casing
Steel pipe cemented into a well to prevent the wall from caving in and to stop unwanted fluids from entering the hole from surrounding rock.

Cast iron
Iron with a total carbon content in excess of the amount which can be retained in solid solution. Carbon varies from 1.8–4.5 per cent. Impurities such as silicon, manganese, sulphur, and phosphorus may be present.

Casting
Object or shape formed by pouring molten metal into a mould.

Castle nut
Hexagonal nut with six radial slots, any two of which can line up with a hole drilled in a bolt or screw. This allows for the insertion of a split pin through the nut and bolt preventing any slackening off from occurring.

Catalyst
Substance altering the speed of a chemical reaction without undergoing permanent chemical change itself during the process. For example, metals and metallic oxides catalyse the **oxidation** of engine lubricants in service.

Catalyst fines
Small particles of the **catalyst** used in an oil refinery **catalytic cracking** plant. Mainly very hard, abrasive alumina and silica particles that can find their way into residual fuels. These particles can cause extreme damage to engine fuel pumps and injectors, therefore, ISO fuel standards for heavier marine

fuels places a combined maximum limit of aluminium and silicon at 80 mg/ kg. This figure assumes that, once treated, the amounts will be much lower.

Catalytic converter
Process where the conversion of certain chemicals is achieved by breaking up the **molecules** into other chemicals or gases. Widely used to break down **noxious** diesel emissions into more environmentally acceptable amounts. Also known as selective catalytic convertor (SCC).

Catalytic cracking
Secondary oil refinery process using a **catalyst** in a high temperature environment to break down large oil **molecules** into smaller, lighter range molecules. This process increases the volume of the more valuable, lighter products, particularly gasoline.

Catamaran
Vessel with double hulls and a deck structure between them.

Catchpot
Container inserted in pipeline to remove liquid droplets or solid particles entrained in a gas stream.

Catenary
Curve produced by a uniform, flexible wire or chain when suspended by its ends providing resilience to any sudden stresses. Anchor chains from a buoy, or wire between a tug and tow will assume this shape.

Cathode
Negative **electrode**.

Cathode ray tube
Display device forming part of an oscilloscope or a television screen.

Cathodic protection
Electrolytic system to protect metal from corrosion by providing an electric current neutralising the current naturally produced in the corrosion process. Current may be provided by sacrificial **anodes**, or through incorrodable anodes in an impressed current system. The electric circuit is completed through the corroding medium to the **cathode**, the metal to be protected.

Cat's paw
Light air producing ripples on the surface of the sea.

Caulking
(1) Making joints watertight by filling seams of wood planks with oakum. **(2)** Method of closing butts and seams of riveted steel plating.

Causa causans
The cause of a cause of a loss.

Caustic embrittlement
Embrittlement of steel occurring when exposed to highly alkaline conditions. May occur in boilers where leakage around rivets or fittings coupled with high stresses allow a concentration of caustic conditions to accumulate in crevices such as between a tube and tube plate.

Cavitation
Formation of cavities round a pump rotor or **propeller** blade, often on the back of the blade, that fill with air or water vapour. The effect of cavitation on a **propeller** is twofold: (a) cavities formed eventually collapse resulting in a severe mechanical action producing erosion of the blade surface; (b) a loss in propulsive efficiency occurs with severe cavitation.

CCAI
Calculated Carbon Aromaticity Index. Empirical formula to indicate the ignition quality of a bunker fuel oil. The value depends on the density and viscosity of the fuel. Shell have developed a simple nomogram that, when using these two parameters, gives a quick guide to an index of a fuel's ignition characteristics. A low number (approximately 890) would suggest high viscosity fuel with good ignition qualities. *See also* **CII**.

CCGT
Combined Cycle Gas Turbine (RN).

CD-ROM
Compact Disk - Read Only Memory.

Ceiling
Timber placed across the floor of a cargo hold to protect it from damage.

Cell
Basic element of a battery in which electrical energy is obtained as a result of chemical action. The cell is filled with an **electrolyte** and the reaction takes place between the enclosed **anode** and **electrode.**

Cellular
Structural arrangement where a compartment is divided into small spaces, such as a **double bottom**.

Celsius
Name for centigrade temperature scale measured in degrees Celsius.

Cement

Prior to epoxy paints, used as a wash for the protection of plating against the action of bilge water to give more effective protection to steelwork.

Cement box

Wooden box or shuttering filled with quick setting cement as a temporary repair for leaking plates, water valves or piping.

Cementing

Pumping cement down the casing in a well and up into the annular space between the casing and the well bore, to hold the **casing** in place.

Cementite

Hard, brittle compound of iron and carbon containing about 6.6 per cent carbon that corresponds to the composition Fe_3C. Plays an important part in ferrous alloys and in reality, alloys of the iron-carbon system are iron-cementite alloys.

CENSA

Council of European and Japanese National Shipowners' Associations.

Centistokes (cSt)

Common unit for **kinematic viscosity,** measured by the time a fixed volume of oil flows through a capillary tube. Kinematic is the viscosity range chosen for determining viscosities of both marine fuels and lubricants. Fuel distillates and lubricants are usually measured at 40°C, intermediate and heavy fuels at 50°C. The corresponding numerically equal **SI unit** is square millimetres per second (mm^2/s).

Centraliser

Device on a casing to hold it clear of a well bore wall prior to cementing.

Centre girder

Continuous girder in double bottom that runs fore and aft on centre line.

Centre of buoyancy (B)

Centroid of underwater volume of ship and point through which the total force of **buoyancy** can be assumed to act. An important feature of form is the longitudinal distribution of displacement as expressed by the longitudinal position of the centre of buoyancy (LCB). For a ship to float on even keel the LCB must be under the centre of gravity (G). The position of the LCB is dictated by the loading of the ship as shown in Figure 12.

Centre of flotation (CF)

Centroid of **waterplane area**. Small angles of trim consecutive waterlines pass through the CF.

Centre of force
Point at which total force exerted can be considered to act.

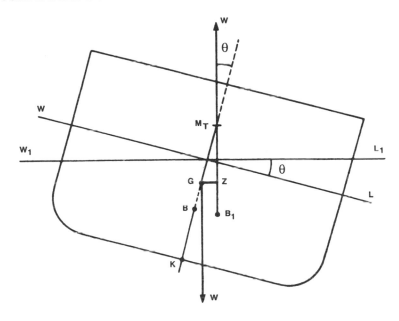

Figure 12 Stability

Centre of gravity (G)
Point through which total mass of ship may be assumed to act as in Figure 12. The position of the centre of gravity of a ship depends on the distribution of masses. Position can be calculated, however, vertical position can only be determined experimentally.*See* **inclination** test.

Centre of oscillation
Point in the axis of a vibrating body where, if the whole matter were concentrated, the body would continue to vibrate in the same time.

Centre of pressure
Point where the entire pressure on an immersed area can be considered to act.

Centrifugal force
Force acting outwards on a body, rotating in a circle around a central point.

Centrifugal pump

A **pump** where liquid enters the centre of a rotating impeller enclosed within a casing and flows radially out through the vanes. A diffuser or volute is used to convert most **kinetic** energy in the liquid into pressure.

Centrifuges

Cleaning unit for the removal of water and particulates from fuels and lubricating oil. Traditional treatment of bunker fuel oil requires two units in series, the first in **purifier** mode, the second working as a **clarifier**. However, because the purifier must have a gravity disc this system is dependent on the density of the fuel being below 991 kg/m^3 at 15°C. If this machinery is fitted, it inhibits the purchase of fuels above that density, which are less expensive. Highly automated alternative units requiring no gravity discs are available from leading centrifuge manufacturers and these are able to process fuels up to 1010 kg/m^3. Lubricating oil usually requires just one unit set up in the purifier mode.

Centrode

Path of the instantaneous centre of rotation of a body.

Centroid of an area

Centre of gravity of an area.

Ceramics

Substances made by firing minerals at high temperature.

Certificates of competency

Verification of competency. The majority of specialised staff on board ship are required to hold the relevant certificates of competency, as issued by the **Marine Safety Agency** in the United Kingdom.

Certificates of safety

In addition to surveys required by classification societies, British ships have to undergo statutory surveys for which certificates are issued; controlled by the **Marine Safety Agency**. For passenger ships, Passenger Certificates can only be issued if a ship complies with the Merchant Shipping Acts. Safety Certificates are also required to meet with the provisions of the Convention Safety of Life at Sea (**SOLAS**).

Cetane index

Empirical measure of the **ignition quality** of a distillate fuel indicating how easily a fuel will ignite when injected into a **compression ignition** engine. It is calculated from **API gravity** and the mid-boiling point of the fuel, or from **density** and various aspects of the boiling characteristics of the fuel. The derived index takes no account of any cetane improver in the fuel.

Cetane number
Measure of the **ignition quality** of a distillate fuel. Indicates the ability of diesel engine fuel to ignite quickly after injection into the cylinder. A high number indicates superior ignition quality with less tendency to knock and is determined by running the fuel in a prescribed test engine.

CFC
Chlorofluorocarbon refrigerant. *See* **Montreal Protocol.**

CGS
Centimetre/gram/second; the basis of the metric system.

Chain drive
Drive mechanism between crankshaft and camshaft of a diesel engine. Sprocket wheels are fitted to both crankshaft and camshaft with a further spring loaded adjustable wheel that runs over all three wheels, maintaining the tightness of the chain.

Chain locker
Compartment where the anchor chain is hauled and stowed. The chain is stowed on a grating to permit drainage overboard through **scuppers.**

Chamber
(1) Enclosed space in a machine. (2) Compartment in a structure. (3) Apparatus designed to reveal tracks of ionizing particles producing a visible effect such as a bubble or spark.

Chamfer
Bevel produced on edges or corners of an object which would otherwise be rectangular.

Characteristics
Criteria used to describe performance or behaviour of a system. May be developed from **static, dynamic** or operating characteristics of machinery.

Charge air
Volume of fresh air supplied to a diesel cylinder prior to compression.

Charles Law
If the pressure of a perfect gas remains constant, the volume of the gas is directly proportional to its absolute temperature.

Charpy test
Beam impact test for metals. A notched specimen is fixed at both ends and struck in the middle opposite the notch by a pendulum. The energy required to fracture the specimen is a measure of the resistance of the material to shock loads.

Charterer
Person or firm engaging a ship with whom the **shipowner** enters into a contract. Any charterer of a ship, except a charterer by **demise**.

Charter party
Contract of affreightment signed between **shipowner** and **charterer** when hiring a vessel for the carriage of goods.

Chart room
Room where all charts are kept as well as other navigating equipment such as **sextants**. Situated on the navigating bridge/wheelhouse.

Chartered Engineer (CEng)
Engineer who has satisfied the Engineering Council's academic standards, backed up by practical experience and having held a position of some responsibility. Registered as a professional engineer and entitled to use the letters CEng after their name. *See* **Institute of Marine Engineers.**

Chaser
Appliance used in anchor-handling to locate a buried anchor and provide a means of securing a pennant to heave it from the seabed.

Check valve
Non return valves regulating the flow of fluids to boilers in piping systems and machinery.

Chemical carriers
Vessels designed to carry chemicals, many of which are highly corrosive, poisonous and volatile. Safety is paramount and related to cargo containment and survival capability.

Chemical change
Change in a substance affecting chemical composition.

Chemical formula
Use of symbols to indicate qualitative and quantitative composition of a chemical substance. For example, H_2O means that a molecule of water comprises two hydrogen elements and one oxygen element.

Chemical reaction
Interaction of two or more substances when chemical change takes place.

Chemistry
Scientific study of the composition and laws of matter.

Chief Engineer
Senior engineer officer of a ship's complement. In the UK, usually qualified to a minimum of **Marine Safety Agency** Class 1 Certificate of Competency.

Chill
Reduce temperature without freezing such as brine in refrigeration systems.

Chinese windlass
Two drums or cylinders of slightly different diameter on the same axis, each with a single coil of rope wound in opposite directions. Rope winds off one drum onto the other creating slow motion with considerable mechanical gain. This allows large weights to be lifted with comparatively small expenditures of power.

Chip
Tiny piece of silicon with an integrated circuit on the surface.

Chlorine injection
A sea water circulating system becomes fouled by organisms unless a biocide is injected into it. Chlorine for injecting can be obtained from a solution of sodium hypochlorite or electrolysis of sea water in a special apparatus.

Chlorinity
Total grams of chlorine, bromine and iodine contained in one kilogram of seawater. For computation the assumption is made that the bromine and iodine have been replaced by chlorine.

Chock
(1) Smooth surfaced fitting at weather deck side through which mooring ropes are led. (2) Wedge for securing a **hatch cover** or adjusting the alignment of an engine or gearbox.

Choke
Coil of high inductance. When used as a filter, it impedes the current in a circuit over a specified frequency range while allowing relatively free passage at lower frequencies.

Christmas tree
Arrangement of valves and fittings designed to withstand high pressures. Found in tankers and other specialised ships and fitted to an oil wellhead to prevent a **blowout.**

Chromising
Process of improving hard wearing properties and oxidation resistance of **ferrous** products by forming a layer of chromium-rich material at the surface by diffusion.

Chronometer
Exceptionally accurate ship's timepiece. Used to ascertain the **longitude** of a ship by comparing local time and **Greenwich Mean Time**.

Chuck
(1) The part of a lathe that holds the rotating workpiece or tool. (2) Name for a fairlead.

CIF
Cost, Insurance and Freight. Type of contract where the seller provides a product and the vessel's operator handles insurance and delivery of the product to the nominated discharge port. The risk of loss or damage usually passes to the buyer when the goods cross a ship's rail.

CII
Calculated Ignition Index. Empirical formula indicating the ignition quality of a residual fuel See also **CCAI**.

CIMAC
Congress International des Machines a Combustion. The International Council on Combustion Engines. Marine applications are well recognised and there are a number of specialised working groups reporting to this Council devoted solely to marine matters, including fuels and lubricants.

Circuit
Combination of electrical devices performing a particular function when connected together in a closed path. A closed circuit is a continuous path, an open circuit is a discontinuous path.

Circuit breaker
Mechanical switching device capable of making, carrying and breaking currents under normal circuit conditions, also breaking currents under specified abnormal circuit conditions such as s short circuit. A safety device.

Circuit diagram
Drawing detailing all essential parts of a **circuit** and its function.

Circulating pump
Centrifugal or **axial** flow type pump drawing water from the sea for cooling condensers and other machinery.

CLA
Centre Line Average. Method of measuring the roughness of a surface by passing a stylus over it and magnifying the profile.

Cladding
(1) Coating of one metal with another. True cladding involves rolling a thin layer of metal onto a basis metal, or depositing a layer by welding. (2) Any covering used to prevent the radiation or conductance of heat.

Clampmeter
Measuring instrument with tongs that clip around a single **conductor**. Flowing current can be measured without interruption.

Clarifier
A **centrifuge** arranged to separate high density impurities from a liquid.

Class expunged
If defects occur in the hull, machinery or any item to make a ship unseaworthy, the **classification society** may strike it out from its present classification.

Classification Society
Society producing its own rules and regulations for the classification of ships. A ship and all its machinery, when built to these rules, will be awarded various class notations. Classification is voluntary, however, a ship's insurance can depend on satisfactory classification. First introduced in 1760 by the UK's, Lloyd's Register of Shipping, now joined by similar societies residing in other countries.

CLEAN
Clean and *Low Soot Engine* with *Advanced Techniques* for *NOx* Reductions. German project aimed at reducing visible **soot** and **particulate** emissions from diesel engines under all operating conditions. Plan to reduce **noxious emissions** to 50 per cent below the IMO 1992 level through changes in engine design and 95 per cent below the IMO 1992 level by use of selective **catalytic convertors**.

Cleat
(1) Fitting with two horns around which ropes can be made fast. (2) Clip on frames to hold cargo battens in place.

Clearance volume
In a reciprocating machine, the volumetric space between end cover and piston when the piston is at the end of its stroke, remote from the crankshaft.

Clench
Making a permanent join such as a clenched shackle with the end of an anchor chain secured to the bottom of a chain locker so it cannot be removed.

Cleveland open cup (COC)
Test method for determining flash point.

Clingage
Cargo remaining in the tank of a ship after discharge. Adheres to the sides, bottom, deckhead, and girders of a tank, and is removed during tank cleaning. Term mainly applies to oil tankers.

Clinker
Solid masses on the grate of a coal fired furnace comprised of **ash** and other substances that have fused.

Clinker built
Each **strake** of shell plating overlaps strake below. Generally used only in small boat building. Known as a lap-strake in America.

Clipper bow
Where the stem has a concave form as it rises from the waterline forming a **bow** shape.

Clogging indicator
Device operated by differential pressure across the filter element; indicates an element has become clogged.

Close annealing
Process of **annealing** metal components in a sealed box preventing the ingress of air and scaling or oxidation of components.

Closed feed system
High pressure **water tube boiler** feed system with no part is open to the atmosphere. It is usual to fit **de-aerating** equipment to remove any dissolved gases which might enter the system.

Close shelter-deck
Ship constructed as a **shelter-decker** with a sealed tonnage opening converting it into a two deck ship similar to a **tween decker** as shown in Figure 13.

Closing appliance
Piece of equipment used to close an opening in the shell, deck or bulkhead of a ship. Strict regulations exist to ensure watertightness.

Cloud point
Temperature at which a cloud or haze starts to appear in a previously dried oil when cooled under prescribed conditions. Since a fuel must be clear and bright for clouding to be observed this only applies to certain distillate fuels.

CLT
Contracted and loaded tip; unique propeller design with sharp, flat tipped blades.

Clutch

Device used to connect two working parts, such as two shafts, to permit easy connection or disconnection without bringing both parts to rest. When connected they must transmit the required power without slip.

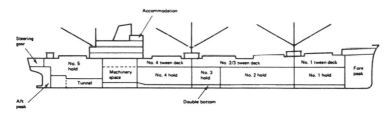

Figure 13 General Cargo Ship

CNC
Computer Numeric Control.

Coagulator
See **coalescer.**

Coal
A solid fossil fuel consisting mainly of carbon produced by the compression of decayed plants.

Coalescence
The combination of smaller particles to form a larger one.

Coalescer
Unit containing material with surface properties that promote **coalescence,** that is the combination of small oil droplets to form larger ones which can then separate more readily under gravity and ultimately form a continuous oil phase. The coalescer is placed downstream of the gravity separator, coalescing and separating those droplets which pass through the gravity stage as a result of their small size. A coalescer has in theory an infinite lifetime. May also be describes as a **coagulator.**

Coaming
Vertical plating bounding a hatchway. Heights of coamings depend on hatch position, some being more exposed than others. Coaming may be omitted altogether if directly secured steel covers are fitted and the safety of the ship ensured. The height of the coaming is dictated by the Merchant Shipping **(load line)** Rules of 1968.

Coatings, protective
Covering adherent to metal offering protection against corrosion. Usually applied to paints and similar compositions of organic origin.

Coaxial cable
Electric cable consisting of two conductors insulated from each other, one in a tubular form wrapped round the other. Used to transmit high frequency signals as it is not affected by external magnetic fields and does not itself produce any field. A practical example is a television aerial.

COBOL
Common Business Orientated Language. Computer language.

Cocoon
The sealed envelope placed around the equipment of **laid** up ships.

CODAD
Combined Diesel And Diesel plant (RN).

CODAG
Combined Diesel And Gas Turbine plant (RN).

CODOG
Combined Diesel Or Gas Turbine plant (RN).

CODLAG
Combined Diesel Electric And Gas Turbine plant (RN).

Coefficient
Number defining a certain characteristic or relationship under consideration. Used to express quantities of change under certain variable conditions such as temperature and volume.

Coefficient of expansion
Proportional increase in length of a solid for each degree centigrade increase in temperature. The coefficient of expansion of a superficial area is twice the linear coefficient, the coefficient of expansion of volume is three times linear.

Coefficient of friction
Ratio of the force required to overcome friction between the weight of a body and the surface it rests on before sliding will occur.

Cofferdam
Void or empty space between **two bulkheads** or **floors** preventing leakage.

Coffin plate
After plate of the **keel** connecting with the sole of the **stern frame**.

Coffin ships
Unseaworthy ships due to serious defects or overloading. Description introduced due to the number of ships lost, perhaps deliberately for insurance, before the introduction of **load line** legislation and other safety regulations.

COGAG
Combined Gas Turbine And Gas Turbine plant (RN).

COGOG
Combined Gas Turbine Or Gas Turbine plant (RN).

Coil
One or more insulated conductors wound in a series of turns.

Cold filter plugging point (CFPP)
Highest temperature at which a cooled fuel will not flow through a test filter under prescribed conditions. The CFPP is usually lower than cloud point and higher than pour point.

Cold temperature sludge
Sludge formed in an engine operating at too low a temperature to prevent the condensation of water or to evaporate volatile contaminants in the oil. Often called mayonnaise sludge due to its appearance.

Cold working
See **work hardening.**

Collar
Projection from a shaft either integrally with it or firmly secured to it. Provides axial location of the shaft in its bearings, such as the thrust collar enclosed within a **Michell** type **thrust bearing.**

Collet
Ring or collar, usually split, to encircle a groove in a stem or shaft that is retained by an outer ring or seating.

Collision bulkhead
Foremost transverse **watertight bulkhead** extending to the freeboard deck. Designed to limit the entry of water in the event of bow collision damage.

Colloidal solution
Apparently homogeneous mixture of a fluid with finely dispersed suspended matter with little tendency to settle, such as Graphite in oil.

Colorimeter
Instrument for determining the colour of a petroleum product.

Colza oil
Oil made from crushed rape-seed used as a lubricant and an illuminant.

Combustion
Act of burning. Chemical action accompanied by the release of heat energy.

Combustion chamber
(1) Space in a direct injection diesel engine bounded by piston crown, cylinder cover and cylinder wall, in which combustion takes place at or near top dead centre. (2) Chamber in the cylinder cover of an indirect injection engine connected to the main cylinder by a relatively narrow passage promoting turbulence. (3) Space adjacent to the burner in a boiler where combustion takes place.

Commodore
(1) Title given to the senior captain and senior chief engineer of a large fleet of merchant ships. (2) In the Royal Navy, an intermediate step between the rank of **captain** and rear admiral. It is not necessarily a promotional step, rather pertains to the responsibility of the position. When duties have been completed, the incumbent may revert to the substantive rank of captain.

Common rail
Type of **fuel injection** system with fuel circulating to all injectors all the time. With this system each injector contains its own injector pump.

Commutator
Mounted on the moving element of a rotating electrical machine. Consists of a cylindrical ring or disc assembly of conducting members individually insulated in a supporting structure, with an exposed surface for contact with current collecting brushes.

Companion
Permanent covering to a ladderway.

Companionway
(1) Set of steps leading between decks. (2) Ladder used for disembarkation.

Compartment
Subdivision of the hull by transverse watertight bulkheads, creating compartments that allow the vessel to remain afloat after **flooding.**

Compass
Instrument used to steer a ship on a predetermined course and to take bearings of visible objects in order to fix a ship's position on a chart.

Compass adjuster
Specialist who adjusts the magnetic compass using a process called swinging the ship. An essential process as true north and magnetic north differ.

Compass adjustment
Deviations of an installed magnetic compass are ascertained for different directions of a ship's head and reduced as much as possible by fixing small magnets in suitable positions in the compass stand to neutralise the magnetic effects of the ship and its equipment on the compass needles. The deviations remaining after the compass adjuster has completed his task are tabulated, or plotted, on a card called the deviation table. This may have three columns headed respectively: Ship's Head by Compass; Deviation; Ships Head Magnetic. The corrections shown are applied in all subsequent navigational operations.

Compatibility
Ability of a petroleum product to form a homogeneous mixture that neither separates nor is altered by chemical, time or temperature interaction.

Compensating winding
A **winding** carrying all or part of the load current designed to reduce the distortion of the **magnetic field** by the load current.

Compensation
Modification of equipment compensating for any shortfalls in requirements.

Compensators
Hydraulically or mechanically operated equipment that compensates for the upward and downward motion (heave) of a floating rig or **drill ship** during drilling operations.

Compiler
Computer programme that converts high level programming language into machine language.

Complement
Total number of suitably qualified and certificated crew on board ship.

Complex liquid
Liquid with a rate of shear not proportional to the shearing stress.

Components
Ingredients or parts required to manufacture a finished product.

Composite
Originally used to describe the construction of a ship during the transition period from wood to iron, where the framing would be iron and the hull wood. Now describes ships built of two or more metals, such as a steel hull with an aluminium superstructure.

Composite boiler
Firetube type steam **boiler** fitted in the exhaust gas flow from a diesel engine. Also has the provision for generating steam by oil firing.

Composite sample
Sample consisting of ingredients from various sections used to obtain an average of the whole. For example, in a bunker tank samples would be drawn from top, middle and bottom.

Compound-wound motor
Direct current motor with two separate field **windings**. Usually the predominating field is connected in **parallel** with the **armature** circuit, with the other connected in **series** with the armature circuit.

Compounded oil
Mineral lubricating oil containing animal or **vegetable fats,** or chemical substitutes. Widely used for lubrication of steam reciprocating engines because of their ability to form strong emulsions which allow them to continue efficient lubrication in the presence of water. Used on oil lubricated **sterntubes**.

Compound steam engine
Engine where steam is expanded in more than one cylinder, such as in double, triple or quadruple expansion steam reciprocating engines. In practice the term usually applies to an engine expanding steam in two cylinders.

Compounds
Chemically, any substance formed by two or more elements.

Compound wound
Applied to dc rotating machines, denotes that the excitation is supplied by two types of windings, **shunt** and **series**. When the electro-magnetic effects of both **windings** are in the same direction it is cumulative compound and when opposed it is differential compound.

Compression ignition
Initiation of spontaneous combustion of the fuel in a diesel engine due to the high temperature and pressure of air compressed by piston movement towards top dead centre.

Compression ratio
Volume of a compression chamber with the piston at the top of its stroke as a proportion of the total volume of the cylinder when the piston is at the bottom of its stroke.

Compressor
Machinery used to increase the pressure of a gas. Reciprocating or rotary.

CONAG
Combined Nuclear And Gas Turbine (RN).

CONAS
Combined Nuclear And Steam Turbine (RN).

Concession
Government licence to drill for oil or gas in a designated area.

Conchoidal fracture
Fractured surfaces exhibiting a series of wave or beach marks under **fatigue** conditions. The markings show the progress of fatigue cracks, often elliptical in form, and can help trace the origin.

Condensate
Liquid produced by vapour condensation, like water from condensed steam.

Condensate extraction pump
Pump in a closed feed system drawing condensed steam from the condenser, which is under vacuum, and pumping it to the de-aerator.

Condenser
(1) Chamber where exhaust steam is led to condense into water. (2) Electrical condenser. *See* **capacitor.** (3) Part of a **refrigeration** system.

Condition monitoring (CM)
Method of determining when maintenance is required rather than carrying out maintenance on an empirical calendar basis. Avoids unnecessary maintenance and stripping of machinery. Techniques involve visual examinations, performance checks (revolutions, output and heat transfer), pressure/temperature tests, ultrasonic tests, lubricant analysis, insulation tests, and vibration measurements. Since 1971, opening of turbines at first periodical survey can be dispensed with if CM readings are satisfactory. The results from CM are accepted by some classification societies for the extension of surveys for a variety of equipment, including stern tube/shaft systems and small engines.

Conductance
In a dc circuit, a reciprocal of **resistance.** In an ac circuit, the component of **admittance** due to a loss of electrical energy in elements carrying current.

Conductivity
Expressed as the ratio of current density to electric field strength and has units of siemens per metre; reciprocal of **resistance.**

Conductor
Body or substance normally offering a relatively **low resistance** to the passage of an electrical current. Usually metallic materials are good conductors.

Conduit
Container for electric wires or cables protecting them from damage.

CONICS
*Con*tainer *I*nformation and *C*ontrol *S*ystem.

Conference line
Two or more shipping lines operating a similar service in common between designated geographical areas. It is common to agree a set of freight rates between them that may include special rates for regular shippers.

Connecting rod
Rod connecting **piston** or **crosshead** to **crankshaft**.

Conning
Directing course of ship.

Conning position
Place on **bridge** with commanding view. Used by navigators when conning vessel underway.

Conradson carbon
Test method to determine the carbon forming tendencies of a petroleum product. *See* **carbon residue.**

Consignee
Party to whom the goods are shipped.

Console
Control panel from which an operator can operate and supervise machinery or equipment.

Constant speed motor
Motor that operates at a constant speed under normal conditions.

Constant tension winch
Towing **winch** designed to take a pre-determined load. When the load is exceeded the winch pays out wire and when the load is relaxed the winch takes in wire.

Constructive total loss
Ship wrecked beyond recovery or so badly damaged that salvage or repair would be uneconomical.

Contact breaker
Device for breaking and re-making an electrical circuit.

Contact feed heater
Boiler feed water heater where the feed water and the heating steam are in physical contact.

Contactor
Mechanical switching device with only one position of rest, capable of making, carrying and breaking currents under normal circuit conditions, including operating overload conditions.

Container box
Portable compartment designed to allow goods to be sent from door to door without handing from the initial packing to final discharge.They may be carried by road, rail or ship, or a combination of all three. The most common sizes are 20ft long by 8ft wide by 8.5 ft high and 40ft long, with other dimensions similar to the 20 footer. Commonly named boxes. A **container ship** capacity is expressed in **TEU,** that is twenty foot equivalent units.

Containership
Containers are loaded at a factory or assembly point, conveyed by road or rail to the dock side, and then placed on board the ship. A cellular container ship carries containers in the holds and on the weather deck. In the holds there is a cellular structure of angle bars forming guides into which the containers are stowed one on top of another. These vessels are virtually single deckers with machinery towards the after end. Very large hatchways are enclosed by flush hatch covers and additional containers are stowed on open deck and anchored in position by wire ropes. Open Hatch Container ships are a more recent development. Special cranes are required at container ports to cope with the containers. Containerships are normally faster than traditional cargo ships and speeds of around 26 knots are quite common.

Containment boom
Floating, flexible boom placed on the surface of the sea to contain an oil slick.

Continental shelf
Sea bottom from shore to a depth of 200 metres. Width varies from nearly zero to 800 miles.

Continuous duty
Requirement of service demanding operation at a substantially constant load for an indefinite length of time.

Continuous maximum rated
Designation for ac and dc motors and generators indicating that they are designed for continuous operation at a designated load.

Continuous sea service rating
Designed power output from a ship's engine obtained during normal sea service conditions on a continuous basis.

Continuous survey
Classification designation where machinery and equipment are examined in rotation over the entire survey period.

Contra rotating propellers
Propulsion arrangement with two **propellers** rotating in opposite directions on the same shaft.

Conract of Affreightment
Term used to describe the **chartering** of a ship.

Control
Any purposeful action on or in a system to meet specified objectives. Control may be an open or closed loop, manual or automatic.

Control circuit
Circuit that carries the electric signals directing the performance of a controller but not the main power circuit.

Control valve
Valve regulating the flow of a liquid. Usually operated from a remote position as part of the correcting unit of an automatic control system. Can be pneumatic, electric or hydraulic.

Controllable pitch propeller (CPP)
Propeller made up of a boss with separate blades mounted onto it. An internal mechanism enables the blades to move simultaneously through an arc to change the pitch angle and therefore the pitch. Astern thrust can be produced without changing the rotation direction of the engine. *See* Figure 14.

Convection
Transfer or conveyance of heat by a freely moving gas or liquid.

Convention
Assembly of interested parties to consider legislation on vital matters. A maritime example is the International Maritime Organisation **(IMO)**, who give consideration to wide ranging issues in the marine world.

Convertor, rotary
A **synchronous** machine with a single **armature** winding and a commutator and slip rings for converting ac into dc, or vice versa.

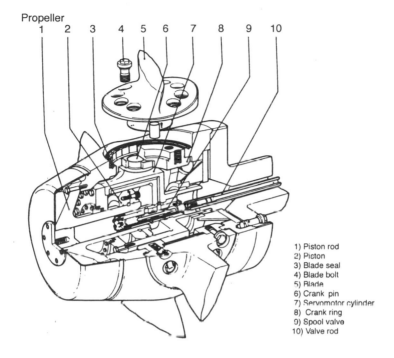

Propeller

1 2 3 4 5 6 7 8 9 10

1) Piston rod
2) Piston
3) Blade seal
4) Blade bolt
5) Blade
6) Crank pin
7) Servomotor cylinder
8) Crank ring
9) Spool valve
10) Valve rod

Figure 14 Controllable Pitch Propeller

Conway Merchant Navy Trust

Founded in 1859, the HMS Conway Merchant Navy Cadet school prepared boys for careers as officers in the British Merchant Navy. The school closed in 1970, however, the Trust as its successor maintains the same objectives and offers full sponsorship to a small number of Deck and Engineer cadets.

Coolers

Heat exchangers arranged to remove heat from a volume or stream of gas or liquid. The latent heat of evaporation of another fluid, frequently water, can be used to absorb unwanted heat and improve efficiency of the system.

Cooling system

Piping and heat exchanger network where a fluid (usually water) is used to remove heat from a piece of machinery. The system normally includes a **heat exchanger**, which is sea water cooled, however, fresh water cooling is sometimes used to avoid corrosion problems.

Copper (Cu)
Ductile material with good electrical conductivity, widely used in electrical equipment. Due to its corrosion resistance it is an integral part of many alloys, especially **bearing** materials such as bronze and brass.

Copper strip corrosion
Measure of a petroleum product's tendency to corrode copper.

Core
(1) Cylindrical section of rock or sediments obtained when a core barrel with annular bits is withdrawn from a well during drilling. (2) Magnetic material upon which the electro magnetising coil is fixed. (3) Conductor and its insulation which are part of an electric cable.

Core plug
Plug for blanking off a core or fettling hole in an iron casting. Such a plug may provide access to the cooling water of a cylinder block.

Corliss valve
Steam engine valve with an oscillating rotary motion over a port for admission of steam and its exhaust, the motion being controlled by an **eccentric**-driven wrist plate.

CO_2 recorder
Instrument providing a record of the carbon dioxide content in any enclosed space or in a gas stream such as engine or boiler exhaust.

Corresponding speed
William **Froude** studied the wave pattern of geometrically similar forms at different speeds and found that the wave patterns appeared to be identical when the models were run at speeds proportional to the square root of their lengths. The corresponding speed is the speed of the model (V1) where:

$$\frac{V1}{\sqrt{L1}} = \frac{V2}{\sqrt{L2}}$$

The formula is used to estimate ship speed (V2) from the results of tank tests on a model. *See* **Froude's Law of Comparison.**

Corrosion
Chemical reaction of a metal with its environment. Any chemical reaction resulting in the conversion of useful materials, generally metals or alloys, into substances of no value. Rust is the most common example of corrosion.

Corrosion clover leaf
Pattern of wear that takes place in the cylinder liner of a diesel engine. Increased wear may take place between lubrication quills due to the possible

reduction in the level of alkaline lubricating oil at this part of the liner. The amount of oil present may not be enough to neutralise the corrosive products of fuel combustion, and a clover leaf pattern of wear appears. The corroded area varies inversely as the distance between control points.

Corrosion fatigue
Deterioration of a metal by the combination of fluctuating stresses and a corrosive environment.

Corrosion inhibition
The prevention of corrosion. Can take a number of forms such as **cathodic protection** or the application of protective coatings and inhibitors.

Corrosion piece
In a salt water cooling system manufactured in copper alloys, corrosion of the alloys is reduced by the introduction of a length of steel pipe or iron sandwich piece. The iron or steel acts as a sacrificial **anode** protecting the adjoining copper alloys from corrosion. Similar arrangements are fitted in steel or galvanized steel salt water systems. Corrosion pieces are fitted in pipe sections where renewal is easiest.

Corrosive wear
(1) Condition where corrosion and wear occur simultaneously. The most common is in **fretting corrosion** where the mutual movement of surfaces in close contact generates wear debris and increased wear between surfaces, such as in a push fit. (2) In diesel engines this term relates to the sulphur content of the fuel which, if not neutralised by an alkaline cylinder oil, may corrode the liner promoting an etching process revealing the **pearlite** and **stellite** (phosphide) structure of the iron. Maintaining temperature above the **dew point** is also vital in combating cold corrosion. If acids are not neutralised in the cylinders, they may enter the crankcase attacking the crankshaft and bearings.

COSAG
Combined Steam And Gas Turbine Plant (RN).

Cotter pin
Pin, usually either tapered or split, inserted through a shaft engaging with holes or castellations in a nut or collar so as to prevent accidental turning or slackening. As a method of locking nuts this application is now becoming less common because of the introduction of lockwashers and adhesive chemical preparations such as Loctite. A cotter may also take the form of a rectangular section tapered key, like those used to set up or adjust the halves of big end bearings, typically those of steam locomotives. A further form, usually of circular cross-section with a tapering flat machined on one side, is

used to locate a crank on a shaft and to enable torque to be transmitted, such as on the pedal cranks of bicycles.

Coulomb (C)
Unit of electrical charge. The quantity of electricity transported in one second by a current of one ampere.

Coulomb friction
Term used to indicate frictional force is proportional to normal load.

Counter
Portion of **stern** overhanging the **rudder.**

Couple
Pair of forces, equal and parallel, acting in opposite directions with a tendency to rotate the body on which they act. The moment of couple is equal to the magnitude of one of the forces multiplied by the perpendicular distance between their lines of action.

Coupling
Mechanical connection between two parts or circuits. Power or energy is transferred from one to the other. May be electrical, mechanical or hydraulic.

Covered electrode
Metal electrode used in **arc welding** with a coating that acts as a flux to assist the welding process.

Cowl
Shaped top of a natural ventilation trunk which can be rotated to draw air into or out of the ventilated space. Also the cover of a ships funnel.

CPD
Continuous Professional Development. Structured way a professional engineer can keep up-to-date with their field of expertise.

CPI
Characters per inch. The amount of characters a computer printer can print in one inch of space.

CPU
Central Processing Unit.

Crack arresters
Design features incorporated into a structure to impede the propagation of a brittle crack, particularly useful in large welded structures. They may take the form of a different weld material or the addition of riveted members. Rivet holes can often stop a crack reaching its own **critical crack length.**

Cracking
A conversion process whereby lighter oils are produced from heavy oils such as **(a) thermal cracking (b) catalytic cracking (c) hydro cracking**. In petroleum refining, refers to breaking large molecules to form smaller molecules, creating lighter compounds.

Crack detection
Method of detecting cracks or inclusions in metallic parts.

Cradle
Supporting framework for launching a ship.

Crank
Offset section of a **crankshaft** to which a **connecting rod** is attached permitting the transfer of motion.

Crank angle
Angle of **crankshaft** crank determined by its relationship to top or bottom dead centre.

Crankcase monitoring
Indicating or recording conditions inside a crankcase with a system of sensors and instruments showing the extent of smoke, ranges in temperature, or the proportion of inflammable gas or liquid particles present. Warns of imminent danger.

Crankshaft
Main rotating member in base of engine transmitting power to both flywheel and power train.

Crankshaft deflection
Measurement taken by a micrometer dial gauge inserted between the crank webs while the crankshaft moves through one revolution. Used to check engine alignment.

Crank throw
Radial distance from centre line of crankshaft to centre of a crankpin. Equal to half the stroke.

Crank web
Arm or side of crank.

Crater
Cup shaped depression in a weld. The arc pushes the molten metal away from the centre of the point being welded forming a crater.

Crawl

(1) When an **induction electric motor** runs to only one seventh of full speed due to a seventh harmonic in the field form. **(2)** Defect on paintwork consisting of the formation of wrinkles before drying.

Creep

Continuous, slow change in deformation of stressed material. Exhibited by most metals at elevated temperatures at stresses well below the yield point at room temperature. Boiler **superheater** tubes are especially susceptible.

Creep rupture

When stress is imposed for long periods at the working temperature until fracture occurs.

Crevice corrosion

Type of **corrosion** from differential aeration cells arising due to oxygen depletion in a crevice. Occurs between adjacent components and in bolted and rivetted joints. Stainless steels are particularly sensitive to this.

CRINE

*C*ost *R*eduction *I*nitiative for the *N*ew *E*ra. Systematic approach to project control in the offshore industry aimed at minimising costs.

CRISTAL

*C*ontracts *R*egarding an *I*nterim *S*upplement to *T*anker *L*iability for oil pollution.

Critical crack length

When a crack exists and is subjected to repeated loading, there exists for each material and each stress level in the material, a length beyond which the crack is producing more energy than it is consuming so the rate of cracking is accelerated.

Critical path analysis (CPA)

Method of planning a complex operation, or series of interdependent processes, to reveal the timing of each stage to ensure completion of the whole operation to target. The analysis highlights long lead items, enabling these to be progressed.

Critical pressure

Pressure at which a gas will liquefy at its critical temperature.

Critical speed

When a rotating shaft or system becomes dynamically unstable. It is influenced by the stiffness of its bearings and their supports. The fundamental critical speed of a shaft is equal to its natural **frequency** in lateral vibration.

Critical speeds for particular pieces of machinery are often shown on their revolution counters.

Critical temperature
(1) Temperature at which magnetic materials lose their magnetic properties, about 800°C for iron and steel, or at which some change occurs in a metal or alloy during heating or cooling. **(2)** Temperature above which a given gas cannot be liquefied, limiting the number of gases suitable for use in refrigeration.

Cross curves
Curves of righting levers (GZ) plotted on a base of displacement for constant angles of heel. *See also* **curve of statical stability** and Figure 12.

Cross flooding
When a compartment on one side of a ship is flooding and the ship is beginning to **heel** excessively, the corresponding compartment on the opposite side may be flooded to return the ship to the upright position.

Cross ties
Horizontal strengthening struts introduced in large wing tanks to stiffen tank side boundary bulkhead structures against transverse distortion under liquid pressure.

Cross trees
Thwartship members on mast to support derricks away from the mast.

Crosshead
Lower end of a piston rod. Carries top end of **connecting rod**.

Crosshead engine
Engine in which the **connecting rod** is connected to a **crosshead** travelling in guides, and the crosshead is in turn is connected to the corresponding **piston rod**. Most often in large two stroke engines.

Crown
(1) Uppermost section of a drilling derrick. *See* Figure 8. **(2)** Denotes the round up or **camber** of a deck.

Crowning
Progressive reduction of tooth thickness towards the ends of a gear tooth. *See* Figure 1.

Crown block
Fixed system of pulleys at the top of a drilling derrick for raising and lowering equipment such as the **drill string and casing**. *See* Figure 8.

Crown wheel
Larger wheel of a **bevel reduction gear** as shown in Figure 5.

Crow's nest
Look-out position on the upper foremast.

Crude assay
Procedure for determining the general distillation and quality characteristics of a crude oil.

Crude oil
Naturally occurring mixture consisting predominantly of hydrocarbons plus sulphur, nitrogen and/or oxygen derivatives of hydrocarbons, that can be removed from the earth or seabed in liquid or gaseous form.

Crude oil washing (COW)
Cargo oil tank cleaning system where crude oil is sprayed onto the surfaces of the tank sides and bottom to remove sludge.

Cruiser stern
Rounded stern which is hydrodynamically efficient and improves water flow into and away from **propeller**.

Crutches
Posts on the deck forming a crutch that the ends of a **derrick** can rest on then be secured to when not in use.

Cryogenic
Pertaining to extremely low temperatures.

Cryogenics
Study and science of freezing mixtures and techniques associated with sub-zero temperatures.

Cupro-nickel
Name given to copper-rich alloys of copper and nickel. The most common alloys contain 10, 20 and 30 per cent nickel and are used in a variety of marine applications such as sea water piping and heat exchanger tubes. Additions of 1 per cent each of iron and manganese are made to produce the best corrosion resistant alloys.

Curie point
Temperature when ferro-magnetic materials lose ferro-magnetic properties.

Current (I)
Flow of electricity along a conductor. **SI unit** is the **ampere.**

Cursor
(1) Movable marker on a slide rule. (2) Small flashing line or rectangle displayed on a computer monitor to indicate position.

Curtis turbine
An **impulse turbine** with more than one row of blades following each row of nozzles, such as in velocity compounding.

Curve of statical stability
Curve of righting arms to the base of angle of inclination for fixed displacement. Such a curve is readily obtained from a set of **cross curves**.

Cut off
Point at which a valve closes the port opening of a steam reciprocating engine cylinder to the admission of steam, generally expressed as a percentage or fraction of the stroke.

Cutter stock
Lighter oils/solvents blended with heavy fuel oils to reduce viscosity and improve stability.

Cybernetics
The science of systems of control and communications in animals and machines.

Cycle
The complete series of a periodic quantity which occur during a period. In alternating current it is one complete set of positive and negative values.

Cyclic hardening
Hardening of a material under repeated loading.

Cyclic softening
Softening of a material under repeated loading.

Cycloidal propeller
Combined steering and propulsion device comprising a number of vertical blades arranged to rotate and revolve to give thrust in any desired direction. *See also* **Voith Schneider.**

Cylinder
Tubular chamber in which the piston of an engine or pump reciprocates; the internal diameter is called the **bore**, and the piston-travel the **stroke**.

Cylinder block
Housing on an engine that contains the **cylinder**.

Cylinder head
Casting containing valves and injectors that bolt to the top of a cylinder block and seal off the cylinder.

Cylinder liner
Machined sleeve pressed into a **cylinder block** in which the **piston** moves up and down.

Cylinder oil stock
Residuum of vacuum distillation generally of paraffinic base. Such oils, compounded or otherwise, are used for lubrication such as in steam cylinders or reduction gears.

D

Dalton's Law
Discovery by John Dalton that in a mixture of gases the total pressure is the sum of the pressures of each of the constituents.

Damper
Hinged flap used to control gas flow in a boiler uptake.

Damping
(1) A ship has six degrees of freedom, **heaving, swaying, surging, rolling, pitching and yawing.** The first three are linear motions. Rolling is rotation about a longitudinal axis, pitching is rotation about a transverse axis, and yawing is rotation about a vertical axis as shown in Figure 15. It is necessary to damp these motions and many devices have been suggested such as passive water tanks and activated fins. (2) Damping units are fitted to control systems to avoid surging and excessive oscillation in machinery systems. Friction and viscosity have the same effect.

Dangerous goods
Potentially hazardous cargo such as toxic or flammable goods. The shipper must notify the shipping company of such cargo, which is then usually carried on deck. **IMO** have produced a code for the carriage of dangerous goods in ships **(IMDG Code).** This code recognises nine broad classes of such goods and is universally accepted.

Dangerous spaces
Cargo or tanker space where **flammable** or explosive vapour can accumulate.

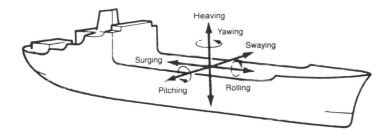

Figure 15 Six Degrees of Freedom

Dashpot
Damping device comprising a **piston** in a cylinder. Liquid or air may be used to provide the fluid friction.

Data base
Assembly of information that can be collected in a computer programme and extracted in a variety of forms to meet specific requirements such as engine type, **bore** size and horse power.

Data logger
Used in centralised instrumentation to continuously monitor machinery.

Date line
Line on the 180th **meridian** where the dates on each side differ by one day

Datum
Level or value used as a base reference point or line to which varying quantities and dimensions can be related.

Davits
Supports under which lifeboats are stored and launched.

Dead angle
Angle of movement of the **crank** of a reciprocating steam engine during which the engine will not start when the steam is admitted due to the ports being closed by the slide valve.

Dead centre
Either of two points in an engine crank cycle at which the crank and the connecting rod are in line. A piston is on dead centre when it is at the top or bottom of its stroke.

Dead man's handle
Handle or lever which must be manually held to maintain engine power. This equipment is widely used ashore in trains as a precaution against the driver suffering a blackout, can also be fitted in some smaller ships.

Dead reckoning
Navigation based upon the distance and direction travelled from a position of known co-ordinates.

Deadlight
Steel cover for a **porthole** in heavy weather, usually hinged and provided with strong screws and wing nuts.

Deadrise
The **athwartship** rise of bottom **shell plating** from **keel** to the **bilge**. Also known as **rise of floor**. *See* Figure 6.

Dead ship
Describes a ship without its own means of steering and propulsion.

Deadweight
Weight (in **tonnes**) of cargo, stores, fuel, passengers, and crew on a ship when loaded to its **maximum summer loadline**. Also the difference between a ship's **loaded displacement** and **lightweight** (light displacement).

De-aerator
Equipment heating boiler feed water under pressure to remove dissolved air and minimise boiler internal corrosion.

Decarbonising
Process of removing carbonaceous matter from the inside surfaces of an engine and of refurbishing the valves and pistons.

Decantation
Separation of a solid from a liquid, or a liquid from a solid, by sucking, pumping or pouring the liquid away without disturbing the solid or liquid settled below.

Decca Navigator
Co-ordinated navigation system developed in the UK.

Deceleration
Rate of decrease in the speed of an engine or moving part.

Deci (d)
Prefix to **SI units** denoting one tenth of the unit.

Decibel (dB)
Unit of sound pressure or noise intensity. *See also* **phon.**

Deck
Platform or horizontal floor on a ship extending from side to side.

Deck head
Underside of a **deck.**

Deck house
Superstructure found on upper deck of a ship which does not extend across the full breadth of the ship.

Deck, main
Principal deck or strength deck that for structural reasons is an essential part of the hull.

Deck pipe
Pipe through which the anchor cable passes to the **chain locker.**

Deck seal
Non-return valve arrangement preventing the back-flow of flammable gases from cargo tanks into an inert gas plant.

Deck, shelter
Deck above the main deck. If not permanently closed against the weather the space is exempt from tonnage dues.

Deck, tween
In a cargo ship, any deck between the bottom of the ship and the main deck, or the main deck and the superstructure deck above. *See* Figure 13.

Deckload capacity
Weight of equipment and stores that a drill rig can accommodate.

Declination
Angular distance north or south of the **celestial** equator. Used as a co-ordinate with **Greenwich Hour Angle** to identify positions of celestial bodies.

Declivity
Angle of launching ways at a shipyard.

Decomposition
Chemical separation of a substance into two or more substances, differing from both each other and the original substance.

Decompression levers
Levers holding exhaust valves open so no compression pressure builds up and the engine turns over easily.

Decrement
Ratio of the **amplitudes** of two successive waves in a train of damped **vibrations,** the amplitudes decreasing with time.

Dedendum
Part of the working surface of a gear tooth towards the root of the tooth as shown in Figure 1.

Deep tanks
Tanks extending from the shell or double bottom up to or beyond the lowest **deck.** May serve the dual purpose of carrying liquid in bulk or ballast when the ship is only partially loaded, provided the vessel does not have segregated ballast. Can be used for bulk or general cargo as it has hatches that are oil-tight. A longitudinal division is fitted to reduce free-surface effect.

Deep well pump
Centrifugal pump to raise the fluid placed at the bottom of a deep bore hole or at any low point in a system containing fluids. Usually driven by an integral electric motor.

Deflection
Linear measurement of the amount of movement of an object or structure subjected to a bending moment, a shear force or a couple.

Deformation
Change in shape of a component under stress. Elastic deformation occurs if the amount of applied stress does not exceed the **elastic limit** of the material as the original dimensions will be restored when the stress is removed. Plastic deformation occurs if the stress is above the elastic limit; the resulting deformation is permanent.

Degaussing
Neutralising the magnetic field of a vessel by direct-current electric coils permanently installed in a vessel. Method of protection against magnetic mines.

Dehumidifiers
Substances or systems removing moisture from the atmosphere. Chemicals such as calcium chloride and silica gel absorb water from the atmosphere.

Dehydration
Elimination or removal of water by chemical action or heating.

Deka (da)
Prefix to **SI units** equal to ten times the unit.

Delay period
Time between fuel injection and pressure rise in a diesel engine.

Delivered power
Propulsive power which must be available at the **propeller** in order to drive the ship at the designed speed. The units **shp** and **bhp** are often used. *See* **horse power.**

Demineralising Plant
Plant for removing the last traces of impurities from water. Ion exchange plants can produce water with only 0.1 parts per million of impurity.

Demise
Temporary transfer of a vessel to another party, taking control away from the **shipowner** for the period of charter.

Demulsibility
Resistance of an oil to **emulsification.** Also the ability of oil to separate from water. The higher the demulsibility rating, the faster the separation.

Demurrage
(1) When the **charterer** delays a vessel beyond the allocated time for cargo loading or discharge. **(2)** Rate of pay or sum payable to the **shipowner** for the detaining of his vessel.

Density
Absolute relationship between the mass and volume of a substance at a stated temperature. Marine fuel and lubricant density is usually quoted as kg/m^3 at 15°C. Typical marine fuel densities are marine diesel fuel 820.0 to 880.0 and marine heavy fuel 930.0 to 1020.0. Lubricants cover a wide range, however, a typical diesel engine crankcase would have a density of 900.0.

Department of Transport
United Kingdom Government department responsible for maritime affairs. Day to day work is carried out by their deputised authority, the **Marine Safety Agency (MSA).**

Deposits
Relating to accumulations of sludge, varnish and carbonaceous residues derived from factors such as unburnt or partially burnt fuel, breakdown of crankcase lubricant, water, carbon residue, dust, and wear particles in diesel engines. Excessive deposits within fuel or lubricant systems can cause blockage of filters, centrifuges, heaters leading to engine stoppage and other damage.

Depreciation
Reduction in the value of plant and equipment over a period of time due to wear, tear and obsolescence.

Depth moulded
Vertical distance at amidships from the **keel** to the uppermost deck, taken inside the plating at the ship's side as shown in Figure 6.

Derating
Operation of a diesel engine at normal maximum cylinder pressure for continuous sea service rating, with lower brake mean effective pressure **(bmep)** and shaft speed. Means of reducing the specific fuel oil consumption **(sfoc)**.

Derelict
Ship, still afloat, abandoned at sea.

Derived fuel
Form of energy produced from a basic fuel source such as coal or oil.

Derrick
(1) Woodspar or steel tube used with the winch for discharging and unloading cargo. Rapid loading and unloading of cargo from holds is an important factor in the economic efficiency of a ship leading to the development of other means such as side loading through doors in the side shell rather than hatches. This permits the use of fork lift trucks as well as cranes. **(2)** Elongated pyramid construction situated on a drilling platform containing all equipment for drilling and servicing oil and gas wells. *See* Figure 8.

Derrick, heavy
Strong derrick for lifting heavy masses with a special heel fitting and socket secured to the deck. *See* Figure 7.

Desalination
Removal of salt from sea water. Ships plants are usually of the multi-stage evaporating and condensing types producing fresh water while discharging concentrated brine.

Dessicant
Substance absorbing moisture, such as anhydrous calcium chloride, used as a drying agent.

De-superheater
Heat exchanger removing all or part of the superheat temperature from the main steam of the boiler before the steam is used for auxiliary purposes.

Detergency
Cleansing, purging action. Is the property in engine lubricating oils that

helps control deposits, preventing particles from adhering to engine parts by keeping them in colloidal suspension.

Detergents
Substances, usually in solution, for degreasing and cleaning. Surface active agents, unlike soaps, do not leave a deposit on the cleaned article.

Deterioration
Any undesirable physical or chemical change.

Detonation
The **combustion** of part of the compressed mixture in an internal combustion engine after the main ignition point, often accompanied by a **knock**. *See* **after burning** and **knocking**.

Detuner
Auxiliary vibrating or rotating mass connected to machinery with springs to dampen vibration characteristics.

Deuterium
An **isotope** of hydrogen with double the mass. Deuterium oxide (D_2O) is heavy water, with density 1.105.

De-vaporiser
Vent condenser gases released by the **de-aerator** pass through to give up their heat energy to the circulating feed water.

Developed area
Area of a curved surface when laid out on a flat surface, such as a propeller blade. *See* Figure 9.

Development well
Well drilled with a view to producing oil or gas in a proven field.

Devil's claw
Claw attached to fore part of a **windlass.** Can be fitted over a link in the chain, a screw arrangement allows it to be heaved tight, taking the weight of the anchor off the windlass when the anchor is housed.

Dew point
If a sample of air is lowered in temperature it becomes saturated. Further reduction creates condensation. The temperature when this happens is the **dew point** for that sample. The amount of water vapour present is important in relation to the maximum amount the air can contain at that temperature. The ratio is called **relative humidity**.

Dezincification
Corrosion of an alloy of copper and zinc (usually brass) that involves loss of zinc and a surface residue of loosely adherent or spongy copper.

DGPS
*D*ifferential *G*lobal *P*ositioning *S*ystem.

Diac
Semiconductor device comprised of two silicon controlled **rectifiers** connected back-to-back on a single piece of silicon without the gate terminal. May be used in the triggering circuit of a **triac**.

Diamagnetic
Material with a relative **permeability** less than unity.

Diaphragms
(1) Partitions in instruments. (2) Disc pierced with circular holes. A diaphragm meter is an instrument with a diaphragm or plate inserted in the pipe, a hole in the plate permits the water to pass. The difference of pressure on either side of the plate gives a measure of the flow.

Dielectric
Liquid, solid or gas in which an electric field can be maintained with little or no external electrical energy supplied. An **insulator**.

Diesel electric drive
System where the ship's main diesel engines are used to drive generators which produce electricity to run motors that in turn drive the main propulsion machinery. Generators also provide electrical power for other electrical equipment on board. Widely used when there is a significant power requirement in addition to the main propulsion, such as in cable laying and dredging craft. Most recent cruise ships are diesel electric due to the huge electrical load in addition to propulsion requirements.

Diesel engine
Predominant marine propulsion engine. An internal combustion engine where the fuel is ignited by the heat of the compressed air. May be of **four stroke, two stroke, trunk piston** or **crosshead** design.

Diesel index
Figure calculated from **aniline point** and **specific gravity** used as an indication to the **ignition quality** of a diesel fuel. Of the same order as the **cetane number**.

Dieso
Joint services Nato designation for a range of distillates suitable for all machinery on Navy ships including boilers, diesel engines and gas turbines.

Differential aereation
Local effect due to differences in oxygen concentration, usually in the same material. An **electrolytic** cell is set up leading to corrosion of the area deficient in oxygen. *See also* **crevice corrosion.**

Differential pressure
Difference in pressure existing between two points.

Diffuser
Chamber surrounding the impeller of a centrifugal pump or compressor, where some of the **kinetic** energy of a fluid is converted into pressure energy due to an increasing cross-sectional area of the flow path.

Digital
Making calculations with data represented by digits. A digit is any number from 0 to 9, using the number base 10. A digital computer uses binary code (numbers to the base 2) to represent numbers or words. Digital Instruments tend to be smaller and more accurate than an **analogue** solution, such as the pocket calculator versus slide rule.

Digital computer
Equipment capable of performing arithmetic computation at high speed. Digital computers are particularly suited to calculations of a repetitive nature and for manipulating large volumes of data.

Diluent
Term used in fuel blending to describe a liquid, often a distillate, used to cut back the viscosity/density of a heavier fuel.

Dilution
In engine system oils, refers to contamination with engine fuel. Distillate fuel reduces flash point and viscosity, residual fuel reduces flash point and increases viscosity.

DIN
Deutche Industrie-Norm. German Industrial Standards similar to **British Standards.**

Diode rectifier
Electronic valve containing an **anode** and **cathode** allowing current to flow in only one direction, such as when the anode is positive; a semiconductor device with two terminals exhibiting a non-linear voltage-current characteristic.

Direct current (dc)
Electrical current flowing in one direction, practically non-pulsating current.

Direct current balancer
Comprises two or more similar **direct current** machines, usually with shunt or compound excitation, directly coupled to each other and connected in series across the outer conductors of a multiple wire system of distribution.

Directional drilling
Form of drilling requiring specialised tools to deviate the well away from the vertical, resulting in a curved profile.

Directional well
Well drilled at an angle away from the vertical. Also called a deviated well.

Direct drive
Coupling of a propulsion engine to a **propeller** using a shaft without intermediate gearing or electrics.

Direct expansion refrigeration
Refrigeration system where the liquid refrigerant is expanded by passing through a regulating valve.

Direct injection
Injecting fuel directly into the combustion chamber of a diesel engine.

Direction finder
Radio receiver with loop aerial that can rotate to determine the bearing of a transmitting station or radio beacon.

Disc area ratio
Developed blade area of a **propeller**, including the **boss**, divided by the area of the circle where the diameter (D) is the propeller diameter. *See* Figure 9.

Discrimination
Smallest change in the measured quantity, producing a notable movement of an index or pointer.

Disengaging gear
Equipment allowing the rapid release of a **lifeboat** from its falls when it is to be lowered into the water.

Dispersancy
Property of a lubricating oil achieved by the addition of metallo additives preventing deposit forming material in the oil from agglomerating into larger particles, by keeping them in a finely divided state. Highly desirable in diesel engine lubricating oils.

Displacement

Weight of water, in tonnes, displaced by a ship. **loaded displacement** includes cargo, stores, passengers, and crew. Light displacement (**light-weight**) is the tonnage displaced without the items detailed in loaded displacement. The weight of a warship is always quoted as displacement tonnage. Ships sold for scrap use displacement tonnage as their sale weight.

Displacement pump

Pump where liquid is displaced from suction to discharge by the mechanical variation of the volume of the pump chamber or chambers. Self priming, they can deal with substances from a level below the pump.

Dissolved oxygen

Natural water, salt or fresh, contains a quantity of air expelled on boiling. The oxygen content is important in its contribution to the corrosion process. Sea water contains about 0.5 per cent by weight of dissolved oxygen.

Dissolved solids

Impurities dissolved in pure water which need to be at a minimum in boilers and evaporators. The preferred unit is parts per million (ppm), one part per million representing one part of solid matter dissolved in one million parts of pure water by mass

Distillate fuel

Fuel extracted from crude oil by distillation. In marine practice the term normally refers to a distillate marine diesel or gas oil.

Distillation

Process for converting liquid into vapour, then condensing the **vapour** and collecting the liquid distillate. An oil refinery fractionating column separates **crude oil** into its various fractions such as gases and gasolines, allowing gases and liquids with different boiling points to be separated at different levels in the column.

Distiller

Unit for converting sea or river water into distilled water for boiler feed or drinking water. **Saturated** or exhaust steam is circulated in a steam coil which heats the sea water under a vacuum. The resulting vapour is condensed in a cooler or distiller. Heating may be carried out by electric coils in smaller units.

Distributed winding

Winding of a rotating electrical machine with coils occupying several slots per pole.

Distribution
Provision of electrical supply to equipment, often at different voltages.

Distribution board
Board where various items of electrical equipment are grouped for ease of distribution. Includes lighting and other minor items.

Distributor
Type of **internal combustion engine** fuel injection pump using one central pumping element with a rotating distributor head that sends the fuel to each cylinder in turn.

Disturbance
Any change inside or outside a control system that upsets the **equilibrium.**

Diversity factor
Ratio of the estimated consumption of a group of power-consuming appliances under normal working conditions to the sum of their nominal ratings.

Diverter
(1) Resistor connected in parallel with a winding of a machine to divert a fixed or variable fraction of the current. **(2)** Inflatable **torus** that, when pressurised, seals the drill rig annulus space allowing drilling mud to be diverted to mud pits on the drilling platform.

DnV
Det norske Veritas. Norwegian **classification society** founded in 1864.

Dock
Place where ships are moored for loading, discharging, repairs or fitting out during construction. A dry or graving dock is pumped out and maintained dry while the ship is within. A wet dock is usually a large area where a ship remains afloat, often isolated from tidal movements by a lock gate. A floating dock can be submerged sufficiently for a ship to be floated onto it and then raised to lift the ship clear of the water.

Dock dues
Payments made for use of a **dock** and its equipment.

Docking bracket
Vertical stiffener fitted between each transverse bulkhead to support the centreline girder of an oil tanker.

Docking plan
Provides essential information to the dockmaster. Consists of an outboard profile and midship section. Frame spacing, extent of **double bottom**, decks, **watertight bulkheads**, and machinery spaces are shown. Positions of all

openings in shell below waterline, **rise of floor, bilge radius, bilge keels,** and bottom longitudinals are also indicated.

Docking plug
Plug consisting of a threaded bolt; fitted in all **double bottom** tanks to allow draining prior to examination in a **dry dock**.

Dodger
Screen used as a protection from spray.

Dog
Small metal fastener or clip used to secure doors and hatchcovers.

Dogleg
Abrupt change in direction of a **well bore**.

Dog shores
Supporting timbers for a ship under construction on a slipway located between the standing or fixed ways and blocks on the sliding way; holds the ship until it is launched.

Dolphin
Island mooring generally constructed of wooden piles or cement blocks.

Donkey boiler
Small, usually vertical, auxiliary fire tube boiler to supply steam to winches or deck machinery when the main boilers are not in steam.

Donkeyman
Rating who attends a donkey boiler and assists in the engine room

DOS
Disk Operating System. A series of programs, referred to as an operating system, used to control and manage electronic files.

Dot matrix
Type of computer printer where a print head comprising a matrix of needles form the letters, numbers and graphics.

Double acting
Steam engine or pump with steam acting on both sides of the piston. Applies to diesel engines where combustion takes place on both sides of the piston.

Double beat valve
Balanced thrust control valve supplying steam to an engine. The valve has two plugs on the same spindle. Steam pressure acts on the top of one plug and bottom of the other, placing the valve in equilibrium. This allows the valve to be operated with minimum effort.

Double bottom
Space between outer and inner bottom plating of a ships hull.

Double insulation
Denotes that, on an electrical appliance with accessible metal parts, a protecting insulation has been provided in addition to the normal functional insulation protecting against electric shock in case of a breakdown in the functional insulation.

Double reduction gearing
Compact arrangement of **gearing** to give two stage reduction from the main engine to the **propeller**.

Double skin
Use of two separate material layers for containment or construction purposes. A double skin construction is used on the sides and bottom of container ships. Because of the number of tanker disasters where extensive spillage has taken place, since 1993 it is compulsory for most newly constructed tankers to have double hulls.

Doubling plates
Extra plates, bars or stiffeners, added to strengthen sections where holes have been cut.

Doublings
Overlaps in a built-up mast where the upper end of the mast overlaps the lower part extending above it.

Dowel
(1) Cylindrical wooden plug in deck plank used to plug a bolthole. (2) Close fitting pin, peg, tube, or bolt for the accurate location of mating parts.

Downcomers
Large bore pipes fitted between the water and steam drums of a watertube boiler, passing outside the furnace to ensure a natural downward flow of cooler water during steam generation.

Down to her marks
When a ship is loaded to the maximum draught for the relevant **load line.**

DRA, Haslar
*D*efence *R*esearch *A*gency, Maritime Division. Originally founded in 1882 as AEW (Admiralty Experimental Works) Haslar, at which time it was concerned with efficient hull forms, propulsion and general improvement in the design and construction of Royal Navy ships.

Drag

Negative slip. Difference between the speed as determined by **propeller** revolutions and the actual speed of a ship, when actual speed is greater than determined speed.

Drag coefficient (Cd)

Non-dimensional ratio of drag per unit of a representative area of a body, to dynamic pressure far ahead of the body.

Drag line

Wire ropes used to arrest the motion of a ship when launching it into a restricted waterway. One system is to use drag chains laid in the form of a horseshoe on either side of the ship with the rounded portion away from the water. This means that the forward portion of the drag is pulled through the remainder of the pile. The wire rope drag lines are attached to temporary pads on the side of the ship.

Drain cooler

Heat exchanger used to reduce the temperature of hot water drains from the lowest pressure feed heater before entering the condenser.

Drain hat

Bilge water collecting point in a continuous tank top designed to excluding large waste material.

Draught

Depth of water a ship floats in; the distance from the bottom of a ship to the **waterline.** If the waterline is parallel to the **keel**, the ship is said to be on the keel. If not parallel, the ship is said to be trimmed. If draught at after end is greater than at the fore end, the ship is trimmed by the stern. If the converse applies, the ship is trimmed by the bow or by the head. Draught marks are cut in the stern and stem giving the distance from the bottom of the ship.

Dredgers

Specialist ship type designed to maintain or increase the depth of port navigable channels, removing shoals and other such obstructions to ensure a clear entry passage. Dredging work demands dredger types that differ greatly in character and operation: multi-bucket; suction; grab; dipper; rock breakers.

Drift

Distance and direction a ship moves in resulting from wind or current.

Drill bit

Part of the drilling tool which cuts through the rock. *See* Figure 8.

Drill collar
Heavy length of pipe placed at the bottom of **drill string** adding weight and stability to the drilling bit. *See* Figure 8.

Drill pipe
See **drill string.**

Drill ship (DS)
Ship fitted with a drilling **derrick** that may be used to drill in waters that are to deep for a **jack-up** or **semi-submersible** rig. *See* **dynamic positioning.**

Drill string
Lengths of steel tubing roughly 10 m long screwed together to form a pipe connecting the drill bit to the drilling rig. The string is rotated to drill the hole, also serving as a conduit for the drilling mud.

Drilling mud
Mixture of clay, water and chemicals pumped down the drill string and up the annulus during drilling to lubricate the system, carry away rock cuttings and maintain the required pressure at the bit end. *See* Figure 8.

Drilling platform
Offshore platform used to drill exploration and development wells without the processing facilities of a production platform.

Drilling table
Table on the **derrick** floor where the drill pipe is rotated. Also called the rotary table. *See* Figure 8.

Drip feed
When lubricant is supplied to oiled surfaces in drops at regular intervals.

Drip proof
Enclosure for electrical equipment providing protection from falling liquids.

Droop
Variation in engine speed following a load change, approximately 4 per cent for a full load change.

Drop point
Temperature at which a grease passes from a semi-solid to a liquid under specified conditions.

Dry bulb temperature
Measurement allowing the determination of **relative humidity** in conjunction with the **wet bulb temperature**; a unit containing two thermometers is called a **psychrometer.**

Dry Dock
Dock with a watertight gate or entrance into which a ship can be floated, then the gates closed and area pumped dry. This allows repairs and maintenance to be carried out on underwater equipment such as **propellers** and **rudders**, and also permits inspection and painting of underwater surfaces.

Dry liner
Thin walled tube pressed into bored-out engine cylinder.

Dry sump
Sump from which engine system oil immediately drains and is returned to a separate tank.

DSV
Diving Support Vessel.

Dual fuel engines
Engines designed to burn either oil or gas, or a mixture of the two, with a simple automatic means of changing from one fuel to the other. Normally the gas is ignited by injection of 2–10 per cent of full load oil, however, some engines have been designed to use spark ignition when running on gas.

Ductile cast iron
Cast iron with carbon in the form of graphite spheroids to give a greater strength and ductility than grey cast iron.

Ductility
Ability of a material to withstand reasonable deformation without failing.

Duct keel
Space formed by twin longitudinal girders in a ship's double bottom. Provides longitudinal strength and is used to carry double bottom piping.

Dummy piston
A disc on the shaft of a **reaction turbine** that balances the steam thrust on turbine blades.

Dump valve
Valve used in steam systems that can open allowing excess steam to be taken to a condenser in the event of a sudden reduction in steam demand. Fitted in plants with high thermal inertia, such as nuclear reactors or exhaust gas boilers where steam generated depends on engine speed not steam demand.

Dunnage
Materials, often timber or matting, placed among cargo to prevent damage.

Duplex filter
Assembly of two filters in parallel with valving for the selection of full flow through either filter. Generally used in lubricating oil and fuel oil lines to allow rapid changeover without interrupting the flow.

Dye penetrant testing
Non-destructive test to detect surface cracks using a penetrant dye.

Dynamically supported craft
Seagoing craft not supported by the hydrostatic or buoyancy force of water displaced by the hull, such as a **hydrofoil** or **hovercraft**.

Dynamic balance
Condition where **centrifugal forces** do not produce couple or resultant force in the shaft of the rotating part due to rotation. Examples of this are the **flywheel** and **propeller**.

Dynamic positioning (DP)
Modern highly sophisticated drilling ships are fitted with fully automated dynamic positioning systems; computer controlled system allowing a vessel to operate independent of anchors or any other mechanical moorings. The system may control **bow thrusters, stern thrusters,** main propulsion **propellers,** and **rudders.** Signals from one or more position reference system indicating the present position and heading of a vessel are processed by the computer. It compares actual values with wanted values and also generates control signals to the thrusters to move or control the vessel as required. The use of mathematical modeling and signal trend analysis in computer systems allows the system to apply predictive control to generate the thrust to counteract displacing forces on a vessel before the forces have moved the vessel off the desired position. DP systems may be single, dual or even triple computer systems, depending on the degree of system redundancy required for the application and classification of the system.

Dynamic stability
Ability of a controlled system to return to a stable state after disturbance.

Dynamics
Branch of mechanics dealing with the motion of bodies (**kinematics**) and action of forces in producing or changing their motion (**kinetics**).

Dynamo
Machine converting mechanical energy into electrical energy.

Dynamometer
Machine coupled to and absorbing the power of an engine on a test bed measuring the engine **brake horse power** output.

Dyne
Unit of force that acts on a mass of one gram for one second imparting a velocity of one centimetre per second.

E

Earth lamps
Indicating lamps detecting the presence of earth faults on the system by comparative brightness, when connected between each phase or pole of an insulated system and earth.

Earth, electrical
A ship's electric circuit is earthed when a pole is connected to the general mass of the ships hull. Metal frames for electrical appliances must be earthed to protect against shock unless double insulated or supplied at extra low voltage.

Earthed system
In an ac 3-phase three or four wire system, the neutral or star point is permanently connected to earth. In a dc system, one pole is also permanently connected to the earth.

Easing gear
Means of manually operating **safety valves** from a position remote from the valves themselves.

Ebonite
Hard black material with good electrical insulating properties made by vulcanising rubber. It contains carbon black and about 30 per cent sulphur.

Eccentric
Disc on a shaft, the centre of the disc displaced relative to the shaft centre. Used to convert a rotary motion into a reciprocating rectilinear motion, such as when operating the **slide valve** of a steam engine.

ECDIS
Electronic Chart Data Information System.

Echo sounder
Instrument located on the keel of a ship to record the depth of water underneath. Works on the **sonar** principle of emitting a vertical pulse of high frequency sound waves. These waves bounce off the seabed and are picked up by a receiver on the hull that measures the time interval between transmission and return. A scale converts the interval to a water depth. *See* **ASDIC**.

ECMAR
European Co-operation for MAritime Research.

ECR
Economy Continuous Rating. Engine rating for fuel economy and speed.

Economical speed
Most cost effective speed. Requires detailed economic analysis.

Economiser
Heat exchanger that consists of a bank of tubes through which the boiler feed water is pumped. Hot boiler exit gases circulate around the tubes and transfer heat from the gas to the feed water, increasing the efficiency of boiler plant.

Eddy currents
(1) Produced in any electrically conducting material influenced by a coil with an alternating current. Used in non-destructive testing for **crack detection** in castings and welds. It is not as penetrating as **ultrasonics** or **radiography,** however, has the advantage of speed, easy automation and no need for physical contact with an object under test. (2) Water particles moving past the hull in streamline flow. When the streamline flow breaks down the water particles revolve in eddies. The energy of this motion is wasted and can be treated as an increase in resistance.

EDT
Electronic Data Transfer.

Eductor
Another name for an **ejector** or jet pump.

EEC
European Economic Community. Referred to as the Common Market.

Effective inertia
The **moment of inertia** of a mass which, if substituted for a part of a system at a given frequency, would have the same vibratory acceleration under the same vibratory torque at the point of separation as the original part. It is measured by the value of the torque.

Effective length
Ship's length that is used for speed-power calculations and the coefficients relating thereto.

Effective power
Power required to tow a ship; product of the **total resistance** and speed of the hull.

Efficiency
Measure of performance expressed as a percentage of output over input.

Effluent
Gas or vapour waste liquid from processes.

Ejector
Type of pumping device used to discharge or expel a liquid or gas from a space or tank. A jet of water, steam or air is forced under pressure from a nozzle creating a partial vacuum or low pressure area which acts on the space suction pipe. No moving parts exist in this device.

Ekranoplans
Form of ultra fast ferry developed by Russia. A combination of ship and aeroplane with speeds said to be in the range of 500 km/h. *See* **wing-in-ground effect (WIG)**.

Elastic centre
Point on section of beam midway between the **flexural centre** and centre of twist; generally all three centres are at a single point.

Elastic limit
Maximum stress that can be applied to a material without causing permanent deformation. *See* **deformation.**

Elastic ratio
Ratio of **elastic limit** to **ultimate strength** of a material.

Elastic solid
Substance in which the **strain** is fully determined by its **stress** whether stress is increasing or decreasing.

Elasticity
Ability of a material to return to its original form or size while sustaining no permanent deformation.

Elasticity, Modulus of
For a material worked within its elastic range, use the following equation:

$$\frac{stress(\sigma)}{strain(\varepsilon)} = constant(E)$$

The constant, denoted by the letter E, is **Young's modulus of elasticity**.

Elastohydrodynamic
Regime of lubrication where concentrated sliding or rolling contacts are separated by a full film of oil. Thickness of the film depends upon the viscosity of the oil and the **elastic** properties of the solids.

Elastomer
Material with properties similar to rubber. Elastomers include natural and synthetic rubbers, and plastics with similar properties.

Elastomeric
After being stretched, the ability of a material to return to its original length.

Electrode
The **conductor** electricity enters or leaves an **electrolyte** through.

Electrolysis
Effect of an electric current passing through an electrolyte transferring **ions** from one part to another.

Electrolyte
Substance in solutions in the form of electrically charged **ions**, capable of conducting electricity. Said of any liquid that can be decomposed electrically.

Electrolytic corrosion
Action caused when dissimilar metals are immersed in an electrolyte (such as salt water) and connected together to form an electric circuit. This causes one of the metals (the anode) to be attacked and wasted away. Sacrificial zinc **anodes** are often used to prevent damage to underwater fittings caused by electrolytic action, however, they must be replaced as they are gradually eaten away. Also called electrolytic electrolysis.

Electromagnet
Ferromagnetic core of soft iron surrounded by a coil. Significant magnetic effect occurs only when current flows in the coil.

Electro-motive force (emf)
Driving force of an electric current measured in volts (V).

Electron
Negatively charged elementary particle of an **atom**.

Electronics
Field of science and technology dealing with the conduction of electricity in a vacuum, gas or semiconductor, and the devices they are based on.

Electroplating
Deposit of one metal on another by electrolytic action. Metal is taken from the **anode** and deposited on the **cathode** through a solution containing the metal as an electrically charged ion.

Electroslag process
Electro fusion welding process for **butt weld**ing thick plates.

Electrostatic
Electrical phenomenon relating to electric charges without magnetic effects.

Elements
Substance that cannot be broken down into more simple forms, the ultimate chemical components of all matter. There are approximately 90 elements regarded as the building stones on which the whole universe has been constructed. *See* Appendix I.

Elevators
Clamps on a **travelling block** attached to the drill pipe of a rig to raise or lower it.

Elongation
Extension of a material when **tensile stress** is applied to it.

EMA
Engineers & Managers Association.

Embargo
Government imposed ban on the movement of ships or cargo within a specified area. Often actuated in a war zone.

Emergency fire pump
Sea water pump supplying ship's main fire pump when the machinery space pump is unavailable. Operates independent of main power sources.

Emergency generator
Diesel driven generator of sufficient capacity to supply essential circuits such as steering, navigation lights and communications. Must be an independent unit with at least two means of starting its own switchboard.

Emissions
Exhaust from diesel engine or boiler. Subject to increasing environmental laws to cut down harmful gases entering the atmosphere. *See* **noxious emissions**.

Empirical
Depending on experience or observation without regard to science or theory.

Emulsification
Mixing two mutually insoluble liquids in very fine particles to form an intimate suspension of one in the other. Emulsification of water and oil sometimes produces **viscous** sludge. Emulsified lubricating oil in turbines or diesel engines is detrimental to their performance. In certain applications, however, notably steam reciprocating engines and sterntube oils, they are deliberately manufactured to emulsify around large amounts of water.

Enclosed space entry
Special procedures adopted for safe entry into any area which can present breathing problems.

Endescope
Special instrument used to visually inspect both gas turbine **combustion chambers** and **blading**.

End float
Play or movement on a shaft in an axial direction. Also known as **end play**.

End play
See **end float**.

End point
Highest temperature reading observed on the distillation thermometer during the distillation of petroleum products. Also called **final boiling point**.

End thrust
Axial force on a **reaction** steam turbine rotor. It must be balanced out by a dummy piston or the use of double flow.

Endothermic reaction
Process accompanied by the absorption of heat.

Endurance limit
Value of alternating stress applied in a fatigue test to a test piece which fractures after a specified number of reversals.

Energy
Ability or capacity of a body to do work. For environmental reasons great emphasis is being placed on renewable energy sources. Solar energy is energy from the sun transmitted by electromagnetic radiation. Wind energy results from pressure variations in the atmosphere leading to the movement of large bodies of air. Wave energy is associated with wave height and results from the action of the wind on the sea surface.

Engine
Machine for converting heat energy into mechanical energy. In the marine environment the heat energy is mainly fuel oil and the convertor the steam or diesel engine.

Engine casing
Plating surrounding deck opening to engine room.

Engine health monitoring (EHM)
Royal Navy procedure for checking condition of gas turbines on a periodic

basis at sea. Includes visual inspection, performance and vibration analysis, and spectrometric oil analysis.

Engine indicator
Instrument connected to an engine cylinder for measuring the power developed in the cylinder at various stages of the cycle producing a pressure volume diagram (**indicator diagram**). By calculating the indicated horse power of each cylinder the entire engine can be developed.

Engineering Council (EC)
Body established in 1981 by Royal Charter to advance education and promote the science and practice of engineering for public benefit, thereby promoting industry and commerce in the United Kingdom.

Engineering Technician (Eng.Tech)
See **Institute of Marine Engineers**.

Entablature
Structure of diesel engine above bedplate and frames to which cylinders are attached. In two-cycle engines the entablature is generally of box form and serves as a manifold supplying scavenge air to the cylinder.

Enthalpy (H)
Measure of the total energy of a system including energy associated with its pressure to volume relationship and internal energy. $H=U+PV$, where $P = pressure$, $V = volume$, and $U = internal\ energy$. The first law of thermodynamics states that the change in internal energy equals the heat absorbed less the work done by the system. The enthalpy of a substance is determined by its composition, temperature and pressure, regardless of what has happened before, therefore, it is not necessary to calculate absolute enthalpy.

Entrance
Immersed body of a ship forward of the parallel middle body.

Entropy (S)
In thermal processes, a quantity which measures the extent to which the energy of a system is available for conversion to work. If a system undergoing an infinitesimal reversible change takes in a quantity of heat dQ at absolute temperature T, its entropy is increased by $dS = dQ/T$. The area under the absolute temperature-entropy graph for a reversible process represents the heat transferred in the process. For an **adiabatic** process, there is no heat transfer and the temperature-entropy graph is a straight line, the entropy remaining constant throughout the process. When a thermodynamic system is considered on the microscopic scale, equilibrium is associated with the distribution of molecules that has the greatest degree of disorder. Statistical

mechanics interprets the increase in entropy in a closed system to a maximum at equilibrium as the consequence of the trend from a less probable to a more probable state. Any process in which no change in entropy occurs is said to be **isentropic**.

Epicyclic gears

System of gears in which one or more wheels travel around the outside or inside of another wheel whose axis is fixed. The different arrangements are known as **planetary, solar** and **star** gears, shown in Figure 16.

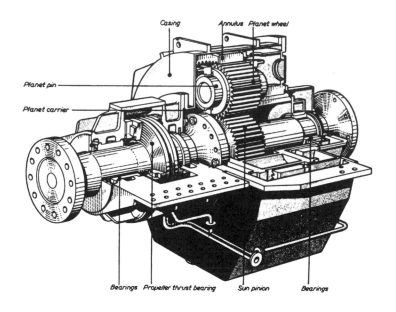

Figure 16 Epicyclic Gears

Epicycloid

Curve traced out by a point on the circumference of a circle as it rolls round the outer circumference of another circle.

EPIRB

*E*mergency *P*osition *I*ndicating *R*adio *B*eacon. **INMARSAT** system that improves the accuracy of reported positions and emergency response times.

Epoxy resins

Polymers derived from epichlorhydrin and bisphenol-A. Chemicals produced from petroleum and natural gas are the bases of epoxy resins, and as paints they have very good adhesion. They can be poured and cured at room temperature and form a tough solid substance widely used for mouldings.

EPSRC
Engineering and Physical Sciences Research Council.

Equilibrium
State of balance; situation when the resultant forces acting on a body are zero whether the body is at rest or moving with uniform velocity.

Erection
Positioning and temporary fastening together of units or fabricated parts of a ship prior to welding.

Ergonomics
Study of humans and machines working together.

Erosion
Wearing away of a material due to the **abrasion** of high speed fluids.

Escape hatch
Hatch with a cover that can be opened from either side.

ESD
Emergency Shut Down.

ESSC
Engineering Service Standing Conference responsible for standards across the Engineering professions.

Esters
Compounds of alcohols and fatty acids forming the major constituent of many **synthetic lubricants.**

Estimated position
Any position, other than a **dead reckoning** position, established from incomplete data or data of questionable accuracy.

ESV
Emergency Support Vessel. Offshore general purpose vessel.

ETA
Expected Time of Arrival.

ETA
Event Tree Analysis. An inductive (bottom up) technique for determining possible accident outcomes from specific equipment failures or human error.

Etching
(1) Method of showing the structure of metals and alloys by attacking a highly polished surface with a reagent that has a differential effect on different crystals with different constituents. (2) Removing films from the surface of materials to allow the subsequent deposition of another coating, such as paint.

ETD
*E*xpected *T*ime of *D*eparture.

Ethane (C_2H_6)
Gaseous **paraffinic hydrocarbon** present in natural gas and petroleum.

ETS
*E*mergency *T*owing *S*ystems. **IMO SOLAS** 74 Regulation 15-1, requires all tankers of 20 000 dwt or more to have ETS fitted to the aft and fore by the end of December 1998. All vessels constructed after January 1996 must have ETS.

Euler's formula
Mathematical relationship which gives the collapsing or critical load for a long straight column which is axially compressed.

Europort
Maritime exhibition held annually in Amsterdam.

Eutectic
Mixture of two or more constituents of a definite composition which solidifies at a minimum temperature below that of any of its constituents.

Eutectic change
Change from the liquid to the solid state in a **eutectic** alloy, involving the simultaneous **crystallisation** of two constituents in a binary system and of three in a ternary system.

Eutectic point
Point on an **equilibrium** diagram showing the composition of the eutectic alloy and the temperature at which it solidifies.

Eutectoid
Similar to **eutectic** except that it involves the simultaneous formation of two or three constituents from another solid constituent instead of from a melt.

Evaporation
Conversion of a liquid into a vapour.

Evaporators
Cylinders containing coils. Sea water is admitted to a **cylinder** and steam passed through coils causing the water to evaporate. Water vapour is then condensed and used for boiler feed, drinking water and domestic services.

Even keel
Condition when fore and aft **draughts** are the same and **keel** is horizontal.

Evolute
Evolute of a given curve is the locus of its centre of curvature. A curve has one evolute but an infinite number of **involutes**.

Exciter
Source of all or part of a field current which will bring about electricity generation by an **ac generator.**

Excitation winding
Winding of a rotating electrical machine to produce a **magnetic field.**

Exfoliation
The flaking off of the outer layers of an article, such as the case of a case hardened component. Also referred to as **spalling** or peeling.

Exhaust gas turbine
Turbine driven by exhaust gas from a diesel engine to power **turbo blowers** or return additional power to the engine.

Exhaust gases
Exit of gaseous products of combustion from a cylinder after completion of the power stroke by a piston. Also refers to combustion gases from a boiler or gas turbine. Major source of **waste heat** and **noxious emissions.**

Exhaust lap
Distance moved by the **slide valve** of a steam reciprocating engine from the mid-position on the port face before uncovering the steam port to exhaust. It promotes cushioning by closing the exhaust early.

Exhaust steam turbine
Low pressure steam turbine taking exhaust or bled steam from another engine.

Exhaust valve
Valve through which combustion gases leave an engine.

Exothermic reaction
Chemical reaction during which heat is generated.

Expansion valve

(1) Auxiliary valve fitted on some reciprocating steam engines used to provide an independent control of the point of cut-off. (2) Valve in **refrigeration** and **air conditioning** systems used to regulate the amount of refrigerant flowing around the circuit. When the liquid from the condenser is reduced in pressure by the valve, some liquid vaporises cooling the rest down. This mixture, mainly liquid, then passes to the **evaporator** which is the cooling medium. The amount of refrigerant passing through the valve is automatically controlled by conditions at the evaporator outlet.

Explosimeter

Instrument for testing atmosphere in an oil tank for the presence of gases.

Explosion proof

Enclosure that can withstand a particular explosion without igniting external **flammable** material.

Explosion relief valve

Valve designed so that once pressure has been relieved the valve must immediately reseat to avoid possible flames entering the engine room and/ or allowing oxygen into the crankcase. It is a requirement that relief valves are fitted to the crankcase doors of engines to release excess pressure.

Extensometer

Instrument for measuring dimensional changes of a material used on test pieces during a **tensile test** to give a close record of extensions. Minute recordings are essential when determining the **limit of proportionality,** or proof stresses.

Extra First Class Certificate

Highest level of **MSA** certification for engineer officers.

Extra Masters Certificate

Highest level of **MSA** certification for deck officers.

Extraction pump

Pump used to draw condensate directly from the condenser of a steam plant and pump it to the **de-aerator,** generally against the considerable static head of the de-aerator.

Extreme breadth

Maximum breadth over the extreme points port and starboard of a ship. *See* Figure 6.

Extreme depth

Depth of a ship from upper deck to underside of the keel. *See* Figure 6.

Extreme draught
Distance from waterline to underside of keel. *See* Figure 6.

Extreme pressure lubricants
Normal mineral oil containing added organic compounds, such as sulphur and chlorine, which react at hot spots (above 200°C) between asperities to form films of sulphide, chloride and phosphide. These films **shear** more easily than substrata meal and are used on hypoid and other heavily loaded gears, where boundary film lubrication prevails and speeds are insufficient to build up a thick film of lubricant.

Extrusion
Forming of sections by applying pressure on the mass of a substance causing it to flow through an orifice of the shape or section required.

Eyebolt
Bolt with an eye at the end for a hook.

F

Fabrication
Manufacture of various sections of a ship, often remote from each other and generally under cover, for assembly later.

Factor of safety
Ratio of **ultimate tensile strength** to working stress (estimated maximum load in service) for a material; always a value greater than one.

Factor of subdivision (F)
Value used to calculation of the permissible **floodable length** of a compartment with respect to the damage stability of a ship. The value is determined by a formula which depends upon the length of a ship and is measured by a Criterion of Service Numeral (numeral based on the relation between the volume of space allotted to passengers and machinery and the total volume).

Factories act
Act under which Dock Regulations derive authority, laying down regulations on how to organise a factory dealing with issues such as safety, first aid and overcrowding.

Fahrenheit
Method of graduating a thermometer in which the freezing point of water is marked 32°F (0°C) and boiling point 212°F (100°C), the interval being180°.

Fahrenheit is rapidly being replaced by the Celsius (Centigrade) and kelvin scales. To convert °F to °C subtract 32 and multiply by 5/9.

Fail safe
System or device that will take up a safe position or condition in the event of component failure or loss of supply and/or operating medium.

Fair
Term applied to the readjustment of ship's plating that has become slightly buckled in a **collision.**

Fairlead
Fitting allowing ropes and mooring lines to go in the required direction unobstructed. Usually fitted in the **gunwhale** or ship's rail at the **forecastle** and **stern** to facilitate a smooth entry for mooring lines.

Fairway
Navigable channel for ships entering or leaving port.

Falls
Rope used with **blocks** for lowering a lifeboat.

Fans
Device for delivering or exhausting large volumes of air or gas with a low pressure increase, fundamental to any system of mechanical ventilation. The three main types are:

Centrifugal. Widely fitted; give the best combination of high volume, high pressure and reasonably high efficiency. There are four types of **impeller:** forward curved (multi blade); backward curved (single blade); backward curved (aerofoil blade); paddle blade. Efficiencies vary from 50 per cent up to 85 per cent for the aerofoil oil blade.

Axial flow fans. Used less due to their higher noise levels and lower pressure; when fitted with a silencer they can be advantageous.

Propeller fans. Limited to roof and wall extractors due to their low pressure.

Farad (F)
Electrical unit of **capacitance** in **SI** system of units.

Fashion plate
Side plate at end of superstructure deck, generally with a curved end.

Fast line
End of offshore drilling line fixed to the reel on the draw works. So called as it travels with greater velocity than any other part of the drilling line.

Fathom
Measurement of sea depth equal to a distance of 6 ft.

Fatigue
Deterioration of the properties of a material which takes place under conditions involving fluctuating stress. Unlike **brittle fracture, fatigue fracture** generally occurs very slowly. Such fractures occur at low stresses which are applied to a structure repeatedly over a period of time. Often associated with sharp notches or discontinuities in structure. One failure mechanism of **gear teeth** and **bearings**.

Fatigue crack propagation
Progression of a crack in a material under a fluctuating stress cycle. The surface of a fatigue fracture sometimes exhibits **conchoidal** or wave marks indicating the mode of fracture. Cracks may be arrested by drilling small diameter holes at each end.

Fatigue limit
When applied in an alternating manner, the maximum stress a material can stand indefinitely without **fracture**. If carried beyond this limit a crack develops at a surface and progresses through the section under repeated alternating stress.

Fatigue test
Test subjecting a specimen to a series of fluctuating stresses until **fracture** occurs. The stress can be applied in bending, torsion, or axially in tension or compression (push-pull). The most commonly used machines (Wohler) apply a weight to the end of a cantilever beam held in a rotating chuck, thus subjecting the specimen to a complete reversal of bending stress at each revolution. The number of applications of stress are recorded on a revolution counter. By subjecting specimens of a material to fatigue tests with increasing loads, the minimum load at which the material will not fracture after a given number of stress reversals can be determined.

Fatty oils
Oils found in certain tissues of animals and plants. The fat of terrestial animals is found in the cells of the adipose tissue, in marine animals in the blubber and in some cases the liver, and in plants mostly in the seeds or fruit. Chemically, most fatty oils consist of glycerol combined with fatty acids.

Fay
Unite closely two planks or plates, bringing surfaces into intimate contact.

FEANI
European Federation of National Engineering Institutes.

Feathering
(1) Positioning of blades of a variable pitch **propeller** so that no thrust is exerted when turning. **(2)** The release of small quantities of steam by a boiler **safety valve** at a pressure below the blow off value.

Feed check valve
Boiler feed water supply valve that is non-return and can be hand regulated.

Feed heater
Heat exchanger that increases the temperature of boiler feed water generally by using some form of waste or exhaust steam which is then condensed.

Feed pump
High pressure pump that forces feed water into a boiler.

Feed regulator
Device that controls the water level in a boiler.

Feed tank
Tank that feeds a service, particularly a tank containing boiler feed water.

Feed water
Water supplied to a boiler to compensate for water lost through vapourisation.

Feedback
Transfer of a signal from the output of a system back to the input to control or stabilise the circuit. A feedback control system is one where the signal is compared with the signal equivalent to the required system condition and corrective action taken if necessary.

Feeder ship
Small ship that carries cargo from the main port to nearby ports.

Feeler gauge
Thin metal strip of a particular thickness and very fine accuracy etched with its actual value. Used alone or with similar strips to measure gaps.

FEMAS
*F*ederation of *E*uropean *A*ssociations of *M*arine *S*urveyors and Consultants.

Fender
Resilient device, generally movable, interposed between a ship's hull and the harbour walls or other ships, to minimise impact and prevent direct contact to reduce the risk of structural damage or chafing. Often of ropework, timber or pneumatic construction.

Ferrite

Name for the substantially pure **alpha iron** phase occurring in iron carbon alloys; applied to alpha iron, the solvent for other elements in alloy steels.

Ferro alloys

Alloys of iron with chromium, manganese, silicon, tungsten, molybdenum, and vanadium. Used to introduce the alloying element into steel or cast iron or to act as deoxidiser.

Ferrograph

Instrument used to determine the size and distribution of wear particles in machinery lubricating oils.

Ferrography

Scientific appraisal using optical and scanning electron microscopes to determine the number, size and composition of metal wear particles found in machinery lubricating oils. Will identify factors such as the type of wear taking place, such as fatigue or cutting, and is a valuable tool for investigating machinery breakdowns. Widely used for condition monitoring.

Ferromagnetic

Metal such as iron or cobalt which has a high magnetic permeability and retains its magnetism in the absence of an external magnetic field.

Ferrule

Metal ring or cap, strengthening or forming a joint. Used to retain tubes in condensers and heat exchangers.

Fescolising

Proprietary process for nickel plating. Enables a very heavy deposit of nickel to be applied, building up worn or undersized metal parts.

Fettling

Removing flashes from castings by a process such as hammering or shot blasting.

FEU

Forty Foot Equivalent Unit. Unit of container measurement equivalent to one 40 foot or two 20 foot containers.

Fibre optics

Use of very fine, optically insulated glass fibres to transmit light. The light can be used as part of a visual inspection system or as a control transmission system.

Fiddley

Space over the top of the boilers with iron gratings and ladders.

Field regulator
A **potentiometer** used to adjust the voltage across the field of a dc generator.

Field-coil
Winding on polepiece of motor or generator.

Filament lamp
Standard electric lamp; a filament housed inside a bulb containing an inert gas is raised to incandescence by a flow of current.

File server
Small microcomputer and large backing store device used for the management and storage of files in a computer network.

Fillet
Rounded corner inside angle of a structure or casting, or at the bottom of a **gear tooth**.

Film strength
Imprecise term denoting the ability of a surface film of lubricant to resist rupture by the penetration of asperities during sliding or rolling.

Filter
(1) Electrical network used in electronic circuits, or an optical device in optical communication systems, for the selective enhancement or reduction of specific components of an input signal. Filtering is achieved by selectively attenuating undesired components of the input signal relative to those which it is desired to enhance. A filter can consist of **inductances** or **capacitances**, resistors and capacitators and gyrators (to transform specified capacitors into inductances); it can contain amplifying stages or rely on **resonances** in **piezoelectric**, ceramic, or magnetic materials.

Digital filters. Depend on the action of externally manipulated gates to selectively block or pass certain of the pulses making up a digital signal.

Fluid filter. It is essential to keep a working fluid free from contamination to ensure reliability of the equipment. This can be achieved by the use of filters. Solid particles in a circulating liquid can be removed by fine mesh strainers in addition to felt or paper filters. Magnetic filters or separators can remove particles of ferrous, bronze and bearing metals.

Air filter. Fitted to oil and internal combustion engines to avoid excessive cylinder wear due to abrasive matter entering the engine. These consist of layers of gauze, felt and paper.

Oil pollution filter. Material which allows water to pass through while collecting or separating oil and dirt. Filters of the coalescer type can be used as the final polishing stage in the overall separation process, however, as they retain oil and solid particles, they have a limited life proportional to the amount of contamination.

Filtration
Process of mechanically removing suspended matter from a liquid or gas by passing through a **filter**.

Fin
Fixed or moveable **hydrofoil** attached to a ship in a longitudinal direction to improve the dynamic stability and manoeuvrability. *See also* **stabiliser**.

Fineness
(1) The ratio of the area of **waterplane** to the area of its circumscribing rectangle. Varies from about 0.7 to 0.9. **(2)** The value of the **block coefficient** gives a guide as to whether a ship's form is full or fine.

Fingerboard
Rack supporting tops of stands of pipe being stacked in the drilling **derrick** or mast. It has several steel fingerlike projections forming a series of slots into which a stand of drill pipe can be set as it is pulled out of the hole.

Finger plate
Fitted to a machine to indicate the running position of the rotor or a shaft.

Finite element
Small part of a large continuous structure being investigated with regard to loading. **Displacements, stresses** and **strains** are determined at the **nodes** where various elements meet. The complete structure is then analysed.

Fire brick
Refractory material used to line parts of a boiler furnace; generally composed of alumina, silica and quartz.

Fire detector
Devices distributed around a ship to detect the presence of smoke or fire. Can be **smoke detectors**, **sprinkler systems** or other specialised equipment.

Fire main
Seawater pipeline of sufficient diameter to provide a copious supply of water to at least two fire hoses. Available on deck and in the engine room.

Fire point
Lowest temperature at which an oil vaporises rapidly enough to burn for at least 5 seconds after ignition under standard test conditions. An index of the **flammability** hazard when handling petroleum products.

Firecracks
Cracks occurring on the surface of metal objects which have been repeatedly heated and cooled.

Firetube boiler
Type of boiler in which the furnace flame passes through a bank of tubes transferring heat to the surrounding water. Most early boilers were fire tube, however, this type of boiler is now used mainly for auxiliary purposes. *See also* **composite boiler.**

Fishing
Offshore term for attempting to recover lost drilling tools.

Fish tail bits
Type of **bit** used in petroleum drilling with tails and wings bevelled to form cutting edges for scraping and gouging. Used in drilling shale, sand and clay.

Fission
The splitting of certain large **atoms** during which part of the mass disappears and is converted into energy.

Fit
The dimensional relationship between mating parts. Limits of tolerance for shafts and holes to result in fits of various qualities.

Fit clearance
A **fit** where the machining limits for mating parts are such that clearance occurs when any pair made within the prescribed limits are assembled.

Fitting out
Completing the construction of a ship, generally after launching.

Fix
Position of a ship found by plotting two or more bearings on a chart, taken at known points. The point where the bearings intersect mark the position.

Flag
Nationality of a ship, the country where a ship is registered.

Flag of convenience (FOC)
The **registration** of a ship in a country where tax on the profits of trading ships is low, or where requirements concerning manning or maintenance may not be so stringent. Sometimes referred to as a flag of necessity.

Flagstaff
Flag pole, generally at the **stern** of a ship, carrying the ensign (flag of the country of registration).

Flake graphite iron
Term for grey cast iron distinguishing it from **spheroidal graphite cast iron.**

Flaking
Condition where particles of metal flake off the surface of a bar or billet during drop forging, or from case hardened or hard surfaced steel in service. Also known as **spalling.**

Flame arrestor
Device containing a metallic gauge fitted to vent lines from equipment containing **flammable** gases, **vapours** or liquids. Should the gas or vapour ignite, the flame arrestor will prevent the flame from flashing back into the equipment. *See also* **crankcase explosion doors.**

Flame detector
Fire detecting device using **ultra-violet** or **infra-red** rays given off by flames. Often fitted near to fuel handling equipment or at boiler fronts.

Flame impingement
Burning gas that reaches a combustion chamber wall. Excessive flame impingement on a diesel engine piston can cause burning **erosion** of the piston material.

Flame monitor
Device to monitor the quality of a boiler injector flame and alert engine staff if it should go out.

Flame retardant
Material and cables used in electrical systems, if ignited they will cease to burn once the source of heat is removed.

Flameproof
Type of protection for safe use of electrical equipment in hazardous zones. The term is applied to a device with an enclosure or casing constructed to withstand any explosion of the prescribed **flammable** gas that can occur within it under practical conditions of operation. Will prevent transmission of flames which could ignite any flammable gas present in the surrounding atmosphere.

Flame trap
Gauze or perforated metal cover over an opening or vent to prevent the passage of flame.

Flammable
Something that can readily catch fire and burn quickly, such as wood, coal, and petroleum.

Flammable limits

There are two flammable (or explosive) limits, upper (UEL) and lower (LEL), the lower corresponding to the minimum proportion of combustible **vapour** in air necessary for **combustion**, and the upper to the maximum concentration of combustible vapour in air for combustion. Quoted as vol/vol. As an example, gasoline has a UEL of 7.6 and an LEL of 1.4. It must be remembered in relation to flammable limits, that with all combustible material it is the vapour given off that burns and when the vapour ceases so does the burning.

Flange

Portion of a plate or bracket bent at right-angles to the remainder; to bend over at right angles.

Flanges

Circular metal plates with central holes and a ring of bolt holes welded to the end of pipes to couple them together.

Flanking rudders

Additional rudders located forward of the **propellers**.

Flap rudder

Rudder with a separately moving flap at the trailing edge; operated at low or moderate ship speed to provide improved manoeuvrability.

Flare stack

Isolated chimney or pipe where waste or unwanted gases are burnt off. Oil production platforms have special nozzles designed to prevent the flame being extinguished in high winds.

Flare

Outward curvature of the side shell at the forward end above the waterline.

Flash point

Lowest temperature at which an oil gives off sufficient **vapour** to form a mixture that can be made to ignite momentarily under standard test conditions.

Flashover

Electrical discharge between two parts of a machine or apparatus.

Flat

Minor section of internal deck, generally without **sheer** or **camber**. It can also be known as a platform.

Flat compounded

A dc generator with field windings arranged so there is little or no variation in voltage between no load and full load.

Flat margin
A **double bottom** construction where the tank top extends horizontally to the ship's side.

Flat of keel
Width of the horizontal portion of the bottom shell, measured transversely. Also called the flat of bottom. *See* Figure 6.

Flat plate keel
Middle or centre line strake of plating in the bottom shell. It is increased in thickness for strength and as a corrosion allowance; difficult to paint this portion when a ship rests on docking blocks in **drydock.**

Flettner rudder
Specially designed **lap rudder** using two narrow flaps at the trailing edge, one above the other.

Flexible couplings
Type of **coupling** that permits a degree of flexibility between shafts that are being coupled. Temperature differences can produce lateral and axial mis-alignment and vibration and shock loading can occur. Types vary from the ordinary flange couplings with bolt holes bushed with rubber to the rubber disc type which can accommodate severe misalignment. Some flexible couplings use springs to give the resilience required and other designs involve hydraulic and electro-magnetic couplings.

Flexural centre
Point on any cross-section where a transverse load produces a bending deflection with no twist of section.

Flexural vibration
Vibration due to the bending of a loaded member. Extremely important if considering a ship and its cargo as a loaded beam supported on waves.

Float control
Buoyant ball or cylinder operating valve or cock.

FLOATEL
*Floa*ting *Hotel*/Accommodation Vessel.

Floating battery
Battery that can be charged while supplying current. This allows a balanced situation to be maintained as the battery remains fully charged and is available for peak loads.

Floating dock
Structure which can be **ballasted** to sink and receive a floating ship then de-

125

ballasted to bring a ship out of the water. It then functions as a **drydock** for ship maintenance while remaining afloat.

Floc
Finely divided solids suspended in a liquid that have coagulated into relatively large lumps.

Floodable length
Length of vessel that can be flooded without sinking below the **margin line** as shown in Figure 17.

Figure 17 Floodable Length

Flooding
Term to describe water entering a tank or compartment either because of damage or routine **ballasting**.

Floor ceiling
Wood covering placed over tank top for protection.

Floor plan
Horizontal section showing a ship divided at a water or deck line.

Floors
Vertical plating mounted in the double bottom tanks. can be watertight, solid or of bracket construction. The floor structure is continuous from the **centre girder** to the side shell and supports the inner bottom shell. The arrangement of flooring will be determined by the type of framing system adopted, which can be either transverse or longitudinal.

Flotsam
Floating items or wreckage lost or thrown overboard from a ship.

Flow meter
Device used in systems to measure fluid flow in closed pipes, conduits and ducts. There are two categories: **(a)** Inferential methods; do not measure volume of flow directly, inferring it from velocity or change in pressure.

(b) Volumetric methods: count the number of times a known volume passes through the instrument.

Flow chart
Diagram showing the principal plant, piping and equipment and their interconnections, in symbolic form, for a specific process of operation.

Flue gases
Mixture of air, burnt and unburnt fuel leaving a boiler combustion chamber. Principal constituents are oxygen, nitrogen and carbon dioxide, however, some carbon monoxide can be present if insufficient air is available for combustion. Information about the combustion of fuel in boilers can be obtained by analysing flue gases. For general control work, an apparatus is used in which 100 ml of gas is taken into a water-jacketed graduated burette and the constituents of the gas removed separately by absorption.

Fluid coupling
Device using oil circulation to effect coupling.

Fluid friction
Frictional resistance due to the **viscous** or **rheological** drag of fluids.

Fluidics
Use of mainly **pneumatic** devices for sensing, logic computation, and actuation. The process is based on the Coanda Effect, the property of a jet stream to attach itself to an adjacent surface and remain there until some external force, normally another air jet, causes it to move.

Fluidised bed combustion
Form of combustion where an inert material on a boiler furnace bed is agitated by combustion air and heated by directing a gas or oil flame onto the surface. On reaching the fuel ignition temperature, fuel is admitted causing a further increase in bed temperature. Suitable for burning poor quality fuels. Has an advantage over a conventional boiler of low combustion temperature as some pollutants are retained in the bed producing cleaner exhaust gas.

Fluke
Palm of an **anchor**. The broad holding portion that penetrates the sea bed. *See* Figure 3.

Flume
A **stabilisation** system using an **athwartships** tunnel connecting two wing tanks, the combination containing a stipulated quantity of water. The liquid movement is out of phase with the roll motion thus creating a damping effect. *See* Figure 15.

Fluorescence
Emission of light from a molecule that has absorbed light. During the interval between absorption and emission, energy is lost and light of a longer wavelength is emitted. This phenomena is used in oil content monitors because oil fluoresces more readily than water.

Flush deck
Upper deck extending along a ships length without side to side **erections**.

Flushing
Required exercise to remove swarf, dirt and other undesirable contaminants left in the lubricant system during engine construction. Flushing should be initially carried out with a low viscosity oil plus filters installed at strategic points throughout the system. Filtration should continue after the in-service oil has been filled into the system, both during engine trials and sea trials.

Flushing oil
Oil used to flush out and clean engine lubricant systems. Essential practice prior to the first charge of in-service oil for a new engine and desirable when an excessively contaminated in-service charge has been removed. Usually a low viscosity such as **SAE 10**. **Paraffinic** oil is the preferred fluid.

Flux
Substance added to a solid or applied when a solid is melted to increase its fusibility.

Flying bridge
Open control position located above an enclosed **wheelhouse**.

Flyweight
Small pivoted weight used in mechanical governors.

Flywheel
Solid wheel fitted to an engine to create an available store of **kinetic energy** to suit the following purposes to assist starting; reduce speed variation; prevent over- running if the load is cut; limit phase variation. Flywheels are generally made in cast iron or steel. The rim speed of a diesel engine cast-iron flywheel with an ultimate tensile strength of 230-290 x 10^2 N/cm^2 would be 30-45 m/s.

FMECA
Failure *M*odes, *E*ffects and *C*riticality *A*nalysis.

Foam
(1) Froth that appears when water is agitated. (2) Suspension of a gas in a liquid, often **colloidal**. (3) Chemically made foam to extinguish flames by

excluding oxygen; will provide limited cooling. Particularly safe and effective on petroleum and electrical fires.

Foaming
(1) **Foam** caused by the churning action on the lubricating oil in pumps, gears or bearings that interferes with the free flow through drain passages, filters or flowmeters, which can seriously impair the effectiveness of the lubrication. In serious cases, the use of a lubricant containing additional anti-foaming additive can be the only satisfactory solution. (2) **Foam** can also gather in a boiler steam drum at the water surface due to the presence of suspended matter, an excess of salts or oil. This can lead to priming, such as water carrying over into the superheater. *See* **foam**.

Foils
Also known as vanes, wings, planes and fins. Fitted underneath high speed craft such as hydrofoils, when a speed of approximately 40 knots is achieved the craft rises out the water onto the foils and starts planing, leaving only the rudder and **propeller** in the water. *See* **vertical lift control**.

Font
Complete set of characters of one size of any typeface (also called fount).

Foot pound
Work required to raise one pound a vertical distance of one foot.

Footprint
(1) Also fingerprint. Set of analysis results that can be compared with another set, giving guidance as to any differences. (2) Underwater area over which a **submersible** vehicle can operate.

Foot valve
Check valve fitted to the bottom of a suction pipe;. a **strainer** is often fitted.

Fopple card
Geometric device for measuring small **amplitude** vibrations. Two lines are drawn on the card at a small angle and symmetrically about a horizontal line. Vertical vibrations make the lines appear to cross over each other at a point horizontally displaced from the true intersection point. This horizontal displacement can be clearly read by observation of the vertical lines drawn at positions where the vertical displacement has been measured between the inclined lines. With the displacement measured and a knowledge of the **frequency**, acceleration forces on a body can be calculated.

Forbes log
Device that can be projected through the bottom of a ship which carries a vane rotated by the motion of a ship in the water to transmit electrical impulses to a remote recorder. Records distance travelled.

Force
Action of one body upon another, causing the second body to move unless it is acted upon by an equal or opposite force.

Force-balance
Balancing of forces to achieve an **equilibrium** condition, generally in a **pneumatic** device.

Force de cheval
French unit of **horse power** equivalent to 32 549 foot pounds per minute.

Forced draught
Air supply to a boiler furnace that increases the pressure and velocity of combustion air by maintaining the boiler room pressure as positive in relation to the atmosphere, or by inducing draught in the uptake by blowing air through upwardly directed jets. Positive air pressure can be obtained by means of fans, blowers, or by suitably shaped inlet ventilators making use of the local wind speed and direction.

Force majeure
Circumstance beyond the control of one of the parties to a contract and which can, according to the terms and conditions, relieve that party of liability for failing to execute a contract.

Fore peak
Watertight compartment between foremost **watertight bulkhead** and **stem**.

Forecastle
Raised deck at **bow**, below which the crew used to be housed.

Forefoot
Lower end of a vessel's **stem** that curves to meet the **keel**.

Forest products carrier (FPC)
Ship designed to carry forest products such as sawn timber. Smooth sided holds are required and the vessels are generally self sustaining with gantries and cranes for loading and discharge.

Forging
Deformation of a metal by heat and applied force to change its shape and/ or enhance its properties, such as by hammering or pressing.

Fork beam
Half beam to support a deck where hatchways occur.

Forming
To shape a beam, frame or other member to the exact form desired.

Formulae
Rule or statement, generally in algebraic symbols and figures.

FORTRAN
FORmula TRANslation. Computer symbolic language.

Forward
In the direction of, at or near the stem.

Forward perpendicular
Imaginary line drawn perpendicular to the **waterline** at the point where the forward edge of the **stem** intersects the **summer load line**. *See* Figure 2.

Forward shoulder
Part of a ship where the **entrance** region meets the **parallel middle body**.

Fottinger coupling
Outward flow water turbine driving an inward flow turbine within a common casing, acting as a coupling, gear or clutch for transmitting power.

Fouling
(1) Restriction of movement by entanglement. (2) Marine growth on a ship restricting its progress. (3) Deposition of substances within pipework restricting the passage of fluid.

Founder
Ship that sinks after filling with water.

Four ball EP test
Method for determining the extreme pressure properties of lubricants.

Four stroke cycle
Operating cycle for internal combustion engine requiring four strokes or two revolutions of the crankshaft. On the first downstroke of the piston (induction) air is drawn in through the inlet valve. The valve closes and on the upward stroke air is compressed (compression) causing its temperature to rise. Fuel is injected then ignites and on the downward (combustion/power) stroke burns and expands. On the return stroke (exhaust) the exhaust valve opens and burnt gases are expelled. *See* Figure 18.

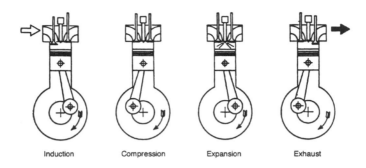

Induction　　　　Compression　　　　Expansion　　　　Exhaust

Figure 18 Four Stroke Cycle

FPS
Floating Production System.

FPSO
Floating Production, Storage and Offloading system.

Fractionating column
In the petroleum industry, generally refers to the refinery column in which the initial distillation of **crude oil** is carried out at atmospheric pressure. It is called fractionating as it separates crude into various fractions.

Fracture
Break or partial break. Fractures in metal have visual characteristics. A brittle fracture is bright and glistening, a fibrous fracture is grey and dull, and a ductile fracture has a smooth, fine and dull grain.

Fracture toughness
Ability of a material to withstand the extension of a crack once it has started. In general, brittle materials can not withstand this extension, whereas **ductile** materials are more resistant to crack propagation.

Frame
Transverse structural member acting as a stiffener to the shell and bottom plate. Can also be longitudinal; known as the ribs of a ship.

Framing systems
Various methods used to stiffen the bottom shell and side plating of a ship against compressive sea forces.

Free alongside ship (FAS)

Term meaning the seller is responsible for bringing the goods alongside a ship at the loading port on the date agreed with the buyer, after which the risk of loss or damage to the goods passes from the seller to the buyer.

Free on board (FOB)

Term meaning the seller is responsible for delivering goods to the port of loading agreed in the contract and for loading them onto a ship nominated by the buyer. The risk of loss or damage to the goods generally passes from the seller to the buyer once goods pass a ship's rail at the port of loading.

Free piston engine

Engine where the firing load on the piston crown is absorbed by compressing air or other gases below the piston underside, which can be of a larger diameter than the working piston. Free piston engines are generally of the **opposed piston** design. Pistons are not constrained by connecting rods and crankshafts, however, there can be a mechanical linkage to keep the pistons in phase. Power output is in the form of compressed gas. This is a composite engine using a gas turbine as the power producer and not a gas turbine. The reciprocating portion serves as a gas generator supplying hot compressed gas to the gas turbine, yet giving no mechanical power.

Free surface

When a tank is slack, that is contains a liquid but is not full, the stability of a ship is reduced by an amount depending solely on the extent of the free surface of the liquid and its relative density. The free surface effect is independent of the depth and volume of the tank and a few centimeters of liquid will have the same effect as a large volume.

Freeboard

Vertical distance from the **summer load waterline** to the top of the **freeboard deck** plating, measured at a ship's side amidships. Has considerable influence on the **seaworthiness** of a ship, the greater the freeboard, the larger the above water volume of a ship. This provides reserve **buoyancy,** assisting a ship to remain afloat in the event of damage. Minimum freeboards are prescribed by International Law in the form of **Load Line** Regulations. *See* Figure 19.

Freeboard deck

Uppermost complete deck exposed to the weather and the sea with watertight means of closure on all the openings located thereon.

Freedom vessel

Of Japanese design, one of the many popular ship designs created to replace the Liberty class ships built during World War II.

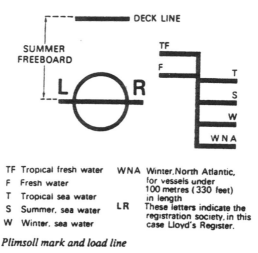

TF Tropical fresh water

F Fresh water

T Tropical sea water

S Summer, sea water

W Winter, sea water

WNA Winter, North Atlantic, for vessels under 100 metres (330 feet) in length

LR These letters indicate the registration society, in this case Lloyd's Register.

Plimsoll mark and load line

Figure 19 Load Lines

Freeing port
Opening in **bulwark** plating to free the deck of water.

Freeing scuttle
Flap fitted to some freeing ports to allow water to drain off but not enter.

Freezing point
Temperature at which a liquid solidifies under controlled conditions. Because of their chemical complexity, petroleum products do not have a sharp freezing point and the **pour point** is the test more commonly used.

Freight
Money paid to a **shipowner** or shipping line for the carriage of cargo.

Freon
Refrigerant gases manufactured from halogenated hydrocarbons, compounds derived from compounds of carbon and hydrogen, replacing some of the hydrogen with chlorine or fluorene. They are virtually non-toxic, non-inflammable, odourless, non-corrosive, and are soluble in oil. Typical examples are R11 (CCl_3F) and R12 (CCl_2F_2). Despite the apparent advantages, CFCs (chlorofluocarbon) are harmful to the environment and more ozone friendly refrigerants such as R134A are gradually being introduced.

Frequency (Hertz–Hz)
A simple pendulum gives a type of motion described as oscillatory or vibratory. The maximum displacement is called the **amplitude** of the motion and the time interval between two successive positions of the body with the same displacement is called the **period**. The period of one complete vibration or **oscillation** could be very small and it is more convenient to consider the number of vibrations in unit time. This is referred to as the frequency of vibration. So that if T is the period and n the frequency then:

$$n = \frac{1}{T} \quad 1\,Hz = 1 \text{ cycle per second.}$$

Frequency changer
Device for converting ac electrical power from one frequency to another.

Frequency filter
Network of **resistance, inductance** and **capacitance** giving minimum resistance to current over a designed frequency range and as much resistance as possible outside this range.

Frequency modulation
Variation in frequency of a carrier wave by frequency of the modulating wave to be transmitted. The transmitted wave is extracted by demodulation.

Frequency of encounter
Frequency with which waves meet a ship as it moves through the water.

Frequency response
Measure of the ability of a device or system to respond to a cyclical input. Using a sine wave input, the system's response to change in the frequency of the input is measured.

Fresh water allowance (FWA)
Amount the **load line** mark can be submerged when loading in water of less density than that of sea water. *See* Figure 19.

Fresh water generator
Piece of machinery used for converting impure water such as seawater to distilled or fresh water. The sea water, normally under vacuum, is brought to boiling temperature by steam or electric heaters and the resulting vapour condenses into distilled water.

Fretting
Wear occurring between two surfaces subject to high contact stress that have **oscillatory** relative motion of small **amplitude**.

Fretting corrosion
Form of fretting in which chemical reaction predominates. Characterised by the removal of particles and subsequent formation of oxides which are abrasive and so increase the wear. Can also involve other chemical reaction products which are not abrasive.

Friction
Force resisting motion when two surfaces are brought into contact and made to slide, one over the other.

Frictional resistance
Resistance experienced by a body moving through a fluid due to the velocity gradient across the boundary layer. For a ship, it depends on **wetted surface** area, length, and the type of surface and density of the sea.

Frigate
Craft originally introduced in the 18th century to seek out, keep in touch and monitor the enemies movements. Now a general purpose warship carrying guns, missiles, helicopters and a variety of armaments and equipment.

Froude number
Dimensionless parameter used to indicate the influence of gravity on fluid motion and in the study of wave making resistance. The following formulae is generally expressed as:

$$F = \frac{v}{(gd)^{-\frac{1}{2}}}$$

F = Froude number $\qquad\qquad$ v = gravity wave
g = gravitational acceleration of fluid $\qquad$ d = depth of flow

See **Froude, William.**

Froude,William (1810–1879)
Engineer and naval architect who influenced ship design by developing the study of scale models propelled through water then applying the results to full size ships. Froude invented the deep **bilge keel** to reduce ship's roll and the **dynamometer** for measuring the power developed by large engines.

Froude's Law of Comparison
If two geometrically similar objects, like two ships or a ship and its model, run at corresponding speeds then their residuary resistances per unit of displacement are the same. $R1_1$ is the residuary resistance of a ship and Rr_2 that of the model, then:

$Rr_1 = Rr_2 \left(\dfrac{L}{l}\right)^3$ Where L = length of ship and l = length of model.

Froude's Law of Comparison can also be used to predict the performance of geometrically similar **propellers.**

FSA

Formal Risk Assessment. To identify hazards, assess the risks associated with those hazards, consider alternative ways of dealing with the risks identified, and decide which option is best.

FTA

Fault Tree Analysis. Deductive (top down) technique specifying an accident event and providing a method to determine the cause.

Fuel

Substance suitable for the economic supply of heat by combustion, such as coal, oil and gas.

Fuel blender

Equipment for mixing two or more grades of fuel, generally a light and a heavy product, to reach the desired final blend of viscosity, density and stability. Most often found at the shore terminal, however, can be on the bunker barge and occasionally a ship itself.

Fuel coefficient

Formula used for comparing operational efficiency of ships of similar type and speed, used for comparing voyage results. Defined by the formula:

$$\frac{D^{2/3} \times V^3}{T}$$

D = displacement in tons
T = tonnes of fuel consumed per 24 hours steaming
V = speed in knots

Fuel compatibility

Two or more fuels of different quality can combine readily to form a stable mixture, or they can separate or form sludge. Fuels that combine readily are said to be compatible while the others are incompatible.

Fuel, diesel

Fuel used in a diesel engines varies from a light gas oil to a residual. Most modern marine engines of reasonable size, whether main propulsion or auxiliary, are designed to burn residual type products. Their fuel systems, from bunker fuel tanks through heating, settling, centrifuging, and filtration, are constructed accordingly.

Fuel economy

Efficient use of fuel. In a ship this can mean choosing the best sea route to take advantage of favourable winds, currents or tides, to ensuring that all machinery is maintained in optimum running condition. Of primary importance, however, is the selection of the most economical speed.

Fuel, low sulphur

Typically marine heavy bunker fuels contain 3 per cent of sulphur (S) and the present highly alkaline cylinder oils satisfactorily neutralise any acids formed avoiding corrosive wear. Occasionally heavy bunker fuels are supplied with a much lower sulphur content (0.5 or less) and cases of high wear have been reported.This could be due to their unusual burning characteristics, however, it is unwise to run for extended periods on highly alkaline cylinder oil when using such fuels.

Fuel pump

Pump supplying fuel to a boiler or prime mover.

Fuel, residual

In the refining of crude oil, many fractions or products are produced and the subsequent remaining fuel is known as residual. The intensity of the refining process determines the quality of the residual. With so much secondary refining taking place, such as cracking, and the mixing of residues from a variety of crudes, the residual can be of poor quality. Bunker quality analysis should be carried out on delivered fuel and the results analysed prior to burning.

Fuel soot

Black material formed in the combustion chamber of a diesel engine due to incomplete combustion. Mostly exhausted into the atmosphere, however, a proportion of soot can enter the lubricating oil system and join other contaminants to form a black sludge, lowering the quality of the system oil.

Fuel stability

A fuel's stability level. Bunker fuel should be a stable homogeneous mixture when delivered to a ship; must remain stable both in storage (time) and when subjected to heat (temperature). *See also* **stability**.

Fulcum

Point or line about which an object balances.

Full bore safety valve

High capacity boiler **safety valve**.

Full flow cargo system

Method of cargo handling on tankers using large sliding sluice valves fitted in the tank bulkheads. By opening these valves the tanks are drained to the after end where the cargo pumps extract oil for discharge ashore. No suction pipework is needed other than a small stripping line.

Full wave rectifier
Device inverting alternate half waves of an alternating input so that the output contains two half wave pulses for each input cycle.

Fulton, Robert (1765–1815)
American pioneer steamship engineer. He demonstrated his first small steamer on the River Seine in Paris in 1803. On his return to the United States he built the *Clermont* powered by an imported Boulton & Watt 20 Nominal HP engine. *Clermont* was 133 ft long with a 13 ft beam. On the 17th August 1807 it made its maiden voyage up the Hudson River from New York to Albany, averaging close on five knots. It continued on this service for many years and was the world's first commercially successful steamship.

Fumigation
Applying fumes to a sealed compartment to destroy vermin and insects.

Fundamental units
Units to which all physical phenomena can be reduced consisting of length, mass, time, dielectric constant, magnetic permeability, and temperature.

Funnel
Uptake sending smoke, combustion and exhaust gases to the open air.

Funnel gas inerting
Using inert, scrubbed, dried, and filtered exhaust gases as a blanket cover over the cargo tanks of an oil tanker.

Funnel guy
Guys or stays supporting the funnel.

Furnace
Interior of boiler where fuel is burned. *See* **combustion chamber.**

Fuse
Wire in a main or branch electrical circuit designed to melt when overloaded to cut the flow of current.

Fuse base
Fixed part of fuse provided with terminals for connection to external circuit.

Fuse carrier
Movable part of a fuse designed to carry the **fuse link.**

Fused isolator
Isolating switch that incorporates a **fuse.**

Fuse link
Part of a fuse, including the fuse element, that must be replaced after a fuse has operated and before it is put back into service.

Fusing factor
Ratio of the minimum fusing current, minimum current that will melt the fuse element, to the normal current rating of the fuse.

Fusion welding
Process where a weld is made between metals in a state of fusion without the need for hammering or pressure.

FZG test
German devised method for determining the load carrying ability of lubricants. Uses calibrated **spur gears** operating at a fixed speed and controlled initial oil temperature. Testing is carried out in 15 minute stages, increasing the load after each stage. There are a maximum of 12 stages. Good load carrying gear oils would be expected to exceed stage 12.

G

Gag
Device that holds one **safety valve** shut while the other is being set.

Galley
Space on a ship where food is prepared and cooked.

Gallon, Imperial
Defined as the space occupied by 10 lb of water under specified conditions. One Imperial gallon = 1.20095 US gallons = 4.546 litres

Gallon, U.S.
One US gallon = 0.8327 Imperial gallons = 3.785 litres

Gallows
U-shaped girder on the deck of a trawler through which trawl warp is led.

Galvanic action
Action that occurs during **electrolytic** corrosion. The term generally implies the presence of dissimilar metals in contact, and their effect on each other in a corrosive environment. In such a system the **anode** is corroded thereby protecting the **cathode** from corrosion.

Galvanising
Generic term for any of several techniques for applying thin coatings of zinc to iron or steel as a protection against corrosion.

Galvanometer
Instrument used to measure or give an indication of a small dc flow.

Gamma iron
An **allotropic** form of iron existing above the upper critical point. Gamma iron is non-magnetic and in steel is known as **austenite.**

Gamma rays
Electromagnetic waves of higher frequency and greater penetrating power than **X-rays.** Emitted by radioactive substances such as thulium, iridium, caesium and cobalt.

Gangway
Ramp or stairs used for embarking or disembarking from a ship.

Garboard strake
Strake of bottom shell plating adjacent and on each side of the **keel plate.**

Gas
Vapour state of any substance that has no independent shape or volume. Also any substance that remains homogeneous, whose volume increases without limit when pressure is constantly reduced at constant temperature.

Gas cap
Layer of natural gas above the oil in a reservoir.

Gas cap drive
Recovery mechanism whereby the oil from the **reservoir** is displaced by the downward expansion of an overlying **gas cap.**

Gas detection
Monitoring of an area or compartment for **toxic** or **flammable** gases. Usually associated with a measurement, an acceptable display, or the triggering of an alarm in the event of an unacceptable value recorded by the equipment.

Gas detection sensor
Device whose resistance varies in the presence of gas. When forming one arm of a balanced circuit, an out-of-balance current resulting from a change in resistance will indicate the presence of gas.

Gas freeing
Removal of pockets of gas from the tanks of an oil carrying vessel after cargo has been discharged to avoid the possibility of explosive mixtures remain-

ing. Various methods are used including inert gas, vacuum, and washing. A tank is gas free when all noxious and dangerous gas vapors are removed.

Gas injection
Process whereby separated associated gas is pumped back into a **reservoir** for conservation purposes or to maintain a reservoir pressure.

Gas oil
Superior quality distillate fuel used for high speed diesel engines. Marine diesel is often a blend of gas oil and a small proportion of intermediate fuel.

Gas to oil ratio (GOR)
Volume of gas at atmospheric pressure produced in association with a unit volume of oil.

Gas turbine
Rotary heat engine converting some of the energy of fuel into work by using the combustion gas as the working medium. Working fluid is gaseous throughout the complete cycle which generally consists of compression, heating and expansion.

Gas welding
Process for joining metals by melting them with a gas flame from a torch. A concentrated gas flame was the first heat source for **fusion welding.** A variety of fuel gases combined with oxygen have been used to produce a high temperature flame. Oxy-acetylene and oxy-propane are the most usual gases.

Gasification
Process manufacturing gaseous fuel from a solid or liquid fuel.

Gasket
Material used to make a joint or seal between two surfaces, such as between two pipe flanges or cylinder head cover and cylinder. Can be rubber, copper, paper or another soft material suitable for the specific application.

Gate valve
Valve allowing unrestricted flow. Can have a wedge action, be parallel sided or have a double disc. Used in circulating systems where small frictional losses are required.

Gauge glass
Glass tube or arrangement of glass plates fitted to a gauge used to give a visual indication of the level of liquid in a tank, pressure vessel, or boiler.

Gauss
Unit of magnetic flux density. The **SI unit** is the tesla which equals 10 gauss.

GCBS

General Council of British Shipping. Formerly known as the Chamber of Shipping. Body formed to promote and protect the interests of British shipowners. Received the Royal Charter in 1922.

Gear

Mechanism for transmitting motion or power where the speed and torque of the input shaft is converted to a lower or higher speed at the output shaft. *See* Figure 1.

Gear, helical

Gear wheels with teeth inclined at an angle, not parallel with the wheel axis. Double helical gears operate with each half of a tooth inclined in opposite directions. This eliminates axial thrust. *See* Figure 20.

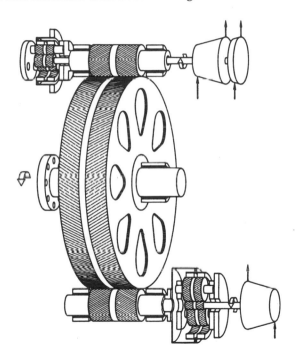

Figure 20 Helical Gears

Gear noise

Noise due to vibrations caused by impact and non-uniform angular velocities of rotating gears arising from pitch errors, inaccuracies of tooth profiles, and eccentricity.

Gear pump

Displacement pump made of two interconnecting gear wheels in a closely fitted casing. Liquid is forced between two meshing gears and discharged.

Gear shaping

Cutters or abrasive wheels. Generally employed in pairs, their inner surfaces are flat unless modified to produce corrected teeth. Cutters are used in a planing or shaving sense, while coarse abrasive wheels are used in the process known as gear grinding.

Grinding. Finishing the profile of a gear teeth by grinding. Process uses shaped smooth abrasive wheels which move relative to the workpiece, which is itself moved, to form the profile of the gear tooth. The Maag system is a well known form of this process.

Rack or circular cutters. Straight sided teeth cut by short lengths of straight rack or circular gear-form cutters fitted in gear shaper machines to generate involute profiles on the spur gear blanks. The cutters reciprocate axially while being fed inwards slowly against the rotating blank, the gears form cutters themselves generated by straight rack form tools. The Fellows system of gear cutting is based on this principle.

Rotating hob cutters. Cutters in the form of helical pinions have been further developed into the helical cutter with so small a lead angle that it becomes virtually a worm. The thread, or threads, of this are gashed and relieved providing cutting edges at intervals along the length. The cutting action of the hob results from its rotation in a form of milling machine. The Gleason system is based on hobbing.

Shaving. Improving the accuracy of the profile of the gear teeth. The shaving cutter is similar to a helical gear where the teeth have been serrated with cutting edges along the tooth spiral. The cutter is fed across the face width of the workpiece while in mesh with the teeth.

Gear, spur

Cylindrical gear with teeth parallel to the axis. *See* Figure 1.

Gear tooth damage

Abrasive wear. Smooth, even wear resulting from prolonged service with a moderately clean lubricant.

Scuffing. Surface damage of a more severe nature. Local welding and tearing of surfaces occurs, indicating inadequate lubrication and/or cooling, with regard to the load and speed. Can also indicate local overloading due to gear misalignment or incompatibility of materials.

Scoring. Fully developed form of scuffing caused by the same factors as scuffing; induced by foreign matter or particles of debris in the lubricant.

Spalling. Pattern of very fine pitting, often giving material a crystalline appearance. Due to impact forces, mostly found close to the pitch line. High speeds and pitch errors can promote this form of damage.

Gear trains
Double reduction. Compact arrangement giving two stage reduction.

Epicyclic. System where one or more wheels travel around the outside or inside of another wheel whose axis is fixed. The different arrangements are known as planetary, solar and star.

Locked train. Type of double reduction gearing which has a single input shaft driving two primary wheels via quill shafts on to two secondary pinions, and finally a single main wheel.

Single reduction. Refers to a simple reduction gear train where the reduction ratio is obtained in one stage by a pinion or pinions on one shaft meshing with a corresponding gear or gears on a single output shaft.

Split primary. Double reduction gear train with double helical secondary pinion placed between each hand of the double helical primary wheel.

Split secondary. Double reduction gear train with double helical primary wheel placed between each hand of the double helical secondary pinion.

Gear wheel
Wheel or hub into which teeth are cut.

Geared steam turbine
Steam turbine with single or double reduction gearing between the turbine and the **propeller.** This allows greater propulsive efficiency and reduced number of revolutions at the **propeller.**

Geiger counter
Geiger-Muller electron tube device used as a radiation counter.

General arrangement
(1) Plan showing general layout of ship design equipment in each compartment. (2) Drawing showing the component parts of an engine or unit in their

correct assembled relationship. Consists of a plan and two elevations and can include sectional arrangements showing internal construction.

General Average (GA)
General indemnity made by all interests in a maritime loss deliberately but necessarily incurred for the safety of the remaining property when in peril. *See* **General Average Act**.

General Average Act
Intentional act or sacrifice carried out during a voyage to preserve the venture from peril, such as putting out a fire in the hold that causes cargo to be damaged by water. The principle of general average is laid down in Rule A of the York Antwerp Rules 1950. The term *average* covers all damage sustained by ship or cargo on a voyage, as well as extraordinary expenses incurred while at sea. *Average* can also refer to partial loss.

General Average expenditure
Extraordinary expenditure voluntarily and necessarily incurred for preserving property in peril.

General Average loss
Loss that is due to a **General Average Act** or Expenditure.

General service pump
Pump serving several purposes such as feeding a **donkey boiler** or supplying drinking water tanks. Must not be connected to a **bilge**.

Generator
Machine converting mechanical power into electrical power.

Geolograph
Recording instrument used in oil drilling to determine the speed and penetration of the bit during the operation.

Geology
Science relating to the history and development of the earth's crust.

Geophysics
Physics of the earth. A hybrid discipline involving a combination of physical and geological principles.

Germanischer Lloyd (GL)
German ship **classification society** founded in 1867.

Ghost lines
Light coloured streaks on a freshly machined surface of steel caused by the segregation of impurities in the original ingot becoming elongated during rolling or forging.

Gill jet thruster
Thruster device using a vertical axis propeller in a T-shaped tunnel. Water is drawn from both sides and leaves through the bottom of the hull. Rotatable gill fins direct the water in one of a number of fixed positions around a circle. More recent developments of the Gill principle utilise a horizontal axial flow pump that draws water through a single fixed grid, which is usually mounted horizontally at or near the vessel's keel. The pump discharges through another grid on or near the Centre Line of the vessel. This grid is ducted so that the outflow of water is effectively horizontal. The grid is also rotatable through 360 degrees by an electric motor, so that the thrust exerted by the pump jet can be controlled to operate in any horizontal direction. The resultant thruster unit, in addition to being part of a vessel positioning system, can also be used as a *get-you-home* device in the event of failure of the vessel's main propulsion system.

Gimbals
Two rings that pivot at right angles to each other to keep a compass in the horizontal plane under any circumstances.

Gin block
Single pulley sleeve in a skeleton frame. Used in **derrick** spans and **derrick** heads in conjunction with a **whip** for handling cargo.

Gipsy
Slotted wheel or cable holder on the horizontal shaft of a **windlass.**

Girder
Continuous stiffening member running through a ship from fore to aft supporting the deck.

Girding
Term used to describe a tug capsized by the action of a ship or vessel being towed. Capsizing can occur when the towline is abeam of the tug (at 90 degrees to the centreline) and sufficient force is generated by the action of the tow to pull a ship over bodily. Also described as **girting.**

Girting
See **girding.**

Gland seal
Sleeve of soft material used to secure a tight packing on a **piston rod, propeller** shaft, pump spindle or electric cable. Synthetic rubber seals are also used.

Gland steam
Steam introduced into shaft gland packing to prevent air leakage into and steam leakage out of a turbine.

Gland steam condenser
Shell and tube type heat exchanger used in a closed feed system to collect and condense steam from the turbine gland steam system.

Glass reinforced plastic
Glass in very fine filaments is mixed with a plastic before curing resulting in a finished product with enhanced properties.

Glass wool
Insulation material derived from molten glass. Extremely light, vermin proof, fireproof, odourless, and does not absorb moisture.

Globe valve
Valve with spherically shaped body enclosing the **valve seat**. Liquid is introduced from below the seat so the upper chamber is not pressurised when the valve is closed.

Glow plug
(1) Heater installed in the combustion chamber of some diesel engines to assist when starting the engine from cold. *See also* **semi-diesel** engine. The heater is switched off once the engine is running. **(2)** Igniter for re-lighting the fuel to a gas turbine in the event of the flame becoming unstable such as under cold conditions.

GM
Metacentric height. Distance from the **metacentre** (M) to the **centre of gravity** (G) of a ship. To be stable G must be below M as in Figure 12.

GMDSS
Global Maritime Distress and Safety System. Concept of satellite and terrestial radio communication services developed by **IMO**.

Go astern
(1) To move stern first. **(2)** To reverse engines. **(3)** To take up a position astern of another ship.

Goal post mast
An **athwartship** structure on the weather deck to support **derricks**. A stump mast is generally stepped in the middle of the structure.

Go-devil
Type of **pig** with self adjusting blades used to clean the interior of pipe lines.

Gog rope
Rope used in ship handling work with European-style conventional screw tugs to control the position of the main towline as a precaution against **girding** (capsizing). Also known as gob rope, stop rope or bridle.

Gooseneck
(1) Fitting on the end of a boom or derrick that connects it to the mast or post and permits a swivel motion. (2) Tube turned over at the head the to prevent the entry of water.

Gouging
Removal of metal from a welded seam to make a back-run for a **butt weld**.

Governor
Controls speed. The centrifugal governor conical pendulum is one in which the rising of a rotating ball with increase of speed controls the speed of an engine by operating levers to check the supply of fuel.

GPS
Global Positioning System.

Grab
Steel bucket in two halves, hinged so the jaws of the bucket open for grabbing a load, close when the bucket is full, and open again when discharging the load. Used for handling bulk cargoes such as coal and grain.

Graduation
Marking or setting out of a scale.

Graphite
Crystalline (hexagonal) form of elemental carbon, either natural or synthetic in origin, often used as a dry lubricant because of its **laminar** structure. An ideal lubricant when mixed with a mineral oil or grease.

Grating
Flooring made of a grid arrangement of steel strips. Used in an engine room to allow comprehensive viewing of machinery.

Graving dock
Dock where ships are repaired or built. Water is pumped out as required. Also known as a **dry dock.**

Gravity davits
Type of **davit**; slides down to position a lifeboat for lowering when released.

Gravity platform
Platform made of reinforced concrete that sits on the sea bed and remains in position independently, without piling, due to its weight.

Gravity separator
Chamber through which oily water is caused to flow in acquiescent manner allowing oil droplets to separate from the water under the influence of gravity due to the density difference between oil and water. The term includes plate separators, a variant where parallel plates are inserted to enhance performance. The bulk of oil contamination is removed by a gravity separator.

Grease
Semi-solid or solid lubricant. Combination of a petroleum or synthetic product and a **soap** (such as lithium or calcium) with selected additives.

Great circle route
Shortest route between two points.

Green sea
Sea that traverses the deck of a ship without breaking any waves.

Greenheart
One of the heaviest, strongest and most decay resistant of all timbers. Guyana is the principal source of supply. Used for piles and underwater work due to its resistance to the boring action of the sea animal teredo.

Greenwich Hour Angle (GHA)
Angular distance west of the Greenwich (UK) **celestial meridian**. Used to identify the positions of celestial bodies for navigation.

Greenwich Mean Time (GMT)
Time at Greenwich by the sun. The standard to which all time related observations can be referred.

Greenwich meridian
The **meridian** through Greenwich used for measuring longitude and time. Also called the prime meridian.

Grim wheel
Free rotating vane wheel for installation behind a ship's main **propeller** developed by the German Professor Grim. Its diameter is about 20 per cent larger that the main **propeller** and it rotates at about 40 per cent less speed. Said to reclaim a part of the energy normally lost in the **propeller** slip stream converting it into additional thrust.

Gripes
Wire ropes that secure a lifeboat when hoisted to the **davits** and chains, holding it to the deck with a claw fitted over the **gunwhale**.

Grommet
Ring of soft water resistant material positioned beneath a nut or bolthead to provide a watertight joint.

Gross registered tonnage (GRT)
The capacity in cubic feet of the spaces within the hull and enclosed spaces above the deck available for cargo, stores, fuel, passengers and crew divided by 100. Thus 100 cubic feet of capacity is equivalent to 1 gross **ton**.

Grounded
Connected to earth. In the case of a ship, its hull is **earth.**

Ground speed
Speed of a ship relative to land. It is measured on trials against marked positions on the shoreline (measured mile) and must be corrected to find the speed in **knots**.

Grubscrew
Setscrew without a full length threaded head with a slot for turning for securing a pulley or collar to a shaft.

Guardian valve
Astern steam isolating valve. Type of maneouvring valve in a steam turbine.

Gudgeon pin
Short shaft connecting **piston** and **connecting rod** in a trunk **piston engine** oscillating in bearings in one or both components; known as a piston pin in the USA.

Gudgeons
Solid lugs on the sterntrame **rudder post**, drilled and fitted with bearings to take the rudder **pintles**.

Guide and shoe
Two interacting components carrying connecting-rod side thrust in a **crosshead engine**. The crosshead shoe is attached to the crosshead and piston rod, and slides in the guide as shown in Figure 21

Guillotine door
Door found at the stern of some **roll-on/roll-off** ships, resembling in its configuration the instrument of execution from which it gets its name. It is found on ships which have no **ramp** fitted and who require a shore based link span. Must be watertight.

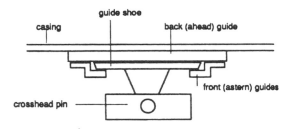

Figure 21 Crosshead Engine Guide and Shoe

Gunmetal
Alloy of copper, essentially a tin bronze. The original Admiralty gunmetal contained 88 per cent copper, 10 per cent tin and 2 per cent zinc. There are many variations and some can contain lead or nickel. Ideal for valve bodies where corrosion resistance is a requirement.

Gunwale
Upper edge of a ship's side next to the **bulwark.**

Gusset plate
Bracket plate positioned in a horizontal or almost horizontal plane.

Guy
(1) Rope used to guide a load while hoisting. **(2)** Rope or wire used as a stay.

Gyro-compass
A **gyroscope** mounted so the diurnal revolution of Earth is made to constrain the North-South line of the **compass** to seek the **meridian.**

Gyroscope
Rapidly rotating wheel mounted to have three degrees of freedom. Active **stabilising** systems have gyroscopes as part of their control system.

H

Hague Rules
Rules covering the carriage of goods by sea identifying the rights and responsibilities of carriers and owners of cargo. First published in 1924 following an international convention.

Half-breadth
Half the breadth of a ship. At any transverse section half-breadth distances can be given as a ship is a symmetrical about the longitudinal centreline.

Half cardinal
A **compass** point halfway between two cardinal points.

Half life
Time taken for the amount of radioactive radiation to decay to half its original value. Depending on the **isotope**, this can take an infinitesimal part of a second to millions of years.

Halon
Halon generated hydrocarbon gas used as a fire extinguishing agent. Two examples are Halon 1301 (BTM) and Halon 1211 (BCF).

Hammering test
Applied to steel castings, such as anchors. The anchor is slung and hammered with a 7lb sledge hammer and should give a clear ringing sound.

Hamper
(1) Necessary but cumbrous equipment. (2) Top-hamper. Extensive superstructure above weather deck.

Hand steering gear
Emergency **steering gear** situated aft. Rods and gear wheels allow the operation of the rudder from an after deck position.

Hard patch
Plate riveted or welded over another plate to cover a hole or break.

Hardening
Increasing the hardness of a metal.

Work hardening. Improving the hardness and strength of a metal by mechanical working in a cold state.

Case hardening. Producing a zone on the outside of a component which is harder than the core of the metal. This can be done by carburising steel to increase the carbon content of the surface layer or by **nitriding**. Flame and induction hardening produce similar effects on certain steels.

Hardness, metals
Resistance to plastic deformation. In engineering, indentation hardness, wear hardness and scratch hardness are the main types. Tests are available to measure these properties and the indentation test has the widest application, generally using the Brinell tester. This test can be made quickly without

destroying the part involved, and is used during inspection to check the quality of products and their heat treatment. Hardness tests giving an arbitrary scale of numbers are also used to check strength and **ductility.**

Hardness, water
Due to the salts of calcium and magnesium. The insoluble carbonates cause deposits in boilers and combine with soap to form insoluble compounds.

Harmonics
Components of **cyclical** movement repeating two or more times per cycle.

Hatch beam
Removable beam fitted over a hatch opening, generally beneath a wooden or steel hatch cover.

Hatch coaming
Vertical plating which surrounds a hatch opening. The hatch cover rests, and is secured, on top of the hatch **coaming**. Its function is to prevent water washing into the hold and to lessen the risk of any person working on the deck falling through the open hatchway.

Hatch cover
Cover creating a watertight hatch to protect the cargo hold. *See* Figure 22.

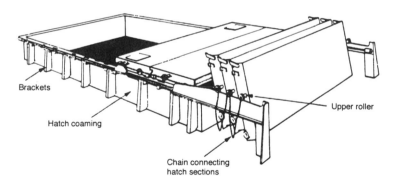

Figure 22 MacGregor Rolling Hatch Cover

Hatches
Openings in the decks of general cargo and bulk cargo ships allowing the loading and discharge of cargo to and from the holds. To close these openings a **hatch cover** shuts onto a coaming to create a watertight seal. On ships such as tankers the tank hatch which is much smaller, is the only a means of

entry for personnel carrying out inspection and maintenance. A hinged lid enables watertight closure when fully fastened down.

Hawse pipe
Tube through which the anchor cable is led.

Hawser
Wire or fibre rope for warping, mooring, hauling or towing.

Hazardous area
Area where explosive gas/air mixtures **(flammable)** are or could be present in quantities large enough to require special precautions for the construction and use of electrical apparatus. In hazardous areas three types of zone are recognised in sequence of decreasing probability of explosive gas/air mixtures:

Zone 0. Zone in which a flammable atmosphere is continuously present, or present for long periods.

Zone 1. Zone in which a flammable atmosphere is likely to occur under normal operating conditions.

Zone 2. Zone in which a flammable atmosphere is likely to occur only under abnormal operating conditions and only for a short time.

Haze
Solid matter like smoke, dust and salt particles suspended in the atmosphere.

HAZCHEM
Hazardous Chemical.

HAZOP
*Ha*zard and *Op*erability Studies. Technique identifying **hazardous** and operational problems.

Head, total
Pressure difference created by a pump between suction and delivery branches to produce a flow of liquid.

Header bar
Cross-bar situated over the doors of an open top shipping **container** that form part of the end frame. During loading or unloading the header bar can be swung out of the way or completely removed, depending on the design.

Header tank
Expansion tank partially filled with water connected to an engine cooling system. Air or other gases above the water are allowed to expand and contract as the temperature changes and can be vented to the atmosphere or allowed to reach a higher pressure limited by a **relief valve.**

Headfast
Mooring rope from the **bows** leading forward. Also known as a headline or headrope.

Head flow characteristic
Diagram or graph showing head against flow for a pump. Exhibits the pump characteristic, system characteristic, and net positive suction head available.

Health monitoring
Checks carried out to ensure a machine or process will not endanger the health of the workforce or the public, by means such as nuclear radiation, radiography, or dangerous chemicals. Also applied to condition and performance monitoring of machinery.

Heat Affected Zone (HAZ)
Zone in the parent metal adjacent to a **weld** that has had its structure and properties changed by the heat of the weld.

Heat, radiant
Heat emitted by heat rays as distinct from heat transmitted by **conduction** or **convection.**

Heat balance calculation
Calculation of quantities of heat discharged from an engine as useful work. Heat available from the fuel consumed minus losses including heat to exhaust, heat to coolant and lubricant, mechanical losses, and heat dissipated from the engine structure.

Heat engine
Engine that converts heat into mechanical energy.

Heat exchanger
Cooling unit using sea, fresh or feed water. To avoid the deposition of salt in marine engines, the direct sea water cooling temperature should not exceed 57°C. A better procedure is to use a closed circuit with fresh water in association with a heat exchanger to transfer the heat to the sea water. By this method corrosion difficulties are avoided.

Heat of combustion
Measure of the available energy content of a fuel under controlled test conditions. Also called **calorific value.** *See also* **specific energy.**

Heat pump
Machine for transferring heat from a low temperature to a region of higher temperature. Heat is extracted from the low temperature body using a refrigerant then compressed to transfer the heat to the higher temperature

body. Finally the refrigerant passes through an expander to repeat the whole process. The low and high temperature media are frequently air or water.

Heat transfer
Transferal of heat from one place to another by **conduction**, **convection** or **radiation**. The term refers to the movement of heat from a fluid to a solid or vice versa such as between combustion gas and a piston or the cylinder liner and cooling water.

Heat treatment
Term applied to the process where steel is subjected to one or more temperature cycles to modify its properties.

Heat
Form of energy released during combustion.

Heave to
Bring vessel to rest with head to wind.

Heave
Up and down motion of a **semi-submersible** drilling platform or **drill ship.**

Heave/motion compensator
Device keeping the **drill string** applied to the well bottom, despite the vertical motion of the rig on the surface of the sea relative to the sea bed.

Heaving
Vertical movement in a sea. *See* Figure 15.

Heavy crude
Crude oil with a high proportion of heavy oil fractions.

Heavy marine fuel oil
The residue from the crude oil refining process blended with lighter fuel to reach the required viscosity and density. It can be mixed with waste and chemical products.

Heavy lift derrick
Cargo handling device, generally of patented design, for large heavy items. *See* Figure 7.

Heavy lift vessel
Vessel fitted with strong **derricks** and gear, designed to lift heavy masses. *See* Figure 7.

Heavy water
Water with a density about 1 per cent greater than that of ordinary water. Used in heavy water nuclear reactors.

Heel
Inclination of a ship from the upright.

Heel block
Block at lower end of **derrick**.

Heleshaw
Type of hydraulic pump consisting of a number of pistons arranged radially around a shaft. The pump runs at constant speed, variation of output being achieved by varying the path or length of stroke. The pistons must follow as they rotate around the shaft axis.

Helical gearing
Helical gears connect parallel shafts and the teeth wind helically round the axis. There are single and double types. The tooth action of the single helical gear produces end thrust; in the double helical gear, end thrust from one helix is balanced by that of the other. Helical gears are suited for very high peripheral speeds over 300 m/min. *See* Figure 20.

Helical gears, double
Also called herringbone gears. Gears with the teeth cut on equal but opposed helices, often employed to cancel out thrust forces. Under load, single helical gears generate an axial thrust reaction that can be undesirable. *See* Figure 20.

Helical gears, single
Used to connect parallel shafts, as with straight **spur gears**, however, the teeth are cut helically on the cylindrical blanks in the form of a very coarse pitch, multi-start thread. This configuration provides a stronger tooth (considered as a cantilever) and smoother transfer of load from tooth to tooth than straight **spur gears**.

Helicoidal surface
Surface generated by rotation and translation in relation to an axis, such as a screw thread or **propeller**.

Helium (He)
Inert gaseous element present in the atmosphere. Used as a shielding gas in helium arc welding; liquefies at temperatures below 4K, and changes to a form known as liquid helium II at 2.2K. Liquid helium is the standard coolant for devices working at cryogenic temperatures.

Helix angle
Angle between the tangent at any point to the helix along which the tooth is cut, and the plane through the point containing the axis of the gear.

Helm indicator
Pointer worked from the steering wheel indicating the angular position of the **rudder**. Can also take the form of an electronic instrument.

Helm
Whole of the mechanism by which the **rudder** is controlled.

Helmsman
Individual who steers a vessel underway.

Henry (H)
Electrical **SI unit** of either mutual or self inductance. An inductance of one H is present if the electro-motive force of one V is induced when the current changes at a rate of one A/sec.

Herringbone gear
Double helical gear. *See* Figure 20.

Hertz (Hz)
The **SI unit** of frequency that equals one cycle per second.

Hertzian stresses
Contact stresses set up when two elastic bodies in point contact press together.

HKSOA
Hong Kong Ship Owners Association.

High expansion foam
Fire fighting foam produced from a liquid concentrate; expands up to 1000 times after passing through a foam generator.

High frequency heating
Heating in which a material, either electrically conducting or electrically insulating, is heated by an alternating electric field of a frequency above normal mains frequency, such as over 50 or 60 c/s.

High pressure stage
Particular point in a process where a high pressure substance is utilised or produced. The high pressure stage of a steam turbine plant utilises high pressure steam for power generation. The high pressure stage of an air compressor produces high pressure air.

High rupture capacity fuse
Electrical cartridge fuse with a high rupture capacity. Used for overcurrent protection in an electrical circuit.

High seas
Maritime areas outside the jurisdiction of any state.

High speed diesel
Diesel engine with a crankshaft rotational speed of 600 rev/min or more.

High speed steel
Highly alloyed tool steel that has been intensely hardened, retaining its hardness at a dull red heat, to accept machining at high speeds.

High temperature sludge
Sludge formed in an engine when a lubricating oil is subject to high temperature, generally resulting from sustained operation under heavy loads and/or high speeds that leads to oxidation of the oil.

Higher tensile steel
High tensile strength steel with good notch toughness, ductility and weldability. Ideal for ship's structures where high stresses occur.

Histogram
Graphical representation of data in the form of rectangles on a base representing intervals that results in a stepped figure.

Hogging
When a vessel drops at the extremities; opposite of **sagging**. *See* Figure 15.

Hoistable car deck
Deck on a car carrying ship taking vehicles between ports. Can be stowed under the deck head when not in use and lowered on wires into its operational position.

Hold
Internal compartment where cargo can be stowed and carried. One of the spaces between **bulkheads** specifically intended for the carriage of cargo.

Holding down bolts
Bolts connecting a machine bedplate to a foundation such as tank top girders.

Home trade
Trading limited to indigenous ports. In the United Kingdom British ships are limited to trading with British and Irish ports while European ports are limited to between Brest and the River Elbe.

Homogeneous cargo
Entire cargo of the same uniform type.

Homogeniser
Machine that blends or emulsifies a substance by forcing it against a hard surface through fine openings.

Honing
Finishing of cylinder liner bores to a high degree of accuracy.

Hooke's Law
Approximate law of **elasticity**. The ratio of stress to strain is a constant within the limits of elasticity. The stress at which this law ceases to apply is known as the **limit of proportionality**.

Hoop stress
Stress in a tube under pressure that acts tangentially to the perimeter of the cross-section.

Horizontal well
Direction well where the final angle of drilling is more than 60 degrees away from vertical.

Horn
That part of a **stern frame** on which a spade type **rudder** is hung.

Horse power (hp)
One hp is equivalent to the work done to exert a force equal to 33 000 foot pounds per minute, 550 foot pounds per second, or approximately 746 watts. The **SI unit** of power is the kW. One kW=1.341 hp. There are various definitions of horse power as detailed below.

Brake (bhp). Actual output delivered by a reciprocating engine at its output shaft, generally measured with some form of brake meter; bhp is always less than ihp as it includes mechanical losses.

Indicated (ihp). Of a reciprocating engine, the horse power developed by the pressure volume changes of the working agent within the cylinder; it exceeds the useful or brake horse power at the crankshaft by the power lost in friction and pumping. The **mechanical efficiency** of the engine is its **bhp** divided by its **ihp**.

Nominal (nhp). This term was used with early reciprocating steam engines, giving an indication of their capability. Based on dimensions rather than performance, it did not indicate the actual power developed by the engine in service.

Shaft (shp). Net power delivered to the **propeller** shafting, such as after passing through reduction gears, thrust block or other transmission devices. Measured by a **torsion meter** situated at the end of the shaft tunnel.

Hose proof
Enclosure for electrical equipment. Indicates high pressure water from a nozzle in any direction under specified conditions will have no harmful effect.

Hot bulb engine
Internal combustion engine in which ignition of fuel does not solely depend on heat from compression relying partly on other sources such as a hot bulb; sometimes called **semi-diesel.**

Hot spot
(1) Area of material on a rubbing component of a machine, such as a piston or bearing, that becomes excessively hot due to a malfunction such as a lubrication failure. (2) In carburetor engines, an area of the inlet manifold wall heated by exhaust gas to aid fuel vaporisation.

Hot working
Mechanical manipulation of metals, such as rolling, forging or extruding, at temperatures above their recrystallisation points.

Hotwell
Chamber storing the condensed exhaust steam from an engine in an open feed system.

Housing
Portion of a mast below the surface of the upper **deck**.

Hovercraft
Craft which can hover over or move across water or land surfaces while being held off the surfaces by a cushion of air. The cushion is produced either by pumping air into a plenum chamber under the craft or by ejecting air downwards and inwards through a peripheral ring of nozzles. Propulsion can be achieved by tilting the craft, by jet, or by air propeller. Over water it can be achieved by a water **propeller** and over land using low-pressure tyres or tracks.

HSE
*H*eath and *S*afety *E*xecutive in the United Kingdom.

HSST
*H*igh *S*peed *S*urface *T*ransport.

Hull
Outside plated frame and body of a ship.

Hull cleaning
Removal of fouling organisms from the external surface of the hull of a ship. This can be done in dry dock by pressure hoses and brushes, or in wet dock or anchorage by divers or special equipment with rotary brushes.

Hull efficiency

Ratio of effective power (product of the resistance of the hull and ship speed) to thrust power (product of thrust delivered to the **propeller** and speed of advance of the **propeller**).

Hull resonance

When a ship moves through regular waves a vertical force is created that generates a heaving motion. The magnitude of this motion depends on, among other factors, the ratio of the heaving period (T_H) of a ship to the period of encounter of waves with a ship (T_E). Maximum **amplitudes** of heave will occur when T_H/T_E approach unity. This is the **resonance** condition.

Humidity

Measure of the amount of water vapour in a given volume of gas. Most measurements relate to air. *See also* **absolute humidity.**

Humidifier

Apparatus controlling and maintaining desired humidity conditions in an air supply.

Humpage's gear

An **epicyclic** train of wheels for speed reduction of a machinery shaft.

Hundred year storm

Conditions only likely to occur once every hundred years. To be taken into account in the design of offshore drilling **rigs.**

Hunting gear

Form of mechanical feedback. In the case of **steering gears,** the position of the **rudder stock** is transmitted through mechanical linkage to the control rod of a variable delivery pump. As the rudder starts to move, the hunting gear starts to remove the stroke from the pump so the pump is off stroke when the rudder reaches the required position.

Hunting

A mechanism producing a follow-up effect so that motion in one plate induces motion in another until equilibrium is established. *See* **hunting gear.**

Hybrid platform

Gravity drilling platform with a base and storage area made of reinforced concrete and upper sections made of steel.

Hydrant

Terminal point of a water main with fittings for the attachment of hose pipes.

Hydraulic control
Use of a flowing liquid as the control medium in pumps, motors, valves, actuators and ancillary equipment.

Hydraulic fluids
The three principle types are aqueous solutions, petroleum fluids and synthetic fluids. The latter two are used in a variety of marine machinery applications, such as in steering gear and deck machinery. It is essential for such fluids to have a high **viscosity index** so that their viscosities remain reasonably stable regardless of temperature.

Hydraulic intensifier
Device used to obtain a supply of high pressure liquid from a greater flow of low pressure liquid using interconnected pistons of two different sizes.

Hydraulic steering motor
Multi-cylinder reciprocating engine driven by liquid under pressure, generally of radial or swash plate design.

Hydraulic test
Test for pressure tightness and strength. Water is pumped into a compartment at a designated pressure.

Hydraulic winch
A **winch** powered by a hydraulic motor. A central pumping station is often used to supply several winches and other hydraulic services on board ship. The advantages of the hydraulic drive include greater flexibility in positioning and installation, limited maximum motor output torque, variable speed control, good winching characteristics, and reduced electrical loading.

Hydraulics
Branch of applied science dealing with fluids in motion.

Hydrazine (N_2H_4)
Colourless alkali used as a reducing agent, rocket propellant, and for the removal of traces of dissolved oxygen from boiler feed water.

Hydrocarbon
Chemical compounds of hydrogen and carbon.

Hydrocracking
Oil refinery **cracking** process that takes place in the presence of hydrogen to produce lighter distillates, particularly **petrochemicals** and **aromatics**.

Hydrodynamics
Branch of dynamics studying the motion produced in fluids by applied forces.

Hydrodynamic lubrication
Thick film lubrication. Relatively moving surfaces, such as bearing surfaces, are separated by a substantial distance using thick film lubrication. The load is then supported by hydodynamic film pressure to prevent contact between the surfaces.

Hydrodynamic power transmission
Power transmission system which, in general, employs a hydraulic coupling, a torque converter, or a reaction coupling.

Hydrofoil
A wing or foil that operates in water. As a vessel moves off and accelerates, the foil lifts the craft until the hull is clear of the water surface.

Hydrogen burning
When steel is heated to a temperature above 700°C in the presence of steam a reaction occurs causing rapid oxidation of the steel, known as burning. Some marine boilers have caught fire and melted due to this phenomena.

Hydrogen embrittlement
Hydrogen in the nascent or monatomic form is readily absorbed by most metals. In the case of steel, it causes loss of **ductility** or **embrittlement**. Nascent hydrogen is formed when produced by a chemical reaction, such as steel pickled in acid, and is the cause of some boiler defects.

Hydrogen (H)
Least dense element; a light gas which, together with oxygen, forms water.

Hydrographer
A surveyor, usually employed by the government, who produces charts of the oceans and seas for navigational purposes.

Hydrometer
Instrument determining the relative density of liquids. The most widely used are the **API** and the **Baume.**

Hydrophone
Instrument used in **seismic** surveying to detect sound waves passing through water.

Hydrostatic release
Mechanism that will release at a pre-determined depth of water. Used to secure life rafts to enable them to float free from a sinking ship.

Hydrostatic curves
Variations of ship hydrostatic data with its draught shown by a set of curves. Extremely useful in assessing end draughts and the stability of a ship in the

various conditions of loading. Calculations are generally made by computer.

Hygrometer
Instrument for measuring the humidity of air or gas.

Hygroscopic
Denoting a substance that absorbs water.

Hyperbaric chamber
Compartment that can be sealed and pressurised to reproduce conditions at various water depths; can be used to enable divers to decompress or for dry work in deep water.

Hypocycloid
Curve traced by a point on the circumference of a circle as it rolls round the inner circumference of another circle.

Hypoid gear
Form of **bevel gear** used in rear axle crown and **bevel** combinations. The bevel pinion meshes with the crown-wheel below its centre line causing some sliding action between the teeth. Requires a special lubricant.

Hypothesis
Explanation of an observed phenomena based on limited evidence.

Hysteresis
Internal energy loss in an element resulting in an output signal that depends on the input signal and whether it is increasing or decreasing in value.

I

IACS
International Association of Classification Societies.

IALA
International Association of Lighthouse Authorities.

IBIA
International Bunker Industry Association.

Ice breaker
Ship specially strengthened and constructed for breaking up ice to open a navigable channel for other ships. The two main types are polar and baltic; polar is used for heavy duty operations.

Ice class
Ice classification notation. Given to vessels with additional strengthening to enable them to operate in ice bound waters.

Iceberg
Huge mass of ice from polar regions that have broken from the ice cap and are floating. Only one third of the total iceberg is visible above the water, the greater proportion is below the surface.

ICHCA
International Cargo Handling Coordination Association.

ICMES
International Conference on Marine Engineering Systems

ICMS
Integrated Condition Monitoring System including temperature/pressure sensing, engine performance characteristics, vibration analysis, and lubricant analysis.

ICS
Institute of Chartered Shipbrokers.

IES
Institution of Engineers & Shipbuilders in Scotland.

IGEMA
I Give Every Movement Accurately.

Igema gauge
Remote reading boiler level indicating instrument; consists of a U-tube manometer containing two different coloured liquids.

Ignition
Mechanism for starting combustion of the fuel/air mixture in the cylinders of an internal combustion engine. Spontaneous ignition occurs in a diesel engine without the help of a spark when the compressed mixture reaches the ignition temperature of the fuel.

Magnetic ignition. There are two types: the rotating armature and the rotating magnet.

Coil ignition. Consists of an electric battery and coil which transforms battery voltage to a high voltage to produce a spark.

Ignition, CD. Mainly fitted to outboard petrol engines. Each sparking plug has a separate coil and there is no distributor. Rotating magnets in the flywheel generate a voltage which is stored in a capacitor. A sensor magnet in the flywheel triggers the discharge of this through the appropriate coil, which multiplies the voltage to give the spark at the plug. CD ignition systems can eliminate the need for contact breakers and other moving parts, to give increased reliability. They generate much higher voltages (up to 50 000) allowing the use of surface gap sparking plugs in which the spark can jump from the central electrode radially in any direction: thus greatly reducing fouling and the need to adjust the gap from time to time.

Ignition delay

Period in a diesel engine between the commencement of injection and start of combustion.

Ignition quality

The ease with which a fuel ignites when injected into the hot compressed air of a diesel engine. The delay period between the first droplets entering the combustion space and the start of combustion is a measure of the ease of ignition. **Cetane** and **diesel indexes** can be used to measure the ignition quality of distillate fuels and **CCAI** and **CII** for heavier fuels.

ILMarE

Institute of Licensed Marine Engineers. A new marine engineering institute launched in October 1997. Introduced to recognise fully the professional competence and responsibility of senior seagoing engineers and to use an **IMO, STCW** recognised standard for membership. There are two grades: Member (MILMarE) who must be the holder of a Class I certificate of competency; Fellow (FILMarE) who will require an additional 5 years serving at sea as a Chief Engineer on an ocean going vessel or a similar position of responsibility in the maritime industry. Members of this body will also be Members of the parent **Institute of Marine Engineers**.

IMDG

International Maritime Dangerous Goods Code.

IMIF

International Maritime Industries Forum.

Immersion

The mass to be added or deducted from a ship to change the mean draft by 1cm. Measured in tonnes per cm (TPC).

$$\text{TPC in salt water} = \frac{A}{97.5} \qquad \text{TPC in fresh water} = \frac{A}{100}$$

Where A = water plane area in M^2.

Immersion suit
Protective, all covering, one piece garment specially designed to stop bodily heat loss; designed to keep a person alive in very cold sea water, it is made of insulated material to keep out both cold and water.

Immiscible
Not capable of being mixed; tends to form two layers such as oil and water.

IMO
International Maritime Organisation The United Nations Conference created a new organization in 1948 called the Inter-Governmental Maritime Consultative Organisation (IMCO), now IMO. It aims to provide co-operation among governments on technical matters affecting international merchant shipping and is a specialist agency of the United Nations.

IMPA
International Marine Purchasing Association.

Impact
Sudden application of a shock load on an object or structure. See **impact test**.

Impact test
Test measuring the resistance of a material to suddenly applied or shock load. The most popular test is the **Charpy**. A pendulum strikes a notched specimen and the amount of energy absorbed in breaking the specimen is measured.

Impedance
Complex ratio of sinusoidal voltage to current in an electric circuit or component. Dependent on **resistance, inductance, capacitance** and **frequency**.

Impeller
Rotating component of a centrifugal pump or blower that imparts **kinetic energy** to the fluid using **centrifugal force**. Fluid enters at the shaft or eye of the impeller and passes out the radius or perimeter via radial vanes.

Impressed current system
System of **cathodic protection** where direct current is supplied through **anodes,** generally made of platinum, protecting steel from corrosion in sea water. The steelwork forms the **cathode** of the **electrolytic system.**

Impulse turbine
Steam turbine where steam expanded in nozzles is directed onto moving rotor blades carried in one or more stages. No change in pressure occurs as the steam passes the blade-ring. The blades are rotated by an impulsive force resulting from changing steam velocity. See also **blading, impulse.**

IMSA
International Marine Software Associates.

Inboard
In a direction towards the centreline of a ship.

Inches of mercury
Scale for measuring small pressure changes, particularly those below atmospheric pressure such as a **vacuum**.

Inclination test
Experiment to determine the vertical position of the centre of gravity of a ship for a specified ship condition. The test is carried out by moving masses across the deck under controlled conditions while noting the resulting angle of **heel**. Carried out once construction is complete or after any major alterations affecting the stability. *See also* **stable**.

Inclined manometer
Instrument used to measure low pressure. The applied pressure acts on a container of liquid and forces some of it along an inclined glass tube.

Inclinometer
Instrument mounted on the binnacle and centre of the engine room bulkhead indicating the angle of **heel**.

Inclusion
Slag or other foreign matter entrapped in a weld.

Incombustible material
Material that neither burns nor gives off flammable vapours in sufficient quantity to ignite a pilot flame when heated to 750°C.

Incompatible
Not compatible. Particularly relevant when dealing with fuels and lubricants as in either case products could separate or stratify creating deposit problems within fuel and lubricant systems.

Incorporated Engineer (IEng)
See **Institute of Marine Engineers.**

Indemnity
Compensation offered by one party to another for the consequence of carrying out, or omitting to carry out, a certain act. An indemnity is generally given in writing, however, is unenforceable in a court of law if the act for which it is given is intended to defraud an **innocent third** party.

Indicator diagram
Graph of the work done by steam or combustion gases while in a cylinder. Produced by an indicator mechanism attached to an engine cylinder under operating conditions, recording pressures throughout the working cycle. Essential when calculating the engine **ihp**.

Indirect drive
Use of mechanical or electrical transmission between the prime mover and **propeller**.

Induced draught
Draught created through a boiler furnace by means of an induced draught fan. This reduces the pressure of products of combustion increasing air flow through the combustion chamber.

Inductance
Property of an element in an electrical circuit carrying a current characterised by the formation of a **magnetic field** and storage of magnetic energy. The magnitude of this capability is its inductance.

Induction motor
Motor with a rotor current induced by the relative motion of the rotor conductors rather than drawn from the supply. The rotating field is produced by stator currents when the stator is connected to the supply.

Inductive
Qualifying term applied to an electric circuit or winding indicating that its self-inductance is appreciable compared with its resistance.

Inductor
Electrical component whose principal characteristic is **inductance**.

INEC
International Naval Engineering Conference. Biennial event organised by the **Institute of Marine Engineers** in co-operation with the world's navies.

Inert
Unreactive; resistant to chemical reactions with other substances.

Inert gas
Gas not readily changed by chemical action showing little tendency to combine with other elements. Will not support **combustion**.

Inert gas system
System installed to ensure that when cargo is pumped from the tank it is replaced by non-explosive gas to avoid the possibility of explosive mixtures collecting in an oil tanker. Exhaust gas is taken from the funnel, cleaned by

water washing, tested and then pumped into cargo tanks; these tanks remain pressurised when not full. A number of other ship types are fitted with **inert gas generators** (Pyrene ED-Hol), generating a continuous flow of inert gas that can be piped to fire affected compartments in the event of fire.

Inertia
(1) Tendency of a body to preserve its state of rest or uniform motion unless acted upon by an equal or opposing force. (2) Relating to a ship, entails continued free movement when power is removed from the **propellers**.

Inflammable
See **flammable,** the preferred term.

Information technology
Assembly of the various techniques associated with information handling. Includes computer technology and telecommunication systems.

Infra-red
Energy radiation that is below the visible spectrum within the frequency band 10^7–10^9 kHz. Used for cooking in certain types of galley equipment and in guided missile homing systems when a missile detects then locks onto ship and aircraft exhaust gases.

Inherent regulation
Process property resulting in **equilibrium** after a disturbance without causing any monitoring feedback.

Inhibitor
Compound decreasing the speed of a chemical reaction. For example the way an oxidation inhibitor slows down the tendency of a lubricant to oxidise.

Initial boiling point
Temperature on a distillation thermometer the moment the first drop of distillate falls from the condenser in the **ASTM** distillation test.

Injection timing
Relationship of the starting point of injection to the rotation of a crankshaft.

Injection well
Used to inject gas or water into **reservoir** rock to maintain reservoir pressure in **secondary recovery** and for conservation purposes.

Injection
Process of introducing fuel into the cylinder of a petrol or diesel engine by means of a special pump and injection valve.

Injector
Device embodying a restricted nozzle through which fluid is passed at high velocity from a region of high pressure to one of lower pressure. Fuel injectors in diesel engines generally have a number of small nozzle holes and a spring loaded valve opened by fuel pressure. In steam plant, injectors passing cold water into a steam chamber are used to produce a vacuum.

Injector nozzle
Part of an injector containing the needle valve and its seat.

INMARSAT
International Maritime Satellite Organisation. Communication network available to all ships worldwide.

In phase
Alternating quantities of the same **frequency** that reach corresponding values simultaneously.

Insoluble
Solid chemical substance that will not dissolve in a given liquid over a specified temperature range.

Insolubles
Contaminants in used lubricating oil, determined under controlled test conditions. Pentane insolubles are entire insolubles as determined under test conditions.

Institute of Marine Engineers (IMarE)
An international body devoted to promoting the scientific and practical development of Marine Engineering in all its branches. Founded in London in 1889 and granted the Royal Charter in 1933. There are various membership categories, the first two of which entitle the member to be registered with the Engineering Council as a Chartered Engineer (CEng):

Fellow. Those aged 30 years and over who meet the requirements for the class of Member and have had experience involving superior responsibility for at least five years in the design or execution of important work in maritime engineering. Can be registered as CEng and use the designation FIMarE.

Member. Those aged 25 years and over who have obtained an honours degree in engineering, or an equivalent qualification, and completed a minimum of two years approved training with a further two years engineering experience. Can be registered as a CEng and use the designation MIMarE.

Associate Member. Those aged 23 years and over who possess a Class 1 Certificate of Competency, BTEC/SCOTVEC Higher National Diplomas,

Certificates or the equivalent, and have had approved training and experience. Can be registered as Incorporated Engineer (IEng) thus permitting the use of the designation AMIMarE.

Companion. Those aged 30 years and over who have attained a standard of education, training and experience, which although not in engineering, is at least equivalent to that required for election to Member class.

Graduate Member. Those aged 21 years and over who have obtained an honours degree in engineering or equivalent qualification. Can be registered at Stage 1 on the Engineering Council's Register of Chartered Engineers.

Associate. Those aged 21 years and over who possess a Class 2 Certificate of Competency, BTEC/SCOTVEC National Certificate or equivalent qualifications, and have had approved training and experience. Can be registered as Engineering Technician (Eng Tech).

Consociate. This class of membership is intended for all who are concerned with or interested in the maritime industry and wish to take part in the affairs of the Institute while holding qualifications not directly related to any of the above classes.

Members who are **Chartered Engineers** can be eligible to register through the Institute with **FEANI** and obtain recognition of their qualifications, training, professional experience and responsibility throughout Europe with the award of the title Eur Ing.

Institute of Petroleum
Body committed to advancing the knowledge of all involved in the oil and gas industries. Founded in London in 1913 as the Institution of Petroleum Technologists, it took its present name in the late 1930s.

Instrument
Any electrical or electronic equipment designed to carry out a specific function or set of functions. Covers a wide range of applications in an electrical network or a displacement measuring unit in an engineering system.

Instrument air
Compressed air suitable for use in **pneumatic** equipment. Must be free of oil and dust and be dry enough to ensure no water condenses in the system.

Instrument range
Range of values over which an instrument is able to measure.

Instrument transformer
A **transformer** specially designed to maintain a certain relationship in phase magnitude between the primary and secondary voltages or currents.

Insulated electrical system

An ac 3-phase 3-wire system in which the neutral or star point is not connected to earth. Also a dc system in which neither pole is connected to earth.

Insulation (refrigeration)

Form of insulation that must be provided at the boundaries of refrigerated compartments because the hull steel structure is an excellent conductor. The main insulation materials used are cork, glass wool and polyurethane.

Insulation

(1) Non-conducting material used to form a barrier restricting the flow of heat/cold or electric current from one body to another. (2) Materials of high **resistivity** and electric strength used to prevent conduction between a conductor and an earth, other conductors or the frame of a device.

Insurance

Payment of money against loss, damage or injury to property or person. *Policy.* Signed contract of an insurer to make good a loss against which insurance has been affected.

Insurance Broker

Person acting as an intermediary between those requiring insurance and those willing to insure.

Integral action time

In a proportional plus integral controller where the deviation is constant, the time interval in which integral action increases by an amount equal to the proportional action signal.

Integral action

Action of a control element in which the output signal changes at a rate proportional to its input signal.

Integrated circuits

Small solid-state circuit consisting of interconnected semiconductor devices like **transistors, capacitors** and **resistors** printed into a single silicon chip. Cannot be subdivided without destroying its intended function.

Integrated monitoring system

Combining all the individual control systems of a **plant** into a single computer controlled system. On board ship this would include all aspects of navigation, cargo, machinery and administration.

Intercooler

Cooler fitted between stages as in a multistage air compressor; the cooling medium is often sea water. The effect of intercooling in a compressor is to reduce the air temperature at a constant pressure reducing the amount of power required to compress air in later stages.

Intercostal
Longitudinal girder between the **floors** and **frames**, not continuous.

Interface
(1) Boundary between two surfaces in chemical contact. (2) Method of computer operation where a user communicates directly with a computer.

Intergranular corrosion
Form of corrosion in which the attack of the corrosive medium takes place preferentially at, and is concentrated on, grain boundaries. This type of corrosion leads to disintegration before the bulk of the grains themselves have been attacked to any considerable extent. *See also* **caustic embrittlement.**

Intermediate shafting
Lengths of shafting between a power source and **propeller** shaft.

Internal combustion engine
Engine in which fuel is consumed internally such as in diesel or petrol engines.

Interpolation
To calculate a value from other known values.

Interstitial Water
Water present in the pores of the oil or gas bearing zone of **reservoir** rock.

INTERTANKO
*Inter*national Association of Independent *Tank*er *Owners*.

Intrinsic safety
Method of protecting electrical circuits and apparatus for safe use in **hazardous zones,** where any spark or thermal effect produced in normal operation or fault conditions could ignite gas or vapour.

Inverter
Static device for converting electrical power in the form of direct current to electrical power in the form of alternating current.

Involute
Most common type of curvature employed as the basic profile of modern **gear teeth.** Geometrically it is defined as the curve described by the end of a taut string as it is unwound from the surface of a circular cylinder, the circle is referred to as the base circle. The true involute form is often modified by tip and root corrections to allow for tooth deflections under load and to promote smooth engagement and disengagement under operating conditions.

It is a matter of convenience that the basic rack which generates involute teeth has straight-sided teeth itself. *See* Figure 1.

In water survey
Survey undertaken whilst the vessel is afloat. Hull plating is cleaned by diver operated machinery and a remotely operated underwater TV camera is used to examine the hull. Difficult in dirty water ports.

Ion
Positively or negatively charged **atom** or group of atoms.

Ionisation
Process by which charged **particles** are formed from neutral **atoms** of **molecules** substantially governing the electrical characteristics between **electrodes** in **fluorescent** or other gas filled tubes.

IOPC
International *Oil Pollution Compensation* Fund

IPD
Initial *Professional Development*. A follow on stage from the initial **Engineering Council, SATOR** academic qualifications that encompasses the acquisition and development of skills needed to practice in a specific area of engineering. It is a requirement that IPD should be recorded by a trainee and verified by a supervisor; an intermediate stage prior to **CPD**.

Iron
A **ductile** metal that becomes steel with the addition of carbon. If further carbon is added it becomes cast iron with increased brittleness.

Isentropic
A process that involves no change in **entropy**.

Isherwood system
Ship constructional system with continuous longitudinal framing as the dominant feature.

ISIS (RN)
Decca machinery plant monitoring system.

ISM
International *Safety Management*. Formed by **IMO**.

ISM Code
International *Safety Management* Code. Introduced by **IMO**, requires companies responsible for operations on board ship to determine clear procedures, standards and instructions for safety management.

ISMA
International Ship Managers Association. Formed by a group of independent ship owners.

ISMA Code
International Ship Managers Association Code. Quality management system based on **ISMA's** Code of Ship Management Standards.

ISO 9002
General **ISO** standard for management and related procedures, that is widely used in the maritime industry.

ISO
International Organisation for Standardisation.

Isobar
Line on a meteorological chart connecting points for which simultaneous barometric pressures, reduced to sea level, have been recorded.

Isoclinic
Within a stressed body, it is the imaginary line along which all points have corresponding principal stresses with the same orientation.

Isolating valve
Valve in a piping system that can be closed to separate one part of the system from another in an emergency or during maintenance.

Isolator
Mechanical switching device that provides an isolating distance in accordance with specified requirements when in the open position. Can carry current for a limited time under both normal and abnormal circuit conditions.

Isometric projection
Engineering drawing projection with three mutually perpendicular axis shown equal to the plane of projection.

Isopach map
Geological map giving the thickness of a particular **stratum**.

Isothermal expansion
Change in volume and pressure of a gas under conditions where temperature remains constant.

Isotherms
Line on a chart connecting points that represent the same temperature.

Isotope
One of two or more forms of an element that differ from each other in **atomic**

weight and in nuclear, but not chemical properties. The nucleon of isotopes contain identical numbers of **protons**, but different numbers of **neutrons**.

ISU
International Salvage Union

ITOPF
International Tanker Owners Pollution Federation.

J

Jack staff
Small staff erected at **bow** for a flag.

Jack stay
Taut ropes stretched for a specific purpose, such as between the heads of **davits** or between **stanchions** to take the lacings of **awnings.**

Jack
Appliance for lifting heavy weights or exerting heavy thrust. Can use a screw thread or hydraulic pressure.

Jacket platform
Drilling platform constructed entirely of steel. Such platforms are generally kept in position by means of steel piles driven into the sea bed.

Jacket
(1) Enclosure surrounding a component such as an engine cylinder through which steam or water is passed to maintain a desired temperature. (2) Enclosure made of insulating material that surrounds a component to reduce the transfer of heat or noise.

Jack-up rig
Mobile drilling unit comprising a flat-bottomed barge through which three or four legs are jacked raising the barge above water.

Jacob's ladder
Rope ladder hanging over a ship's side.

Jalousie
Hanging or sliding slatted wooden shutter. Provides ventilation while restricting the entry of wind or rain.

Jerk-pump
Timed fuel injection pump with a cam-driven plunger that overruns a spill port causing the abrupt pressure rise necessary to initiate injection through the atomiser.

Jerque Note
Certificate given by Customs when a ship has been searched and no unentered goods are on board.

Jet
(1) High velocity stream of liquid projected forward or upward from a small orifice. (2) Spout or nozzle through which a liquid is emitted.

Jet bit
Modified drill bit using a hydraulic jet to increase the drilling rate.

Jet condenser
Condenser in which exhaust steam and cooling water spray are mixed in an airtight vessel. A vacuum is then formed by the condensation of steam.

Jetsam
Goods which have been thrown overboard.

Jettison
The act of deliberately throwing overboard or jettisoning goods, for example to lighten a ship that has run aground.

Jetty
Structure that projects into the water to a allow a ship to come alongside in a reasonable depth of water. Also called a **pier**.

Jib
Projecting arm of a crane or **derrick**.

Jig
Appliance used in the manufacture of (interchangeable) parts to locate and hold the work while guiding the cutting tool.

Job evaluation
Means of measuring the relative content and worth of a job, generally by an analysis of the job content under headings such as qualifications needed, specific skill requirements, environmental conditions, and special hazards.

Joggle plate
Plate shaped so that the longitudinal edge of the plate curves and overlaps the plate next to it.

Joggle shackle
Cable shackle with a quick release pin used in anchor work to haul the cable of one anchor when mooring two anchors.

Joint
Piece of compressible material shaped to fit between two surfaces to create a water, oil or gas tight seal.

Joule (J)
The **SI unit** for all forms of energy.

JOT
Journal of Offshore Technology; quarterly journal published by the **Institute of Marine Engineers.**

Journal
That part of a shaft or other revolving member which transmits weight directly to and is in close contact with the bearing in which it turns.

Jumbo derrick
A **derrick** for heavy lifts.

Jumper stay
A **stay** going horizontally from one mast to next or other point; also called a **triatic stay.**

Junction box
Joining place of electric cables.

Junk ring
Ring on upper part of piston.

Junked well
A **well** abandoned due to a blockage that is too costly to remove.

Jury Rig
Temporary equipment replacing a part that has failed or been lost such as a temporary mast to replace one that has been damaged.

K

K factor
The stress-intensity factor. Limiting load on **gear teeth** from consideration of wear depends on the radii of curvature of the co-operating profiles, pressure

angle of gears, **moduli of elasticity,** relative hardness, and surface endurance limits of the materials.

Kapok
Mass of silky fibres that clothe the seeds of the ceiba tree. Used in life jackets, belts, sleeping bags and for insulation.

Kedge anchor
One or more anchors carried in addition to the main or bower anchors, generally stowed aft. Can be dropped while a ship is under way, carried out by a tender or ship's boat enabling a ship to be winched if run aground, used to swing a ship onto a particular heading, or even to hold a ship steady against a tidal stream.

Keel blocks
Heavy wood or concrete blocks a ship rests on during construction and when in **dry dock.**

Keel plate
Strake of bottom plating on the middle line.

Keel
Principal fore and aft structural member running along the middle of a ship's bottom. Often referred to as the backbone of the hull. *See* Figure 23.

Keelson
Girder above the bottom shell on each side of centre-line, running fore and aft.

Keep
Removable part of a housing that holds a machine part in place, such as a bearing keep.

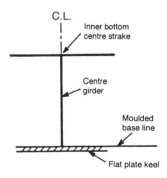

Figure 23 Keel

Kelly
Square or hexagonal hollow shaft that fits into the corresponding hole of the **kelly bushing**, itself fixed to the **rotary table**. *See* Figure 8.

Kelly bushing
Relaceable bearing with a square hole in which the **kelly** slides, that is attached to the **rotary table** during drilling.

Kelp
Large brown seaweed.

Kelvin (K)
The **SI unit** of temperature defined as the fraction, $1/273.15$ of the thermo-dynamic temperature of the triple point of water (where water, ice and water vapour are in equilibrium). The degree kelvin (K) as a unit of temperature difference is exactly equal to the degree **Celsius**, $0°C = 273.15°K$. To change degrees Celsius into degrees kelvin, add 273.15. Absolute zero is $0°K$, that is equal to $-273.15°C$.

Kent-ledge
Permanent iron ballast.

Kerosene
A product between gas oil and gaseous fuels used for heating, lighting and aircraft type gas turbine fuel. Obtained by distillation of petroleum, coal or bituminous shale. Also known as paraffin.

Ketones
One of a class of **organic** compounds containing the group CO, with a double bond to carbon. Acetone CH_3COCH_3 is one of the simplest. The group contains low, medium and high boiling point solvents and also provides important intermediate materials for further chemical synthesis. Because of their high solvent power they are widely used in the formulation of surface coatings and in extraction processes.

Key
Machined element used to connect a component to a shaft, such as a pulley or a **flywheel** that is keyed to a shaft. A key with a rectangular cross-section is called a flat key and is placed so the smaller dimension is in the radial direction. Keys with a circular cross section are called pin keys and can be assembled along the shaft or through it.

Key way
Groove in which a key fits. A key way cut into a shaft weakens the shaft and introduces concentrations of stress. Consideration must be given to this at

the design stage. **Propellers** were originally keyed to the tapered scew shaft **(tail shaft)**, however, most connections are now made without using keys.

Kick
Situation that occurs when the formation pressure in a well exceeds the hydrostatic head of the mud column, allowing formation fluid to enter the well bore. In certain circumstances a **blowout** can occur.

Kill a well
To fill a well with **drilling mud** of sufficient density to stop the flow of oil.

Killed steel
Name given to steel that has been fully de-oxidised before casting, as distinct from balanced and rimming steels. Silicon, manganese and aluminium are among the commonly used de-oxidents.

Kilogram (kg)
The **SI unit** of mass. One **tonne** equals 1000 kg.

Kilowatt (kW)
Unit of power equal to 1000W and approximately equal to 1.34 hp. The watt (W) is the **SI unit** of power.

Kilowatt hour (kWh)
Energy expended when a power of 1000W is supplied for one hour.

Kinematics
The science of pure motion.

Kinematic viscosity
Ratio of the absolute viscosity of a liquid to its specific gravity at the temperature at which the viscosity is measured. Testing is carried out under prescribed conditions and the common unit is the centistoke (cSt). The corresponding numerically equal **SI unit** is square millimetre per second (mm^2/s). Widely used in the marine industry, distillate fuels are reported at $40°C$, heavy fuels at $100°C$ and lubricants at $40°C$.

Kinetics
The science of relations between the motions of bodies and the forces acting upon them.

Kinetic control system
System to control the displacement, velocity, acceleration, or any higher time derivative of the position of a controlled device.

Kinetic energy
Energy stored in a body in motion, given up when a body is brought to rest.

King post
Vertical post fitted to support a **derrick**. Also known as a **samson post**.

Kingston valve
Large valve fitted in a **submarine's** main **ballast tank**, used to control the flooding and blowing of ballast.

Kirchhoff's Law
The ratio of the coefficient of absorption to the coefficient of emission is the same for all substances and depends only on the temperature and frequency of the rays.

Kite
Mark of approval given by the **British Standards Institution.**

Kitchen rudder
Consists of two curved plates shrouding the **propeller**. For going ahead the two plates are parallel with the **propeller** race. For astern the plates are closed behind the **propeller**. Used on some small craft to obviate requirement for reversing gearbox.

Klaxon
An audible alarm used in conjunction with many control systems.

Knee
Metal bar fashioned into a right angle to provide strengthening and support. Used to connect structural members perpendicular to each other such as deck beams and side frames.

Knocking
Noise from a diesel engine characteristic at slow speeds or when starting from cold. If occurring at normal speeds and temperatures it could be due to incorrect timing, faulty combustion or a mechanical defect.

Knot (kn)
Nautical mile, unit or rate of speed equal to 1,853 m or 6,080 ft per hour. The ship speed is always quoted as knots rather than knots per hour.

Knuckle
Abrupt change in the direction of plating.

Knurl
A protuberance. A knurled surface has a series of protuberances produced by milling, to facilitate grip by hand.

Kort nozzle
To increase thrust at low speeds a **propeller** can be enclosed in a shroud or

nozzle. An example is the patent Kort nozzle, often fitted to tugs and trawlers where under a heavy tow the **propeller** is working at a high slip.

L

Labile
Likely to undergo change.

Labouring
When a ship slowly rolls and pitches heavily in bad weather. During this process the internal distortion of the structure causes audible creaking noises.

Labrador Current
Cold water current flowing south along the coast of Labrador. The principal carrier of the icebergs that menace the shipping lanes of the North Atlantic.

Labyrinth-packing
Form of seal mainly used on the shafts of steam turbines to control steam leakage along the shaft. A series of fixed and rotating fins wire draw turbine steam which builds up a back pressure causing the steam to reduce to atmospheric pressure.

Lag
(1) Delay between cause and effect. (2) Thermal insulating material with poor heat transfer characteristics used to restrict heat transference.

Lamellar tearing
Stepped form of fracture in a series of tears that link up. Occurs in some rolled steel plates and beneath welds parallel to the plate surface. This is due to contracting stresses opening up weaknesses in the through-thickness direction of the plate.

Laminar flow
When water in the wake moves in a series of layers without mixing, the flow is said to be laminar. *See also* **Reynold's number.**

Lanchester balancer
Balancing device for certain **four stroke engines** with a uniform crank sequence. Two shafts carrying balance weights are utilised, each suitably phased and rotated in opposite directions.

Lantern ring
Spacing ring inserted into the **stuffing box** of a valve to form a pressure relief or condensing chamber.

Lanyard
(1) Rope or cord used for securing. (2) Rope loop worn around the neck tied to boatswain's pipe. (3) Part of a midshipman's uniform.

Lap winding
Distributed winding of a rotating electrical machine whose sequence of connections is such that it completes all its turns under one pair of main poles before proceeding to the next pair of main poles.

Lap
(1) Amount by which a **slide valve** or piston valve overlaps the steam and exhaust ports in a reciprocating engine. Steam and exhaust laps are necessary to provide for cut off before the beginning of the exhaust, and to provide the cushioning necessary to reduce the load on the piston as it changes direction. (2) Joint in which one edge of a plate overlaps the other.

Lapping
Process of grinding two parts together to create an exact fit.

Laquer
Product of oil oxidation with a varnish like appearance which may form in an engine, usually on the liner, piston or ring lands. Oil insoluble, it has a hard, dry and lustrous nature. Should be removed immediately as it will rapidly increase lubricating oil consumption.

Large angle stability
Stability of a vessel when the angle of inclination is greater than four or five degrees. The criterion for measuring large angle stability is the righting lever, GZ. *See* Figure 12.

Laser
Light Amplification by Stimulated Emission of Radiation. A laser produces a concentrated unidirectional beam of monochromatic light. The active medium that produces the beam is contained in a transparent cylinder with a reflecting surface at one end and a partially reflecting surface at the other. The stimulated waves of light make repeated passages along the cylinder some of which emerge as a concentrated but narrow beam through the partially reflecting end.

LASH
Lighter Aboard Ship. Barge carrying ship. Barges are loaded with cargo and brought to the mother ship ready for the main river or ocean crossing.

Lashings
Wires, chains, ropes, or straps used to secure cargo on a ship, or in a **container**.

Latent heat
Latent heat of fusion of a substance is the amount of heat required to convert the unit mass of a substance from a solid to a liquid without change in temperature. The latent heat of vaporisation is the amount of heat required to convert the unit mass of a substance from a liquid to a vapour without a change in temperature.

Latitude
Measure of the angular distance north or south of the equator.

Launch
Transferring a new ship from its building position on land into the water.

Launching ways
Foundations on which a new ship is launched, usually coated with a special launching grease.

Law of Comparison
See **Froude's Law of Comparison.**

Lay days
Days allowed by a **charter** for the loading or discharging of cargo.

Lay up
Anchor or moor a ship for an indefinite period, either when no charters are available or when a ship is taken out of commission for any reason.

Layout
Drawing showing the positions of the items of plant and control equipment, in a ship's engine room or other space, normally referred to as a plant layout drawing.

Lazarette
Store or provision room.

Lead
(1) Amount by which one operation precedes another in a machine as for instance the number of crankshaft degrees in an **opposed piston engine** between the exhaust crank and scavenge crank. (2) Another name for an electric cable. (3) Amount the steam port is open on a slide valve when the piston is at top dead centre, about to start its working stroke.

Lead (Pb)
(1) Soft heavy bluish grey metal obtained mainly from the mineral galena. One of the most stable metals that is soluble in nitric acid, however, not in sulphuric or hydrochloric acids. (2) Lead weight attached to a rope for taking soundings in shallow water. The bottom of the sinker may be tallow or wax for taking samples of the sea bed. (3) Lengths of thick lead wire placed between the journal and bearing cap during assembly to check the bearing clearance.

Lead acid cell
Cell used in an ordinary storage battery. The **electrodes** are grids of lead that contain lead oxides that change in composition during charging and discharging. The **electrolyte** is dilute sulphuric acid.

Lead line
Left hand vertical line in an **indicator diagram** representing the rise in pressure at the start of the working stroke.

Lead screw
Master screw that controls the longitudinal motion of a lathe tool.

Lead soap greases
Fluid grease made with lead soap and used mainly for reduction and **worm gear** lubrication.

Leading block
Type of block used to change and guide rope in the required direction, such as to a capstan.

League
Nautical measure equal to one-twentieth degree of **latitude** or three geographical miles.

Leak detector lamp
Gas powered lamp, in general butane, used to check for refrigerant leaks. If a **freon** refrigerant is drawn into the flame it will change colour.

Leak-off test
In offshore work, the process of applying pressure to the formation below the casing seat to test the quality of the **cementing** and determine the fracture pressure in the **permeable** zone below the casing seat.

Lean mixture
When the mixture of air and fuel fed into the cylinders of an **internal combustion engine** contain more oxygen than necessary to completely burn the fuel.

Ledeborite
Name given to **eutectic** of **austenite** and **cementite** in the iron-carbon alloy steel system. Contains 4.3 per cent carbon and solidifies at 113°C. Found in cast irons and certain highly alloyed steels.

Lee
Area sheltered from the wind.

Leeward
On the **lee** or sheltered side of a ship.

Leg
Vertical column of a **jack-up drilling rig.**

Length between perpendiculars (LBP)
Distance on the **summer load waterline** from fore side of **stem** to after side of **rudder post,** or to centre of **rudder stock** if there is no rudder post. *See* Figure 2.

Length on waterline
Length of a vessel measured along the **waterline** from forward to aft. *See* Figure 2.

Length overall (LOA)
Distance between the extreme points of a ship forward and aft. *See* Figure 2.

Lever
Rigid rod or beam pivoted at a fulcrum. Load is applied at one end while force is applied at the other.

Liberty ships
Ship of about 7000 Gross Tonnage mass -produced by a number of shipyards in the USA. Between 1942 and 1945, during the Second World War, 2700 Liberty ships were constructed to meet the need for sea transport.

Lid
Component of a valve closing the aperture of the valve.

Lien
Right to retain control of the property (ship) of another party until a debt relating to it has been paid.

Life factor
Design factor providing for the scatter of results in **fatigue tests,** effects of possible deterioration in service, and possible inadequacies in the assumed pattern of repeated loading. The estimated mean fatigue life is divided by this factor to obtain the safe fatigue life.

Lifeboat
Boat carried by a ship for use in an emergency. Provided with oars, a sail and sometimes a small engine; also carries water and provisions and is specially constructed for heavy weather.

Lifeline
Any line or rope for saving life or for security of persons.

Liferaft
Inflatable rubber circular shaped survival vessel stored and deflated in a cylindrical container, secured to the deck in a stand. A **hydrostatic release** is used so it can float free if a ship sinks. Carries water and provisions similar to a lifeboat.

Lift
Amount that the valve **plug** or **lid** moves away from the **seat** when the **valve** is opened.

Light crude
Low density crude oil containing a high proportion of lighter fractions such as gas and gasoline. North Sea crude is mainly light.

Light displacement
Weight of an unladen ship, measured in tonnes. The difference between the **loaded displacement** and light displacement is a ship's **deadweight.** Also known as light weight.

Light running
Running of machinery such as engines and shafting under no load, with the minimum of **friction.**

Light spring diagram
An **indicator diagram** taken with a specially weak control spring to reproduce the low pressure part of the diagram to a large scale.

Lightening hole
Hole cut out of a plate to make it lighter without reducing its strength. Also to make a passage through a plate.

Light-emitting diode
Semi-conductor diode that radiates visible light when energised.

Lighter
Flat bottomed non-propelled barge for carrying goods to and from a ship.

Lightship
Vessel with distinct markings anchored at an assigned place to exhibit a major navigational light.

Lignite
Brown coal showing traces of plant structure. Intermediate between bituminous coal and peat. Used for domestic and industrial purposes, and the manufacture of smokeless fuel.

Lignum vitae
Hard wood heavier than water. An evergreen tree of medium size with abruptly primate leaves, that yields a resin used in medicine. The heavy black heartwood may be used in ships for water lubricated **A-bracket** and **stern tube** bearings.

Limber hole
Drain hole in the vertical structure at the bottom of a tank to allow liquid to drain towards the suction well for a complete tank draining.

Limit of proportionality
In applying load to a test piece, the limit of proportionality is the **stress** at which the **deformation** (**strain**) ceases to be proportional to the corresponding stress. In practice, if a stress/strain diagram is plotted, the limit of proportionality is the point where the line ceases to be straight.

Limiting range of stress
Greatest range of **stress** (mean stress zero) a metal can withstand for an indefinite number of cycles without failure. Also called **endurance limit.**

Limits of size
Maximum and minimum sizes allowed for a dimension. The difference between these sizes is equal to the **tolerance.**

Linear programming
In computers, linear software for solving sets of equations.

Liner
(1) Separate and relatively thin sleeve fitted within an engine or pump cylinder to mate with the piston to form a renewable and durable rubbing surface. A dry liner is in continuous contact with the cylinder wall while a wet liner's inner surface makes contact with a cooling medium. (2) Sleeve or bush press fitted over a shaft in way of a bearing or gland seal. Any wear that takes place on the sleeve that can be renewed without damage to the shaft itself. (3) Cargo ship carrying on a regular trade between specified ports. Also used to describe a large passenger ship.

Lines plan
Drawing that shows the form of a ship. Consists of profile, half breadth and body plan. Shows three sets of sections through the form obtained by the intersection of three sets of mutually orthogonal planes with the outside surface.

Link motion
The eccentric sheaves, rods and radial link for regulating the steam cut off and reversing the motion of a reciprocating engine.

Linked
Term applied to electrical switches and circuit breakers that have their moving contacts linked mechanically in order to operate either simultaneously or in a definite sequence.

Lip seal
Means of leakage protection used on **tail shafts** to prevent the loss of lubricating oil and the ingress of sea water. Consists of specially shaped rubber or synthetic rings held against a sleeve on the shaft by means of either spring and oil pressure or by the water/oil differential pressure. *See also* **sterntube.**

Liquefaction
Change of a gas or solid into a liquid state. Natural gas consists of methane, ethane, propane and butane. The propane and butane are removed by liquefaction and marketed as **liquefied petroleum gas,** the methane is separated and marketed as **liquefied natural gas.**

Liquefied natural gas (LNG)
Consist mainly of varying proportions of hydrocarbons in the paraffin series; the lightest member methane CH_4, with a boiling point of -163.5°C, predominates at 93–95 per cent. Shipped in pressurised tankers at about -162°C, the liquid occupies one-six-hundredth of its gaseous state. The low temperature of this liquid makes steel brittle, therefore, special insulation is required and it cannot be distributed as liquid in containers.

Liquefied petroleum gas (LPG)
Petroleum gases separated in the refinery fractionating column. The heavier gases propane C_3H_8 and butane C_4H_{10} are compressed into liquid and stored under pressure in steel cylinders for industrial and domestic use. They are transported by sea in their liquid condition in special LPG ships.

Liquid
State of matter between a solid and a gas where the **molecules** are relatively free to change their positions with respect to each other, restricted only by cohesive forces that maintain a relatively fixed volume. A liquid is practically incompressible.

Liquid crystal display
Liquid crystal cells whose light transmitting properties vary with the applied electrical field. Numbers or letters can be displayed by the use of an array of straight lines.

Liquid slosh
Movement of liquid in a partially filled tank. The additional forces resulting from this movement must be considered in the design of tank bulkheads and sides. Alternatively wash bulkheads or reduced cross sections must be used in the tank construction.

Liquidus
Line in a constitutional diagram indicating the temperatures at which solidification of one phase or constituent begins or melting is completed. *See* **solidus.**

List
Transverse inclination of ship. Also called **heel.**

Lithium (Li)
Alkali metal similar in general properties to sodium and potassium. Lithium soaps are used in both speciality and general purpose greases.

Litre (l)
Unit of liquid volume. The **SI unit** of volume is the cubic metre (m^3) and the litre is the volume of a cubic decimetre (dm^3). One litre is equal to 0.219969 Imperial gallons and 0.264172 US gallons.

Littoral
The coastal region.

Live
When an electric circuit is charged with current and voltage.

Lloyd's Register
The world's first **classification society** started at Lloyd's Coffee House in the City of London in 1760; also publish the internationally recognised **Register of Ships.**

Lloyd's Register Number
A unique seven digit identification number given to all ships remaining unchanged during the life of a ship, regardless of a change of name or ownership. Recognised by **IMO.**

LMAA
London Maritime Arbitrators Association.

Load
(1) In an electrical system, the electrical **impedence** to which the output source is connected. The source can be an electrical generator, a **transformer**, an **amplifier**, or a single **transistor**. (2) The **horse power** requirement of a propulsion engine for a given loading that varies depending on speed and environmental conditions.

Load carrying capacity
Maximum load a sliding or rolling system can support without failure or excessive wear outside the design limits.

Load factor
Ratio of average load to maximum load.

Load line convention
Rules governing **freeboard**, as laid down by an International **Load Line** Convention.

Load line
A group of lines marked on the outside of both sides of a ship to mark the minimum **freeboard** permitted in different parts of the world during the different seasons. Sometimes called a plimsoll mark. The following load lines are used, *see also* Figure 19.

Summer load line. The waterline to which a ship can be loaded in summer, indicated in the freeboard markings.

Winter load line. The waterline to which a ship can be loaded in winter.

Winter North Atlantic load line. The waterline to which a ship can be loaded for North Atlantic conditions.

Fresh Water load line. The waterline to which a ship can be loaded for fresh water conditions.

Tropical Fresh Water load line. The waterline to which a ship can be loaded for tropical freshwater conditions.

Loaded displacement
Weight in tonnes of a ship's hull, machinery equipment, spares, cargo, bunkers, fresh water and people when a ship is immersed to its **summer load line**. The difference between the loaded displacement and the **light displacement** is a ship's **deadweight**.

Loading port survey
Survey of a ship's cargo spaces prior to loading to ensure clean and hygienic conditions exist suitable for the intended cargo.

Load-on-top
Practice of loading a fresh cargo of oil on top of oil recovered from tank cleaning operations. Widely used on tankers engaged in the crude oil trade. The on board water and oil mixture from ballasting and cleaning of tanks is pumped ashore at loading terminals with special reception facilities to reduce the risk of oil pollution at sea. If the mixture cannot be pumped ashore, the new cargo can be loaded on top and pumped ashore at the discharge port. Effective control of this system requires quantitative monitoring of the ballast prior to discharge.

Locked rotor torque
Torque developed by an **ac induction** motor the instant of starting.

Locker
Compartment in which gear may be stowed. *See also* **chain locker.**

Locking bars
Bars across hatchways locked to **coamings** to prevent unauthorised access.

Locking nut
Fitted to secure the **propeller** on the shaft. *See* **pilgrim nut.**

Locking pintle
A **rudder pintle** with a collar on the lower end to prevent the **rudder** from accidental displacement.

Log
Device for measuring the distance run or a ship's speed through water. Generally comprised of a small impeller of negligible **slip** projected through the bottom of a ship, then withdrawn into the hull when not in use.

Log abstract
Extract of a ship's **log book** giving details of speed and weather conditions encountered at sea. Normally available to a **charterer** so a ship's performance can be accurately calculated and compared with any warranty in the **charter party.**

Log book
Book in which events connected with ship are entered. Main logs kept on board ship are the navigating log and the engine log. Required by law.

Logic
To reason and examine problems in a formal sequential way.

Logistics
Planning and organisation of supplies, stores, and accommodation necessary for the support of personnel movements and expeditions.

Loll

When the **metacentric height** is negative G above M, a vessel will loll over until the **centres of buoyancy** and gravity are in the same vertical line. At the angle of loll a ship has a positive **metacentric height.** *See* Figure 12.

Longitude

Arc of the equator expressed in degrees East or West of the **Greenwich Meridian.**

Longitudinal bulkhead

Hull framing that runs fore and aft instead of transversely. In a tanker it can run along the entire length of a ship separating side tanks from centre tanks.

Long ton

Imperial measure equal to 2240 pounds. Equivalent **SI unit** is 1016.047 kg.

Long stroke engine

Term given to a two stroke diesel engine where the ratio of stroke to bore is in the region of 3 to 4 times. Four stroke engines may also have increased stroke to bore ratios, with reduced magnitude.

Loop scavenge

Piston engine scavenge system in which inlet and exhaust ports are approximately diametrically opposite to each other in the mid/lower section of the cylinder. The inlet ports are shaped so air flows up one side of the cylinder, across the cylinder cover and down the other side before reaching the exhaust ports.

Loran

*LO*ng *RA*nge Navigation. Medium or low frequency system of radio navigation. Transmissions sent from ground stations are received by the ship, enabling the plotting position on a lattice chart.

Loss core

Sum of all losses obtained by multiplying resistance in ohms by the squares of the currents flowing through the windings of an electrical machine or **transformer.**

Loss, windage

Power absorbed by rotating or oscillating parts in disturbing or impelling air, gas or vapour when such action is only incidental to the working of the part or machine.

Lost motion

Difference between the rate of motion of driving and driven parts within a mechanism.

Lost motion clutch

Servomotor arrangement moving the **camshaft** through the angular period between top dead centre in one direction to top dead centre in the other direction. Used when directly reversing a slow speed diesel engine.

Lower critical point

When carbon steel is heated, the point where the micro-constituent **pearlite** changes to **austenite** (730°C). On cooling, the reverse takes place at 695°C. Relevant to the heat treatment of steel.

LP stage

Low pressure area in a steam engine, turbine or air compressor.

Lubricating oil additives

Chemicals added to straight mineral oils to enhance existing properties or confer new properties. They are customarily named in terms of their function such as anti-corrosion, anti-oxidant, detergent, dispersant, viscosity index improvers, pour point, extreme pressure, anti-foam, anti-rust, anti-wear and multifunctional; generally used in small proportions the maximum in diesel cylinder lubricants is approximately 5 per cent.

Lubrication

Process of minimising friction and wear between moving parts by including a substance between them.

Lubricator Quill

Attachment in the cylinder wall of a reciprocating engine through which oil is passed lubricating the piston and cylinder.

Lubricity

An inexact term to give an overall impression of the performance of an oil and its ability to reduce friction within a machine. There is no specific quality test.

Luders lines

Surface markings resulting from localised deformation appearing on some alloys after slight straining.

Luff

(1) Weather side of vessel, opposite to **lee**. (2) Weather edge of a fore and aft sail. (3) In sailing, to turn head on into the wind.

Luffing

Vertical movement of the **jib** of a crane. Either the whole jib is luffed or a small part of the jib at the top is moved vertically. A luffing crane is a crane whose jib can be moved at different angles to the horizontal.

Lug
(1) Projection from a casting. (2) Extremity of a shackle.

Lumen (lm)
Luminous flux emitted within a unit solid angle of 1 steradian by a point source having a luminous intensity of 1 **candela**.

Lux (lx)
The unit of illuminance that equals the illuminance of 1 lumen per square metre (1 lx = 1 lm/m^2).

M

Machine
Apparatus consisting of an assemblage of parts, both fixed and moveable, for overcoming a resistance at one point by the application of force at some other point. Typical simple machines are the inclined plane, the lever, the pulley, and the screw.

Machinery control room
Enclosed space, generally at the top of a ship's engine room, where control and monitoring equipment for all machinery is located.

Machine language
In a computer, a set of binary instructions that can be interpreted or executed directly by the computer.

Macrograph
Reproduction, in general a photograph, of the low power magnification of a metal, polished and usually etched.

Macrostructure
Structure of a metal as seen on polished or etched surfaces with low magnification, revealing crystalline formation and distribution of particles.

Magma
Molten material originating from deep within the earth's crust, from which igneous rocks form.

Magnesium (Mg)
Light brilliant white metal element (sp gr 1.7) that, when alloyed with aluminium and other metals, has a high strength to weight ratio. It corrodes

rapidly in sea water and is used as deoxidiser for copper, brass and nickel alloys. Magnesium ribbon burns in air giving off brilliant white light.

Magnet
Material with the power to attract **ferrous** metals. Its magnetic properties can be possessed naturally or be induced by contact with another magnet. When a straight magnetised bar or needle is freely suspended it will align itself approximately north and south.

Magnetic compass
Compass depending on the **magnetic field** of the Earth for its directive force.

Magnetic crack detection
Non-destructive investigative technique. A thin white paint containing iron filings is spread over the area of interest. A large **magnet** is held over the area and any surface irregularity shows up as a concentration of iron filings.

Magnetic disk
Relating to computers, a thin circular disk with magnetic surfaces upon which data can be written. A floppy disk is an example of a portable removable magnetic disc.

Magnetic Field
Space adjacent to a conductor carrying an electric current or permanent magnet, in which magnetic forces can be detected.

Magnetometer
Instrument for measuring the strength and direction of a magnetic force.

Magnetometer survey
Geological survey method where sedimentary basins are identified and their size determined by measuring the magnetic properties of the underlying igneous rocks.

Magnus effect
Force undergone by a spinning ball or cylinder in a fluid. The effect is responsible for the swerving of golf and tennis balls when hit with a slice; has been applied in ship propulsion and for rudders.

MAIB
Marine Accident Investigation Branch. UK Government body for ship accident investigation. A branch of the **Marine Safety Agency.**

Maierform
Distinctive type of **bow** with a very pronounced rake.

Main bearing
Bearing within which a **crankshaft** rotates, supporting the crankshaft within the engine block.

Main circuit breaker
Circuit breaker installed at the main switchboard that the operation of other switching devices depends on.

Main deck
The **deck** from which the **freeboard** is determined.

Main hatch
Hatch used for the heaviest cargo with a ship's **official number** and **registered tonnage** cut into the **coaming.**

Main inlet
Sea water inlet for circulating or cooling water pumps. Typically refers to the larger pumps in the system.

Main stop valve
Large valve, generally of the non return type, that is the main steam supply line from the **boiler.**

Main vertical fire zones
Sectioning the hull, superstructure and deckhouses into A Class divisions for fire control. Their mean length must not exceed 40 metres.

Maintain class
To pass surveys carried out periodically by a classification society to determine whether a ship is fit to continue trading according to the society's rules.

Make-up feed
Water used to replace losses in a feed system.

Male and female
Engineering terms applied to inner and outer members that fit together, such as threaded pieces.

Malleability
Property of a metal enabling it to be rolled or hammered into shape.

Mandrel
Accurately machined bar or rod, drawn or shaped during working so as to create or preserve desired axial cavity. A tapered mandrel is also used for holding and locating a bored component so that external diameters can be machined true to the bore. Also called mandril.

Manganese (Mn)
Metal element (sp gr 7.4) added to alloys to impart special properties. In steel it refines the grain structure and imparts toughness and in aluminium bronze it improves castability.

Manganese bronze
Applies to high strength brass containing up to 4 per cent manganese. Ideal for propeller castings, such alloys are really high tensile brass. A typical propeller alloy would be 54 per cent copper, 36 per cent zinc, 5 per cent manganese, and a mixture of aluminium, nickel and tin.

Manhole
Access hole in tank top.

Manifest
Complete list and description of a ship's cargo once it is on board. Includes numbers and marks on all packages, descriptions, weights, and the names of the shipper and consignee.

Manifold
(1) Assembly attached to an engine block conducting air into the engine or exhaust gases from the engine. (2) Box shaped compartment on which a number of pipes, pump suction and delivery valves can be grouped.

Manning scale
Minimum number of qualified persons who must form part of the crew by law.

Manoeuvre
Change of direction, speed or position.

Manoeuvring valve
Valve varying the amount of steam supplied to the main engine to alter speed. A typical arrangement is one valve for ahead steam and one valve for astern steam.

Manometer
Pressure gauge for gases and vapours.

Maraging
Compound word for **martensite** and ageing to describe a heat treatment process for certain highly alloyed steels containing nickel, cobalt, molybdenum, and small additions of titanium and aluminium. Such steels are considered to have a martensitic microstructure as **annealed,** attaining a high strength on being age hardened.

Margin line
A line drawn 76mm below the upper surface of the bulkhead deck at the side. A passenger ship is subdivided into watertight compartments in such a way that this line is not submerged if two adjacent watertight compartments are flooded.

Margin plate
Outer boundary of the **double bottom**.

Marine Engineers Review(MER)
The leading technical Journal in the Marine Industry, published by the **Institute of Marine Engineers.**

Marine Information Centre (MIC)
Comprehensive library facility serving the maritime industry located at the headquarters of the Institute of Marine Engineers. Searches from the database of Marine Technology Abstracts (MTA) can be emailed, posted, faxed or telephoned to the inquirer. A variety of databases, including MTA, are available for purchase in CD ROM format.

Marine riser
Large diameter pipe that connects the drill floor of a floating rig to the well head. The **drill string** passes through it then the **mud** returns to the rig.

Marine Safety Agency (MSA)
Section of the British Department of Transport responsible for maritime affairs. Formerly known as the Surveyor General's Organisation (SGO), the agencies overall task is to develop, promote and enforce high standards of marine safety, minimising the risk of pollution to the marine environment from ships. Responsibilities include issuing **certificates of competency,** inspecting UK and foreign ships at British ports to ensure safety standards are being observed, and carrying out accident investigations (**MAIB**). They are also required to offer timely and accurate advice to Government Ministers on maritime affairs and to provide input necessary for drafting legislation.

Marine Society
The oldest public maritime charity in the world founded on June 25, 1756 by Jonas Hanway to encourage men and boys of good character to join the Royal Navy at the beginning of the Seven Years War. The society still operates today offering a wide range of services to the maritime industry.

Marinisation
Modifications to machinery or equipment not originally designed for marine use.

Maritime court
Special court set up to handle any legal action or official enquiry relating to ships or shipping.

Maritime lien
On a vessel, the claim the master and crew has for payment of wages due.

Maritime Technology
A term embracing the wide ranging technological activities of the maritime world. Encompasses knowledge of the sciences of marine engineering, marine electrical, naval architecture, nautical, offshore, naval, as well as many other less technical disciplines including marine management, legal, and insurance, each providing their own individual expertise.

Marlin spike
Tapered metal pin used in splicing a rope.

Marline
(1) To moor or tie. (2) Small tarred line. (3) To bind with a line such that each turn is an overhand knot used for seizing and as a covering for rope.

MARPOL
International Convention on Prevention of Pollution from Ships. An **IMO** Convention.

Marry
(1) To interlace the strands of two ropes when preparing to splice. (2) To place ropes side by side to be hauled simultaneously, as when lowering a boat.

Marsh gas (CH4)
Colloquial name for **methane**.

Martempering
Process for hardening steel where it is quenched from the **austenitic** range to a temperature just about the upper limit for **martensite**. When the temperature of the steel is uniform it is then allowed to cool, generally in air. Distortion and cracking of non-uniform sections can therefore be minimised.

Martensite
Micro-constituent of steel with a needle shaped structure. Formed when steel is rapidly cooled from the hardening temperature. The cooling rate must be faster than the critical cooling rate so that transformation is suppressed to occur at 400°C or lower in accordance with the composition of the steel. It is the hardest decomposition product of **austenite**.

Mass
Property of matter to which **inertia** is ascribed, commonly taken as a measure of the amount of matter a body contains, however, the amount of matter in a body does with velocity.

Mass number
Number of nucleons in a given atomic nucleus, used in nuclear physics.

Mass spectrometer
Instrument for analysing metals. The metal to be analysed is ionised by flame. Charge particles are accelerated in an electrical field, deflected in a **magnetic field** according to their mass, then finally impinged on a photographic plate that records their mass spectrum. From this constituent, elements and proportions can be identified.

Mast
Long vertical pole of tubular steel. Originally only carried a sail, now used for equipment such as navigation lights, radar scanners and **derricks**.

Mast step
Foundation on which a **mast** is erected.

Mast table
Small platform generally attached to **mast** to support hinged heel bearings of **derricks**.

Master
Senior officer in command of a ship. Also called **captain**.

Master bushing
Device that fits into the drill rig **rotary table.** Accommodates the slips and drives the **kelly** bushing so the rotating motion of the rotary table can be transmitted to the **kelly.** *See* Figure 8.

Matrix
Place or core in which something is developed.

Matter
Any body, substance or particle which is subject to gravitation, therefore, any body which occupies space.

Maul
Heavy hammer of metal or wood.

Mayday
Radio distress call.

Maximum continuous rating (mcr)

In diesel engines, the designed maximum continuous power rating. Engine builder's quoted **specific fuel oil consumption (sfoc)** rates are tied in with the mcr. It is common to operate a ship's engine at around 85 per cent mcr placing less **stress** on the engine parts.

Maxwell

The **CGS** electromagnetic unit of **magnetic force.**

Mean specific heat

Amount of heat required to raise the temperature of the unit weight of a substance from a given base temperature to a higher temperature, divided by temperature rise.

Mean time between failure (MTBF)

Term used to indicate the reliability of an engine or machine. A bathtub curve gives the instantaneous failure rate over the life cycle of the equipment. This is calculated by taking the total operating time of the identical units being analysed divided by the number of failures. An example would be 100 identical units in various systems each operating for 16 000 hours with a total of 80 defects. See below and Figure 24.

$$\frac{100 \times 16000 \ hours}{80 \ defects} = 20 \ 000 \text{ hours per defect; } 0.05 \text{ defects per 1000 hours.}$$

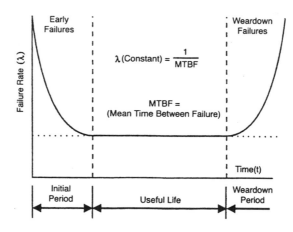

Figure 24 Mean Time Between Failures Curve

Measured mile
Distance of one nautical mile marked onshore. A ship, especially a new construction, will use these markers for sea trials.

MECAL
Marine Engineers Certifying Authority Ltd. A subsidiary company of the **Institute of Marine Engineers** authorised by the **Marine Safety Agency** to survey vessels for compliance with its Code of Practice for the safety of small commercial vessels under 24m in length, used for sport or pleasure. Other Codes of Practice are under development, all authorised by the MSA.

Mechanical admittance
The reciprocal of mechanical impedence.

Mechanical advantage
Ratio between force applied and force or weight exerted or lifted by machine gears, levers, purchase or any other mechanical device.

Mechanical efficiency
Relating to diesel engines, the ratio **bhp** divided by **ihp** is a measure of the mechanical losses in an engine. *See* **horse power.**

Mechanical impedence
In a mechanical vibrating system, the ratio of force to velocity. An example would be a mechanical seal vibrating with uniform **amplitude** at the specified **frequency**; the reciprocal of **mechanical admittance.**

Mechanical resonance
At a given frequency, the enhanced response of part of a mechanism or structure to a constant magnitude disturbing force.

Mechanical seal
Shaft sealing arrangement fitted to pumps, replacing a **stuffing box.**

Mechanical stoker
Device for stoking or firing a steam boiler. It receives fuel continuously by gravity, carries it progressively though the furnace, then deposits or discharges the ash.

Mechanics
Branch of science and technology studying the action of forces on bodies and of the motions they produce. Statics deal with forces in **equilibrium,** **dynamics** deal with motions in relation to forces, **kinematics** covers the theory of motions without reference to forces, and **kinetics** deal with relations between motions of bodies and the forces acting on them.

Median line
Dividing line between two national sectors of an ocean or sea, the locus of points equidistant from the territorial boundaries of the countries concerned.

Medium voltage
Voltage in the range 250 to 650V.

Meehanite
Trade name for certain cast irons treated with calcium silicide while in the molten state, said to increase tensile strength.

Megger
Apparatus for measuring insulation resistance by generating a high voltage.

Melting point
Temperature at which a solid starts to liquify. Pure chemicals melt at a constant temperature. Mixtures, like most **petroleum** products, melt over a temperature range.

Membrane tank
Contains **liquid natural gas** within a thin metallic liquid-tight lining completely supported by a load bearing insulation. This in turn is supported by the structure of a ship.

Membrane wall
(1) Form of tube arrangement in a boiler furnace. A strip of steel is welded between the tubes making the furnace completely gas tight. As the furnace is completely water cooled, no refractory is required in this part of the boiler.
(2) Double skinned tanks for the carriage of **liquid natural gas and liquid petroleum gas** at very low temperatures, designed to allow for large expansion and contraction movements.

Memory
Data **storage element** of a computer.

Meniscus
Curved **free surface** of a liquid in a tube. Mercury in a barometer is convex.

MEP
*M*ean *E*ffective *P*ressure. The average pressure exerted on a piston during the working stroke, generally quoted in bar (b) units. Developed from engine **indicator cards;** also known as mean indicated pressure (MIP).

MEPC
*M*arine *E*nvironmental *P*ollution Prevention Committee. Convention of **IMO** whose primary objective is to protect both sea and air from marine pollutants.

Mercaptans
Sulphur compounds occurring in **petroleum** with a strong odour.

Mercury (Hg)
Silvery-white heavy (atomic weight 200.6) metal, normally in liquid form. Used in barometers and thermometers; also known as quicksilver.

Mercury switch
Switch consisting of fixed contacts suspended above a pool of mercury, all enclosed in a gas-tight envelope. Operation responds to mechanical movement and occurs when the mercury level is disturbed creating a conducting path between contacts.

Meridian
A semi-great circle joining the geographical poles of the Earth and cutting an observer's horizon in the north and south points. All positions on the Meridian have the same **longitude**.

Merchant Shipping Acts
Acts of British Parliament relating to Merchant shipping.

Mesh
(1) The travel of a tooth between engaging with and disengaging from the co-operating tooth is termed the meshing cycle. **Gears** may also be said to be put into or out of mesh signifying movement axially or radially, into or out of engagement. The depth of mesh is determined by the centre distance between the two shafts. (2) A measurement of the size of openings in items such as in filters and sieves.

Messenger
(1) Endless rope passing from a **capstan** to any cable used to haul it in. (2) Small rope attached to a large wire or **hawser** so that it can be pulled between ship and shore.

Metacentre
Measure of the stability of a vessel at small angles of heel, indicating its likely behaviour when **rolling**.

Metacentric height
See **GM** and Figure 12.

Meteorology
Study of atmospheric motions and phenomena used to forecast the weather.

Methane (CH$_4$)
The simplest **alkane**. A gas that occurs naturally in oil wells and as **marsh gas**. Residual LNG is mostly methane, a popular industrial and domestic

fuel. *See* **liquid natural gas.**

Methyl chloride (CH$_3$CI)
A colourless poisonous gas, also known as chloromethane. It is used as a refrigerant for cold storage.

Metre (m)
The basic **SI unit** of length. One metre = 3.281 imperial feet.

Metric tonne
Equal to 1000 kgs and 2204.6 imperial pounds.

Meyer hardness number
The ratio of the load divided by the projected area of the indentation, obtained using the same test as for the **Brinell** hardness number.

MHD
Superconducting Magnetic Hydrodynamic. Form of propulsion for ships involving **thrusters** utilising a **magnetic field** as its power source.

Mica
Mineral composed of aluminium silicate and other silicates that can be split into thin transparent plates. Used as insulation in the electrical industry.

Michell thrust block
Thrust **block** where thrust is taken primarily on segments that can tilt slightly away from the collars on the shaft to allow perfect **hydrodynamic lubrication**. *See* Figure 25.

Micro seizure
Partial welding of materials in close contact; caused by **friction** and results in small particles tearing away from the surfaces. *See also* **fretting.**

Microbiological attack
Organisms that feature under three main headings, bacteria, mould or yeast. Under certain conditions they can multiply and produce corrosive growth products that clog filters, create corrosive dispersions of oil and water, change viscosity, reduce the effectiveness of additives, or promote electro-chemical corrosion. They can be very dangerous as they have been known to penetrate a ship's plating and clog up fuel and lubricating oil systems. Microbes can be found in distillate fuel, lubricating oil, coolants, domestic, bilge and ballast water and can be detected by their unpleasant odour.

Microfarad
One-millionth of a **farad.**

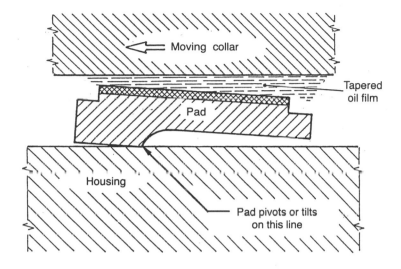

Figure 25 Thrust Collar and Pad

Micrometer
Tool for making precision measurements.

Micron (m)
A sub-multiple of a metre, the SI Unit for length. One micrometre is equal to a thousandth of a millimetre.

MicroProcessor
A computer's central processing unit (CPU), located on a single silicon chip.

Microwave link
Communications system between two points involving the use of a beamed carrier wave in the microwave region of the electromagnetic spectrum.

Midship area
Immersed area of the midship section.

Midship section
Section at the middle of a ship's length.

Mild steel
Alloy of iron containing small amounts of carbon (0.10 to 0.25).

Millibar
One thousandth of a **bar.**

Milligram (mg)
Unit of mass, one thousandth of a gram.

Milling
The action of a milling machine on a work piece subjected to the cutting action of rotating cutters. The work piece may be fed horizontally or vertically into the cutters.

Millscale
Magnetic oxide of iron (FE_3O_4) formed on steel at high temperature. It is formed on steel products both in processing mills and on solidification and is very adherent to the basic metal.

Mimic diagram
Single-line system diagram generally attached to switchboards or control boards with visual indicating devices that show the operational condition of various elements in the system.

Mineral acid
Acid derived from inorganic raw materials. The strong mineral acids most common in a marine environment are hydrochloric, nitric and sulphuric acids.

Mineral oils
Pertoleum and other hydrocarbon oils obtained from mineral sources.

Miniature circuit breaker
Small air circuit breaker fitted into a moulded plastic case with a current rating of 5–100 amps. Often used in a final distribution board, instead of a fuse, as it is fitted with a thermal overload trip.

Misalignment
When one or more parts of a machinery arrangement that should be in line depart from co-linearity.

Miscible
Substances, generally liquids, that mix to form a homogeneous whole.

Mist
Airborn particles of a liquid that have condensed on dust particles.

Mitre joint
Joint between two pieces of material meeting at an angle of 90 degrees, with a common surface of 45 degrees.

Mixtures
The intermingling of two or more substances with no constant percentage where each component retains its essential original properties. *See* **compounds.**

Mobility
Measure of the rate at which a solid continuously deforms after the **yield value** has been exceeded. Mobility is a more general term than fluidity, which is the mobility when the **yield value** is zero.

Mode
Term used to describe the shape of a curve in a periodic oscillation. Modes are coupled when the motion in one mode causes motion in another mode or modes. They are uncoupled when motion in one mode does not cause motion in the other modes.

Model
Scale reproduction of the hull of a proposed new vessel that is tested in a towing tank to determine the resistance and power requirements of a full sized version of a similar vessel.

Modem
*Mo*dulator-*dem*odulator. Electronic device for converting computer data into electronic signals that are compatible with a telephone system for long distance transmission.

MODU
*M*obile *O*ffshore *D*rilling *U*nit. Any **drilling rig** designed for use in a marine environment. Capable of moving, self-propelled or assisted, from one location to another.

Modulation
Method of using radio **frequency** carrier waves to transmit audio **frequency** signals. Achieved by varying either the frequency or **amplitude** of the carrier wave at audio frequency.

Module
(1) Basic length or ratio used to compare different items. An example would be the circular pitch for gear teeth = number of teeth module. (2) A production limit, or component part, standardised to enable straight forward assembly, replacement, or exchange. These units are used in control and electronic equipment to enable repair following fault-finding routines to identify damaged modules. (3) In ship-building, a collection of machinery and equipment assembled for installation as a self -contained unit.

Modulus of elasticity

Ratio of **stress** to **strain** for a material within the range of **elasticity** measured in units of stress. *See* **Hooke's Law** and **Young's Modulus**.

Modulus of rigidity

Ratio of unit shear stress to angle of distortion in radians within the elastic limit. Corresponds to **elasticity** in a tensile test.

Modulus

Measure of a force, properties of a material or their effects, constantly converting a proportionality into an equation.

Molasses

(1) Uncrystallised syrup drained from raw sugar. (2)Refers to a problem cargo due to the high viscosity of any treacle-like substances involved.

Mole (mol)

The amount of substance that contains as many entities (atoms, molecules, ions, electrons) as there are atoms in 12g of ^{12}C. The SI Unit replaces older terms such as gram-atom and gram-molecule, and will correspond to a mass equal to the relative molecular mass in grams for any chemical compound.

Molecular

Applying to the **molecule** of a substance, that is the smallest amount which can exist in a free state.

Molecular weight

Sum of the relative molecular masses of the constituent **atoms** of a **molecule**.

Molecule

The smallest portion to which a substance can be reduced by subdivision without losing its chemical identity.

Molybdenum (Mo)

Heavy metal element (sp gr. 10.0) used as an alloying element to strengthen steel as it does not corrode in sea water. Also used as a sprayed coating on steel to which it has good adhesion.

Molybdenum disulphide

Solid occurring in laminar form. Used as a solid lubricant or oil additive due to good anti-wear properties.

Moment

Product of a force or vector about a point. The distance of the point from its line of action expresses the power of causing rotation about that point.

Moment causing unit trim

The moment acting on a ship that can change its trim by one unit. With **SI units,** this is the moment to change the trim by one metre or one centimetre.

Moment of force

Turning effect of a force about a given **point.** Measured by the product of the magnitude of the **force** and the perpendicular distance of the point from the line of action of the force. Generally, clockwise moments are called positive and counter-clockwise moments are called negative. *See* **torque.**

Moment of inertia

Product of the mass and the square of its perpendicular distance from the datum axis summed for all particles in the system under consideration.

Moment to change trim one inch (MCT)

The moment taken about the centre of flotation which will change the trim by 1 inch. Expressed in foot-tons.

Momentum

Impetus as a result of movement. Momentum of a body is the product of its mass and velocity. Angular momentum is the product of the **moment of inertia** and the angular velocity of the body.

Monel metal

Nickel-copper alloy containing 68 per cent nickel, 29 per cent copper and small quantities of iron-manganese and carbon. Has high corrosion resistance and is often used for **condenser** tubes.

Monitoring

Gathering information by surveillance of the actual behaviour and performance of a ship/**plant.** Facilities provided for this purpose may include equipment for indication, recording and alarm operation. Where centralised monitoring is provided, information is relayed to a central area such as a control room for ease of assessment by the duty officer.

Monkey board

High level platform where the **derrick** man works on an offshore structure **derrick.**

Monkey island

Navigating position above the **wheelhouse.**

Monkey tail

Curved bar fitted to the upper, after end of a **rudder** used as an attachment for the rudder pendants.

Monobloc
Integral casting of all cylinders of an **internal combustion** engine in one block.

Monomer
Substance composed of **molecules** capable of reacting with like or unlike **particles** to form **polymers**.

Monsoon
Periodical persistent wind of the China Sea, Indian Ocean and East African Coast. The southwest monsoon is always accompanied by torrential rain.

Montreal Protocol
Guidelines agreed at the International Convention held in Montreal, December 1991, setting limits on the amount of harmful CFCs (chlorofluorocarbon refrigerants) and halons (fire fighting chemicals) released into the atmosphere. Scientific evidence continues to reveal a more rapid depletion of the stratospheric ozone layer than initially indicated.

Moon pool
Open hole in the hull of a **drill ship** through which drilling takes place.

Moor
Secure a vessel by rope or cable to a **buoy** or position ashore; secure in position at an anchorage.

Mooring ring
Oval casting set in **bulwark** plating through which mooring lines are passed.

Mooring system
Offshore **semi-submersible** drill rigs and workover vessels may have a multi-point mooring system, in which there are 4, 8, 12 or 16 mooring positions around the vessel. At each one there is a mooring anchor winch, with chain, cable or a combination anchor line and large anchor. The size of the anchors can require an anchor-handling tug to deploy each anchor in the required position. *See also* **position mooring system**.

Mooring winch
A **winch** with a barrel or drum used to haul in or release mooring wires.

Moseley's formula
Equation for calculating **dynamical stability**.

Motor, electric
Accommutator. Polyphase **induction motor** with primary **winding** on the rotor and an insulated secondary winding on the **stator** connected across two sets of brushes that can be moved in opposite directions round the **ac commutator**.

Asynchronous. An ac motor where the speed bears no fixed relation to the frequency of supply varying with the load; known as an **induction motor.**

Double squirrel cage. An ac **induction motor,** the rotor of which comprises two cages of different resistances; also called Boucherot squirrel cage motor.

Induction. An ac motor in which the current in one member (usually the rotor) is generated by electro-magnetic induction.

Repulsion. A single phase ac motor in which the field and armature fluxes repel each other to produce a torque in the rotor.

Slip-ring. An **induction motor** with a wound rotor and **slip-rings** for connection to an external resistance or other means of starting or speed control.

Squirrel cage. **Induction motor** with a rotor whose winding consists of a number of bars with their extremities at each end of the rotor connected by rings or plates.

Synchronous. An ac motor whose average speed over a long period is directly proportional to the frequency of supply, independent of load.

Synchronous induction. Synchronous motor started by means of a resistor in the secondary circuit, ultimately run in synchronism using dc excitation.

Motor starter
Electric controller for starting a motor from rest, accelerating to normal running speed and then stopping.

Mould
(1) Template used in ship construction from which steel plates are formed to the correct shape. (2) Metal structure having cavities of the required shape in which fluid or plastic material is cast or shaped. (3) Structure of sand having cores or cavities of the requisite shape in which molten metal is cast.

Moulded breadth
The greatest breadth at amidships from heel of frame to heel of frame. See Figure 6.

Moulded depth
The vertical distance at amidships from the top of the keel to the top of the upper deck beam at side. Also referred to as depth moulded, *see* Figure 6.

Moulded draught
In general, the maximum summer draught amidships. In certain ships of special construction the afterend figure is used to record the maximum draught. *See* Figure 6.

Mousing
Few turns of yarn passed round the open end of a hook to prevent the load becoming unhooked.

Moving coil meter
Instrument used to provide a measurement of voltage or current; consists of a coil wound on a soft iron cylinder that is free to move within a radial **magnetic field.**

Moving iron meter
An instrument that provides a measurement of voltage or current; consists of a fixed coil that carries the current to be measured and causes the movement of a pivoted piece of soft iron.

MSC
*M*aritime *S*afety *C*ommittee. An **IMO** committee.

MTTR
*M*ean *T*ime *T*o *R*epair.

Mud
See **drilling mud**.

Mud box
Strainer to intercept and retain insoluble matter and sludge. In machinery spaces and shaft tunnel, bilge pipes are led to mud boxes that are accessible for regular cleaning.

Mud hogs
In rotary drilling, pumps that force a continuous flow of mud-laden fluid through the drill stem and bit. This mud returns to the rig between the drill stem and casing or wall of the hole carrying the drill cuttings. *See* Figure 8.

Muff coupling
Used to connect two shafts without the use of flanged ends or coupled bolts. Consists of two sleeves tapered to fit each other. These sleeves fit over the two shafts. When the outer sleeve is forced into the taper the inner sleeve grips the shafts to form a solid coupling.

Muffler
American expression for an exhaust silencer.

Multigrade oils
Lubricating oil containing additives known as **viscosity index** (VI) improvers. They may fall into more than one **SAE** grade and are designated by two extreme **SAE** Numbers. 10W/30 would be a low temperature viscosity appropriate to the W grade at $0^{o}F$ ($17.8^{o}C$). A high temperature viscosity

appropriate to the non W grade would be at 210°F (98.9°C). Multigrade oils can therefore be used over a wider range of climatic air temperatures than ordinary lube oils. *See* Appendix 3.

Multi-hull ships
Vessels with multiple hulls such as a **catamaran** (two) or Trimaran (three).

Multimeter
Electrical instrument measuring current, voltage and resistance over a wide range in ac or dc.

Multiplexer
A selector connecting various inputs, one at a time, to a common output.

Multi service vessel (MSV)
Support vessel designed to provide a variety of construction, fabrication, diving, emergency and other services to offshore installations.

Multivibrator
Oscillator producing a repetitive pulse or rectangular wave form.

Muntz-metal
Old name for a copper alloy containing two parts copper and one part zinc by weight.

Muriatic acid
Hydrochloric acid (HCl). A solution of the pungent gas hydrogen chloride in water. Also known as spirits of salts. Used as a pickling agent to remove scale. Concentrated acid contains about 40 per cent hydrochloric acid by weight.

Mushroom valve
Mushroom shaped valve made of heat resistant steel used for the inlet and exhaust valves of diesel engines. Consists of a circular head with a conical face seated over the inlet or exhaust valve face. A guiding stem lifts the valve when moved by a rocker or tappet. Also known as a **poppet valve**.

MW
Megawatt, a million watts.

N

Nadir
Point on the **celestial** sphere vertically below the observer, or 180 degrees from the **zenith**.

Naphtha
A **flammable** oil obtained by dry distillation of an organic substance such as coal, shale or petroleum. Gasoline blending stock, mineral spirits and a broad selection of petroleum solvents are included in the naphtha classification.

Naphthenic
Description of a lubricating oil in which the naphthenic (cycloparaffinic) portion of the oil is predominant in the characteristics of the **oil**, giving it a low to medium **viscosity index and** low natural **pour point.**

Napiers curve
Graph based on observations of **compass** deviations at a number of points. By interpolation, deviation at intermediate points can be determined.

Narrows
Navigable area, narrow due to shoals or adjacent land.

Natural draught
Boiler furnace draught caused by the temperature of furnace gases unassisted by forced or induced draught fans.

Natural frequency
Frequency at which free **oscillation** occurs.

Naturally aspirated
Refers to an engine that draws in air solely by the aspirated action of its pistons without the help of a supercharger or turbocharger.

Nautical Institute
Founded in 1971 to promote and co-ordinate public interest in the development of nautical studies and all its branches.

Nautical mile
Internationally accepted distance of 1852 metres or 6076.1 feet. *See* **knot.**

Navel Pipe
Pipe leading down to the **chain locker** through which the anchor chain passes. *See also* **hawse pipe.**

Navigate
Control and direct the course of a ship.

NCVQ
National Council for Vocational Qualifications. Established in 1986, the council had issued over one million NVQs (National vocational qualifications) by 1996. Qualifications are based on what is done in the workplace and prove the recipient has the skills, knowledge and understanding to meet

the requirements of the particular NVQ. Whilst NVQs will continue to be offered for vocational qualifications, the council itself is merging with the **SCAA** (School Curriculum and Assessment Authority). The name for the new combined body is **QNCA** (Qualifications and National Curriculum Authority), aiming to secure the highest ratings for both vocational and academic standards.

Neap tide
Applied to a tide at its smallest **amplitude**.

Neaped
When a ship is unable to leave a port, harbour or river because the depth of high water on **neap tide** is insufficient compared with its draught. Also refers to a ship run aground on a neap tide.

Necking
Decrease in cross-sectional area of a material over a short longitudinal length just prior to failure. Can be seen in test specimens undergoing tensile testing.

Needle rollers
Bearing rollers with a length many times their diameter.

Needle valve
Valve in an injector nozzle for diesel engine fuel systems.

Negative earthed system
A dc system with the negative pole permanently connected to an earth.

Negative slip
When the distance travelled by a ship is greater than the figure calculated from propeller revolutions.

Neoprene
Polychloroprene rubber having fair to good resistance to petroleum-based fluids together with good resistance to ozone and weathering. Widely used for protective bellows and gaiters.

Nest of tubes
Arrangement of tubes, generally parallel to each other, used in **heat exchangers** to provide a large area for heat transfer.

Net positive suction head
Difference between the absolute pump inlet pressure and the vapour pressure of the liquid, expressed in metres of liquid.

Net registered tonnage
Derived from the corresponding **gross tonnage** by deducting spaces used for accommodation of the crew, navigation and propelling machinery. Is in accordance with a formula developed by the International Convention on Tonnage Measurement of Ships in 1969.

Network analysis
Graphical method of planning a project in a logical sequence by plotting major activities with start/finish dates and times for each activity. This allows an estimation of the overall time required to complete the project.

Network scheduling
Scheduling or time-tabling of production, assembly, despatch or some particular activity, by use of networks and **network analysis** techniques.

Networking
Connecting two or more computers allowing them to communicate with each other. This differs from a multi user environment as each system is self contained and can operate independently.

Neutral
(1) The middle wire of a dc 3-wire system. In 3-phase star electrical connected systems it denotes the common point to which the corresponding end of each phase winding is connected; the other end of each phase winding is connected to a separate line terminal. (2) Being neither acid nor alkaline like pure water.

Neutral axis
Dividing line between the tensile and compressive components of a structure under stress, an example being the line of zero stress.

Neutral conductor
Any conductor connected to the **neutral**.

Neutral earthing resistor
A **resistor** fitted in the earth path of a high voltage system. Its value is chosen to limit the maximum earth fault current to no more than the generator full load current.

Neutralisation number
Test method used to determine the acidity and alkalinity of an oil.

Neutralise
Adding acid to an alkali, or vice versa, until reaching a chemically neutral state.

Neutron
Atomic particle having no electric charge.

Newton (N)

The SI derived unit of force defined as that force which, when applied to a body having a mass of one kilogram, gives it an acceleration of one metre per second squared. One Newton = 1 kg m/s^2.

Newton's Laws

These three laws were first stated by Newton in his *Principia* and form the basis of all classical mechanics.

a) Every body remains at rest, or moving at a constant speed in a straight line, unless it is acted upon by an external force.

b) If an external force acts on a body it will accelerate it in proportion to the size of the force and inversely in proportion to the mass of the body.

c) Every action is opposed by an equal and opposite reaction.

Newtonian fluid

A fluid with a constant **viscosity** at a given temperature and pressure regardless of the rate of shear. Most petroleum products are newtonian fluids, their rate of shear being proportional to the shearing stress.

Nickel (Ni)

Ductile metal element (sp gr 8.9) used in pure form for electro-plated finishes, added to alloys to impart special properties. In steel, it increases susceptibility to heat treatment. In copper, a range of alloys (cupro-nickel) are produced for their resistance to corrosion in sea water. Certain percentages can increase the alloy's tensile strength and resistance to impact.

Nimonic alloys

Alloys with a nominal composition of 80 per cent nickel and 20 per cent chromium with minor amounts of titanium, cobalt and nickel. Used mainly in turbine blading and other components for high temperature service.

Nitriding

A means of surface hardening special steels. The steel is heated in an atmosphere of ammonia gas to a temperature of approximately 500°C. The depth of hardness depends on how long the steel is left at this temperature, a useful thickness is evident after approximately 100 hours.

Nitrile rubber

General term for **copolymers** of butadiene and acrylonitrile. Resistance to petroleum-based fluids vary from good to excellent according to the acrylonitrile content of the **polymer.** Heat resistance is moderate to good but resistance to ozone and weathering is generally poor. Nitrile rubbers are widely used for sealing duties with mineral oils.

Nitrogen (N)

Gaseous element forming approximately four-fifths of the earth's atmosphere. It is an inert gas but can cause brittleness in steel if introduced during manufacture.

NKK

Nippon Kaiji Kyokai. Japanese ship **classification society.**

NLGI

National Lubricating Grease Institute. An American organisation that, amongst other things, develops grease standards. *See* Appendix 3.

No cure no pay

Provision in a **salvage** agreement that salvage money is not payable unless the property is salved in accordance with that agreement.

Node

(1) Point of rest in a vibrating body. **(2)** Point at which a curve crosses itself. *See* Figures 26 and 27.

Nodule

Small round lump of substance, such as carbon in cast iron.

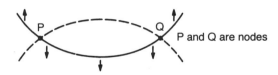

Figure 26 Primary Mode

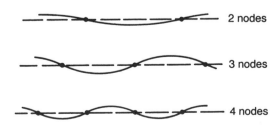

Figure 27 Modes of Vertical Vibration

Noise

Any unwanted sound, signal or disturbance. Sound is defined in BS661: 1969 as a mechanical disturbance, propagated in an elastic medium of such a character as to be capable of exciting the sensation of hearing. This capability is determined by the **frequency** of the disturbance. The audible frequency range for a young person is approximately 20 to 20 000 Hz. The lower limit is difficult to determine because low frequency vibrations of air can be perceived although not heard in the normal sense of the word. The upper limit reduces with age (presbyacusis) and hearing damage. Frequencies below and above the audible range are known as **infrasonic** and **ultrasonic** respectively.

Nomenclature

System of naming

Nominal horse power (nhp)

See **horse power.**

Nomogram

Comprised of three lines marked with scales representing three different quantities. There is a tangible relationship between the three quantities and the values of all scales. When numerical values of two of the units are known, the third can be obtained by drawing a straight line connecting the other two. A well known nomogram for marine bunkers is determining the Shell **CCAI** (ignition quality) number from the **density** and **kinematic viscosity**.

Non associated natural gas

An accumulation of natural gas that exists without the presence of oil.

Non combustible material

Material that neither burns nor gives off **flammable** vapours in a sufficient quantity to self-ignite when heated to 750°C under specified test conditions.

Non-condensing engine

A steam engine that exhausts its steam directly to the atmosphere.

Non destructive testing (NDT)

Methods of testing the properties, quality, or soundness of materials or components that can be applied without causing damage that could render the subject of the tests unserviceable. Typical non-destructive test processes include **radiographic,** dye penetrant, magnetic particle, supersonic testing for detecting internal flaws or cracks, **hardness** testing, inspection by electron microscope, and spot chemical tests.

Non newtonian fluid

A fluid with viscosity characteristics that vary with the rate of shear and decrease as shear rate increases. High **viscosity index** lubricants (**multigrade** engine oils and hydraulic fluids) and greases are examples, primarily because of the additives they contain.

Non return valve
A valve in a pipeline that will automatically close if the direction of fluid flow is reversed.

Normalising
Form of heat treatment for steel. The temperature is raised to about 50°C above the upper critical point and maintained to ensure uniformity throughout, then it is cooled to room temperature in still air. This results in grain structure refinement, reducing internal stresses and improving mechanical properties.

Norman pins
Pins or rollers that can be erected at the tug's after bulwarks to guide the towline and prevent it passing over the vessel's beam. Also known as Molgoggers or Stop Pins.

Nor-Shipping
Biennial shipping exhibition and conference held in Norway.

Notch ductility
Ability of a material to withstand stress, especially when the component contains a notch or has a shape that causes stress concentrations.

Notch effects
A reduction in the ability of a component to withstand shock loads due to the intensity of stress near the notch.

Notch steel
Steel having good notch ductility properties making it difficult for a crack to propagate. Notch ductility is a measure of the toughness of the steel.

Notice of abandonment
Formal notice given by the assured, following a ship loss, that he intends to claim for a constructive total loss (CTL).

Not under command
A ship unable to manoeuvre properly due to steering gear or some other mechanical failure. Signals must be displayed to warn other craft.

Noxious Emissions
Exhaust from diesel engines are comprised mainly of Nox, SOx, soot and particulate emissions. It is anticipated that IMOs, Marpol Convention will require a minimum 30 per cent reduction in the level of 1992 Nox and SOx emissions, although these levels are constantly under review.

Nozzle

Outlet orifice for a pressurised fluid specially shaped to convert the pressure energy into velocity energy, causing the resulting jet to conform to requirements such as shape, concentration or dispersion. Typical examples are injector nozzles, ejectors, fire hoses, or nozzle forming passages that direct the flow of live steam or gas into the moving blade of a turbine. The term may also be applied when a ship's propeller is shrouded by a ring or duct, increasing thrust at low speed; or a pivoted nozzle ring to direct the slip stream to improve rudder action when manoeuvring, particularly at low speeds or in confined waters.

Nozzle Body

The housing at the end of an injector containing the needle valve in a diesel engine fuel system.

Nozzle Group

A segment of the complete nozzle plate in a steam turbine containing multiple nozzles in a single nozzle plate. The nozzle group have their own separate section of box and control valve. For efficient operation, the minimum number of nozzles should be open to achieve a given power.

NPD

Norwegian Petroleum Directorate.

NPL

National Physical Laboratory. British Government laboratory for research in physics, metallurgy and kindred subjects. Located at Teddington, Middlesex.

NRM

Noise Reduction Measure.

Nuclear propulsion

The use of energy produced by a nuclear reaction to provide propulsive thrust through heating the working fluid or providing electric power for an ion or similar propulsion system. A nuclear power reactor is a source of heat, on a par with a boiler furnace, but with several years fuel supply contained in the reactor's core. With nuclear power, heat is exchanged from the core and used to make steam. Once steam is generated, it is treated exactly like steam produced from an oil-fired boiler. The source of heat, the reactor core, is made up of sealed tubes containing uranium fuel pellets. The pellets are then heated by the fission process. The application of nuclear power to merchant ship propulsion is a developing subject that has not achieved any sort of finality due to environmental problems. It is widely used in submarines, eliminating the problem of exhaust gas disposal, to allow a submarine to spend long periods under water.

Nucleate boiling

Occurs when the bulk of the fluid is at saturation temperature or slightly above. Large bubbles are formed on the hot surface that travel through the liquid to the free surface. The agitation of the fluid by the bubbles greatly improves the heat transfer rate.

Nucleus

Internal core of an **atom**. A particle of matter acting as focal point from which reactions or changes of state may evolve.

Nuclide

Type of **atom** with a specific mass number, atomic number and energy state.

NUMAST

National Union of Marine, Aviation and Shipping Transport Officers.

Nusselt number

A **coefficient** of heat transfer.

Nylon

Polyamide thermoplastic materials characterised by their high strength and resistance to abrasion. They do not have rubber-like properties and in hydraulics are used mainly as bearings and bushes rather than for sealing.

O

O and M

Operations and Methods.

Oakum

Material made of tarred rope fibres for caulking the seams of a wooden deck.

OBO ship

Ore-Bulk-Oil. This ship type has been designed to carry its full deadweight with dry cargo in bulk, such as ore, coal, and grain, or a liquid cargo such as crude oil.

Observation Tank

A tank that receives drains from fuel oil heating, tank heating, and other possible contaminated steam heating lines. Also known as an observation drain tank.

Occlusion
(1) As applied to metals, means absorption or retention of gases. (2) Line on a meteorological chart denoting the junction of warm and cold fronts.

OCIMF
Oil Companies International Marine Forum. An association of oil company tanker owners.

Octane
Relates to gasoline type fuels used in **internal combustion engines**. The octane number or rating is a measure of the resistance of a fuel to pre-ignition (**knock**) and is equal to 100 for one type of octane. The development of high octane has permitted a corresponding increase in engine compression ratios with good anti-knock properties. Originally obtained by the addition of lead in gasolines but because of environmental laws on lead pollution must now be a natural quality of the fuel.

Odometer
An instrument sheave used for recording the amount of line paid out when making oceanographic depth soundings.

Odontometer
Instrument for testing the accuracy and uniformity of gear tooth profiles and tooth spacings during manufacture.

OECD
Organisation for Economic Co-operation and Development.

Oertz rudder
Special design of **flap rudder**.

Off hire survey
Inspection carried out when a ship is redelivered to its owner by a **charterer**. The inspection is carried out to determine if a ship is in the same condition, wear and tear excepted, as on delivery.

Official number
Identification number assigned by the national authority.

Offing
Vaguely defined part of the sea that lies between the entrance to a harbour, or the shoal water of a coast, and the horizon; can be very hazardous.

Offset
(1) One of a series of distances, measured from reference planes (normally from the centreplane) to define the size and shape of a body or ship. (2) Continuing deviation typically occurring when proportional action is used alone.

Offshore
Applied to any structure or activity located or carried out at sea.

Ogee ring
Steel ring connecting the bottom of the furnace to the shell of a vertical boiler.

Ohm (Ω)
Unit of electrical resistance between two points of a conductor. A constant potential difference of one volt applied to these points produces a current of one ampere in the conductor.

Ohmmeter
Instrument measuring electrical resistance.

Ohm's Law
In metallic conductors at constant temperature and zero magnetic field, the current I flowing through a component is proportional to the potential difference V between its ends, the constant of proportionality being the conductance of the component. So $I=V/R$ or $V=IR$, where R is the resistance of the component. This law is strictly applicable to electrical components carrying direct current and for practical purposes to those of negligible reactance carrying alternating current. Extended by analogy to any physical situation where a pressure difference causes a flow through an impedance, such as heat through walls or liquid through pipes.

Oil
Greasy, unctous liquid of vegetable, animal, mineral or synthetic origin.

Oil consumption
Amount of fuel and lubricating oil consumed by an engine in a specific period. Fuel is usually expressed in tonnes per day and lubricants in kgs per day. *See also* **SFOC**.

Oil control ring
Piston ring designed to return excessive lubricant on cylinder walls to the crankcase.

Oil, crude
Petroleum prior to refining; a mixture of various hydrocarbons including **paraffinic, napthenic** and **aromatic** derivatives. Varies greatly according to crude source.

Oil fuel register
Arrangement of vanes and air swirler plates fitted between the inner and outer casing of a boiler at each burner position. The register regulates the

supply of air to the burner to ensure complete combustion of the oil. Usually referred to as the air register.

Oil in water monitor
Measuring instrument that determines the concentration of oil in discharging water. Where the permitted level is exceeded, an alarm is given and the water is diverted to a slop tank.

Oil lubricated sternshaft
A **sternshaft/sterntube** system with a steel sternshaft running in a white metal bearing, sealed at each end, running in pressurised lubricating oil. The greatest danger is if the outboard seal leaks allowing sea water to gain access to the lubricating oil. See Figure 28.

Oil mist detector
Instrument fitted inside a diesel engine crankcase to detect dangerous accumulations of oil mist that could give rise to a crankcase explosion.

Oil, non persistent
Oil that evaporates in air leaving little or no trace, such as petroleum spirit and kerosene.

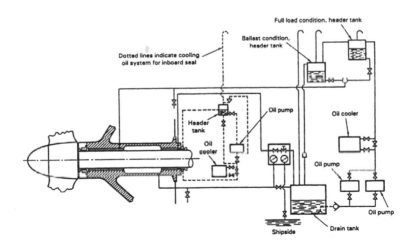

Figure 28 Oil Lubricated Sternshaft

Oil, persistent
An oil which does not normally evaporate in air, such as fuel oil and lubricating oil.

Oil ring
Loose ring fitted on a journal dipping into a reservoir of oil. As the journal rotates the ring moves over it and carries oil up from the reservoir.

Oil separator
Device used to remove water and other impurities including some solids from lubricating or fuel oils. Normally of the **centrifuge** type although static types are available for dealing with oily bilge or ballast water.

Oil slick
Layer of oil floating on the surface of the sea; Usually caused by accident or spillage but can also be caused by natural seepage from the ocean floor.

Oil tanker
Ship designed specifically for the carriage of oil in bulk. They range from a small coastal tanker usually carrying a finished product to an ultra large crude carrier (**ULCC**) that may be half a million tons deadweight.

Oil trap
Geological structure that traps migrating hydrocarbons causing the formation of an oil field.

Oil treatment
Preparation of fuel and lubricating oil for use in boilers and engines. Involves settling, heating, centrifugal treatment and filtering.

Oiliness
Ability of oil molecules to cling to metal surfaces or the property that causes a difference in friction when two lubricants of the same viscosity at the temperature of the film are used under identical conditions. It depends on the presence in the oil of substances that are readily absorbed on and firmly held by the metallic surfaces.

Oily water separator
Term used to denote equipment designed to separate oil from oil-water mixtures to achieve acceptably clean water.

Olefins
Unsaturated, relatively unstable **hydrocarbons** characterised by the presence of a double bond between two carbon atoms in their structure. These compounds are very chemically reactive, such as ethylene and propylene.

Oligocyclic stress
Level of stress in a body that, although insufficient to cause immediate failure, would cause failure after only a few repeated applications.

Ombrometer
Instrument for measuring rainfall.

On hire survey
Inspection of a ship delivered to a **charterer** to establish its condition. The ship must be returned in a similar condition at the end of the charter. *See also* **off hire charter.**

On stream
Stage in oil exploration when production commences and the oil or gas begins to flow.

OPEC
*O*rganisation of *P*etroleum *E*xporting *C*ountries.

Open
When a ship has discharged its last cargo and is ready to steam to another port, if necessary, to load the next cargo.

Open circuit fault
Electrical circuit fault resulting from a break in a conductor causing the circuit to break down.

Open sea
Any ocean or sea outside territorial limits.

Open shelter-decker
A **shelter-deck** ship where the tonnage opening is kept permanently open. Designed so that registered tonnage would not include the shelter-deck space, although this space is capable of carrying cargo.

Operational research
Use of scientific techniques to obtain quantitative values to assist executive decision making. Also refers to an examination of working methods and processes to improve productivity.

OPOL
*O*ffshore *P*ollution *L*iability Agreement.

Opposed piston engine
Internal combustion engine with two pistons in each cylinder. Charging, compression, ignition and exhaust take place between pistons, each of which

are separately connected to the crankshaft. The Doxford is the best known marine engine of this type, although it is no longer manufactured.

Optimal
Highest achievement possible working within a particular set of conditions.

Order number
Number of vibrations or impulses occurring per revolution during the torsional **oscillations** of an engine crankshaft.

Ordinate
The y co-ordinate of a graph, a quantity represented on a curve graduated in a vertical direction from the axis of the graph. Distances above the graph are positive, those below the graph are negative.

Ore Carrier
Single deck ship designed to carry a homogenous cargo throughout the length. Machinery located right aft.

Organic acid
Acid derived from organic compounds often containing **atoms** of carbon, hydrogen, and oxygen only. Organic acids are weaker than **mineral acids**.

Organisation and methods (O&M)
The study of the way an organisation carries out its various functions with a view to improved efficiency.

Orifice
Device partially restricting flow through a pipe, the difference in pressure on two sides of the orifice plate are used to measure flow rate through the pipe.

O-ring
Torroidal ring made of an elastomer such as rubber, used for sealing circular flange joints or the gap between piston and cylinder in **pneumatic** or **hydraulic** mechanisms.

Orlop
Lowest deck in a ship.

Orsat apparatus
Portable apparatus for analysing flue or exhaust gases. A measured amount of gas is passed through three tubes successively, containing potassium hydroxide to absorb carbon dioxide, pyro-gallol to absorb oxygen, and acid cuprous chloride to absorb carbon monoxide. The reduction in the volume of gas after it has passed through each tube indicates the amount of each constituent gas thus absorbed.

Oscillation

(1) Movement of a ship that, if excessive, can increase stresses in the structure and cause distress to passengers and crew. Principal ship oscillations are **rolling, pitching** and **heaving**. *See* Figure 15. **(2)** Periodic change in a variable. An oscillation can have decreasing, constant or increasing **amplitude.**

Oscilloscope

Measuring or display instrument using a cathode ray tube to show the instantaneous values of various electrical quantities with respect to time or some other quantity.

Osmosis

Passing of solvent through a semi permeable membrane separating two solutions of different solute concentration. Can be observed by immersing a tube partially filled with an aqueous sugar solution, closed at the end with parchment, in water. An increase in the level of liquid in the solution results from a flow of water through the parchment into the solution.

OSO

Offshore Supplies Office.

Otto cycle

Working cycle of a 4-stroke engine where burning of the fuel and exhaust event are both considered to take place at constant volume. The cycle which encompasses suction, compression, combustion and exhaust requires two revolutions of the crankshaft.

Outboard

In a direction away from the centreline of a ship.

Out of balance

In rotating parts, if rotation generates a resultant non-axial force.

Output Signal

Signal from one element to the next element in the loop.

Outreach

Maximum distance loading or discharging equipment can extend outwards to lift cargo. There are various points from which this distance may be measured, such as the quay wall or fendering, or the landside end of the jib of a shore crane. Can also describe the distance between ship and shore that a ramp can breach, also called reach.

Outrigger

Extension to increase spread of stays to topmast.

Overage
When the amount of cargo discharged is in excess of the quantity on a ship's **manifest**.

Overall length
Maximum length between the extreme ends, forward and aft of a ship. *See* Figure 2.

Overcarriage
Carriage of cargo beyond the port for which it was intended.

Over compounded
Term applied to a compound wound dc generator meaning the series winding is proportioned so that voltage increases with load.

Overdamping
Amount of **damping** greater than that required for critical damping.

Overfall
As related to a **propeller**, the turbulence caused by the flow of a strong tidal stream over an abrupt change in depth or the meeting of tidal streams.

Overlap
(1) Crank angle or period during which inlet and exhaust valves in an **internal combustion engine** are open together. (2) Distance by which a plate, sheet or strip of material partly covers or extends beyond the edge of an adjacent part. (3) Imperfection at the toe or root of a weld caused by metal flowing on to the surface of the parent metal without fusing to it.

Overlap ratio
Ratio of the face width to axial pitch of a **helical gear.**

Overload
(1) Load in excess of the authorised rating, such as in an engine, motor, or electric cable. (2) Take on excess cargo so that the appropriate **freeboard** lines are submerged.

Overload coupling
Coupling designed so that when a preset **torque** becomes exceeded the transmission of power is terminated.

Overload protection
Device that will interrupt the flow of **current** if it reaches an excessive value.

Override
Means for countermanding the effect of an automatic device such as an engine **governor.**

Overshot
Fishing tool for recovering lost drill pipes or casings.

Overspeed trip
A device, usually mechanical, that will stop a rotating engine when its speed is about 15 per cent above the rated value. Also used on electric motors.

Overtones
Frequencies of **vibration** higher than the lowest frequency of interest, not always integral multiples of this lowest frequency.

Overvoltage
Voltage above the rated or normal operating value of an apparatus or circuit.

Owner
Registered owner or disponent owner, including a charterer by **demise** of a ship. A disponent owner is a person or company to whom ownership of a ship has been made over to, such as a company managing a ship for the owners.

Oxidation
The reaction of a substance with oxygen. (1) The chemical term is used for a reaction which removes hydrogen from a compound or in which an **atom** loses **electrons**. Most metals react with their environment and the result of this reaction is the creation of a corrosion product. Protection against atmospheric corrosion is important in ship construction not only at the building berth but also in the fabrication shops. Serious rusting may occur where the relative humidity is above 70 per cent. All steel material in ship construction, plates and sections are shot blasted to remove rust and millscale. Shot blasting in shipyards involves an abrasive thrown at high velocity against the steel surface, which may be re-circulated and thrown again. Following shot blasting the plates and sections pass through an airless spray painting plant. (2) All petroleum hydrocarbons are subject to oxidation of some extent and this reaction increases with a rise in temperature. With lubricating oils, oxidation produces oil insoluble oxidised materials that can result in an increase in viscosity and the formation of deposits.

Oxides
Chemical compounds resulting from the combination of substances with oxygen.

Oxter plate
Steel plate that fits around the upper part of the **rudder post**.

Oxy-acetylene welding
Welding in which the combination of oxygen and acetylene produces intense heat.

Oxygen (O)
Gaseous element forming approximately one-fifth of the earth's atmosphere. It is a reactive gas that supports combustion and is essential for the respiration of most life forms. It is the most abundant element and is manufactured from liquid air for use in hot welding flames, steel manufacture, medical practice and anaesthesia; liquid oxygen is widely used in rocket fuels.

Oxygen analyser
Instrument used to determine the quantity of oxygen present in an atmosphere or a gas sample. Used to ensure the safety of an enclosed space or to establish the oxygen content of boiler flue gas or **inert gas** for tankers.

Oyster fitting
Electric light fitting designed for bulkhead mounting, to emit light simultaneously on both sides of the bulkhead to which it is attached.

Ozone
Condensed form of oxygen with the molecular structure O_3. A powerful oxidising agent, it is formed when air is subjected to silent electrical discharge or ultra-violet rays and can cause damage to cargoes such as fruit.

P

Packer
In offshore drilling, a mechanical device containing a rubber packing element that can be expanded against the well bore or **casing** to isolate the annular sections above and below the element.

Packing
Material inserted into the **stuffing boxes** of pumps or other machinery as a sealant and/or to assist the lubrication of a journal. For normal water duties soft cotton packing is preferable. Packing may be impregnated with graphite or soaked in oil for initial running in; for chemical and oil duties metallic packings are often used.

Paint primers
Paints used on bare metal as a basis for subsequent coats of paint. Adhesion of the primer to the metal is particularly important. **(a)** Prefabrication primers

are for the first coat on steel plate before it is fabricated into a ship's structure and should protect the steel from corrosion during the building period. **(c)** Wash primers contain a proportion of phosphoric acid that converts traces of rust to iron phosphate and forms an adherent base for subsequent coats. **(c)** Zinc based primers apply a thin coat of zinc that protects steel from corrosion.

Paints
Paint consists of pigments dispensed in a liquid referred to as the vehicle. When spread out thinly, the vehicle changes to an adherent dry film. The primary object of painting steelwork is to provide a coating that will protect the surface from the oxidising effect of the air or water. *See* **oxidation**.

Palaeozoic era
Geological era comprising the Cambrian, Ordovician, Silurian, Devonian, Carboniferous and **Permian periods** that began roughly 600 million years ago and ended roughly 230 million years ago.

Pallet
Consists of bearers and decks or platforms, in or on which cargo can be placed. As they are to be transported by fork lift truck the dimensions and weight must be at a maximum for handling by this equipment.

Panama chocks
Steel casting with oval opening. Chocks must be fitted at each end of a ship passing through the Panama Canal, for use in the locks.

Panamax
The maximum size of vessel, by virtue of its breadth, that can transit the Panama Canal.

Panting
The in and out movement of a ship's plating.

Panting beams
Additional beams in the forward and after portions of the hull to prevent or reduce the **panting** action of the shell plating.

Panting plates
Vertical plates supporting a steam turbine at one end. They are able to flex or move axially as expansion takes place.

Pantograph
Instrument for copying a diagram on any desired scale.

Parabola
Plane curve formed by the intersection of a cone with a plane parallel to its side.

Paraffinic

Description of a lubricating oil in which the straight chain, normal paraffinic portion is predominant. This gives the oil a waxy character with a high **viscosity index** and **pour point**, and good **oxidation** stability in its refined state.

Parallax

Apparent difference in position of an object when viewed from different points. For example when reading a **hydrometer** the eye must be at the level of the liquid or a parallex error will be introduced.

Parallel connection

Electrical connection in parallel, the converse of a **series** connection. All positive terminals are joined together and all negatives are similarly joined. Current then passes from one joined set of terminals to the other, each component taking only a proportion of the total current.

Parallel middle body

Ship's length where the midship section is constant in area and shape. *See* Figure 29.

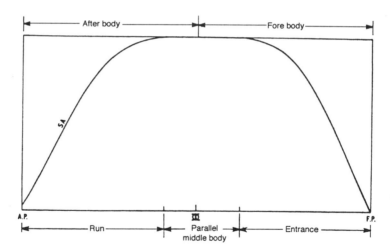

Figure 29 Parallel Middle Body

Parallel operation

Connecting two or more power sources to each other, such as a diesel engine and gas turbine, so the sum of their outputs lead to a common load.

Paramagnetic

(1) Ability of a body to become magnetised in the presence of a **magnetic field**. (2) Material with a relative **permeability** just greater than one.

Parameter

One of several variables used to identify the scope or boundaries of a scheme or system.

Paravane

Device used as a defence against hidden floating mines. Employs a steel cable running from each side of the bow to move the mine away from a ship. Severing its mooring wire allows the mine to float to the surface where it can be seen and destroyed.

Parbuckle

Roll a rounded object, such as a cask or spar, up a ramp or ship's side by passing the loop of a rope under it, making fast the loop and hauling on the standing ends. May also be applied to careening or righting a vessel or boat, or to any operation that involves rolling the object.

Parbuckling

Method by which a damaged ship lying on its side is righted. Two methods are used, one by the application of external forces which pull a ship upright and the other by an internal selection of combinations of **flooding** and **buoyancy**, depending on the conditions. As well as the problem of rotating the vessel care must be taken to prevent the vessel going over in the opposite direction.

Parkerising

A **corrosion** resistant treatment and finish on iron and steel parts.

Parsons, Sir Charles A. (1854-1931)

Designer of the first commercial marine **steam turbine**. In 1897 at the Spithead Review to celebrate Queen Victoria's Diamond Jubilee, his 2010 **shaft horse power (shp)** torpedo boat **Turbinia** raced through the gathered Navies of the world at a speed of 34.5 knots. The first merchant ship driven by Parsons turbines was the 3500 shp Scottish ferry *King Edward* in 1901. By 1907 Cunard's 68 000 **shp** Parsons steam turbine vessels, *Lusitania* and *Mauretania* were capturing the Blue Riband of the Atlantic.

Particle

Any small entity or portion of matter.

Particulates

Atmospheric particles made up of natural materials such as pollen and dust, and man made pollutants such as metallic ash, smoke, and soot. Diesel engines that burn residual fuel with high ash content lubricants produce large amounts of particulates in their **exhaust gases.**

Particular average

Marine insurance term denoting a partial loss.

Pascal (Pa)

The derived **SI unit** for pressure, a name given to the newton per square metre (N/m^2). The multiples kilopascal (kPa) and megapascal (Mpa) are often used.

Pawl

Pivoted catch engaging the teeth of a ratchet to permit rotation in one direction only, such as on a **winch.**

Peak pressure indicator

Instrument used to measure the maximum compression or ignition pressures developed in high speed engines or peak pressure in a hydraulic system.

Pearlite

A micro-constituent of steel with a **lamellar** structure consisting of iron and iron carbide formed when steel is slowly cooled.

Pedestal

Vertical member supporting a machine component, such as a bearing from a foundation below.

Peen

Spherical or thin end of a hammer head used to shape or mark metals.

Peltier effect

Condition arising at a joint between two different metals where an electric current passes giving rise to liberation or the absorption of heat.

Pendant

Short length of steel wire attached to the end of a fibre rope towline to resist wear and chafing.

Penetration

An arbitrary measure of the consistency (hardness) of grease using prescribed test methods.

Penetrameter

Instrument to test the quality of the penetration of a structure using a **radiographic** technique. Particularly useful when examining weld formations.

Penetrometer

Instrument for measuring the penetration of semi-solid substances.

Pensky-Martens tester
Testing apparatus to measure the closed cup flash point under prescribed test conditions.

Performance claim
Claim made by a time **charterer** against a **shipowner** when a ship has been unable to achieve the speed agreed in the **charter party**, has consumed too much fuel, or both.

Performance monitoring
The automatic calculation and recording of critical plant performance criteria, such as specific fuel consumption (**SFOC**), at predetermined intervals to monitor gradual changes in efficiency that occur in service. A valuable aid to watchkeepers for obtaining optimum performance from an engine or machine. Up to 150 sensors can be fitted to a large diesel engine to record cylinder and fuel injection pressures, piston ring clearances, differential pressures, and the temperatures of key units.

Period
Time taken for one complete cycle of a periodic phenomenon; the reciprocal of **frequency**.

Period of roll
Time taken for a complete cycle of the **rolling** motion of a ship.

Period of wave
Time interval between two wave crests passing the same point.

Periodical survey
To maintain its assigned class a vessel has to be examined by a **classification society** surveyor at regular periods.

Permanent set
Extension remaining in a test piece after load has been removed, the **elastic limit** of the material having been exceeded.

Permeability
The percentage volume of a space that can be flooded When a compartment contains cargo or fuel, the amount of water that can enter on damage is less than the volume of the empty compartment. The ratio of the volume entering to the volume of the empty compartment is called the permeability. For cargo spaces it is taken as 60 per cent, for passengers and crew spaces it is taken as 95 per cent.

Permian period
Geological period that began roughly 280 million years ago and ended roughly 230 million years ago; period in which the gas-bearing Rotliegendes sandstone formations were laid down in the southern North Sea.

Permissible length
Length between bulkheads on a ship to ensure it will remain afloat if one or more compartments are flooded. Permissible length is some fraction of the **floodable length,** called **factor of subdivision.**

Perpendiculars
The **forward perpendicular** (FP) is a vertical line through the intersection of the load waterline and the stem contour. **After perpendicular** (AP) is where the aft side of the **stern post** meets the load waterline, or if there is no post the centre of **rudder stock. Length between perpendiculars** (LBP) is the horizontal distance between AP and FP. *See* Figure 2.

Petrochemicals
Range of chemicals made from petroleum, such as ethyl alcohol, paraldehyde, acetone, and isopropyl.

Petroleum
Naturally-occurring green to black coloured mixtures of crude hydrocarbon oils, found as earth seepages or obtained by boring. The principal producing land areas are North America, Venezuela, Irabian Gulf area, Russia, West Africa and Indonesia. In the last two decades the search for petroleum has been extended to offshore continental shelves and production has been developed in the Gulf of Mexico and the North Sea.

Petroleum coke
Solid fuel with a low ash content, non-clinkering and generally low in sulphur content, produced as a by-product in the cracking and distillation of petroleum.

pH value
A convenient method of specifying the effective acidity or alkalinity of a solution. Pure water has a pH value of seven. Strong acids are below four and strong alkalis are above eleven.

Phase
(1) Circuit or terminal of a polyphase electrical system or apparatus. **(2)** Any homogeneous portion of a system.

Phase angle
Angle by which current lags voltage in an ac circuit containing **resistance** and **reactance** or leads the voltage in an ac circuit containing resistance and

capacitance. At zero phase angle, current and voltage are said to be in phase.

Phase diagram
Graphical representation of the limits of temperature and composition at which the constituents (or phases) of an alloy system exist under equilibrium.

Phase modifier
A machine, the chief purpose of which is to supply leading or lagging reactive volt amperes to the system to which it is connected. Phase modifiers may be either synchronous or asynchronous.

Phase sequence indicator
Instrument indicating when the order **conductors** in a polyphase system reach their maximum current or voltage.

Phon
Unit of noise or sound level measurement. Normal conversation is about 10 phons, therefore, sounds above 120 phons can cause acute discomfort.

Phosphor bronze
Bronze alloy of copper and tin with added phosphorus to increase its strength This produces a number of useful alloys resistant to corrosion in salt water containing quantities of tin ranging from 3 per cent to 12 per cent.

Phosphoresence
Luminous effect on the surface of the sea caused by the presence of minute organisms.

Photoelasticity
Method of determining the location and direction of **stress** distribution in bodies under complex systems of loading by passing polarised light through a model made of transparent plastic material. Light is polarised and transmitted only on the planes of principal stress. Stress distribution is then observed through a second piece of polaroid material called the analyser.

Photoelectric cell
Light sensitive sensor that produces an electrical output. Different types of cell exist, namely photo emissive, photo conductive and photo voltaic. Used in equipment such as crankcase **oil mist detectors**.

Pickling
Process for removing oxide films from metals by dipping into a bath of acid. Sulphuric or hydrochloric are the most usual acids employed.

Pier
See **jetty**.

Piezoelectric pressure transducer
Sensor which responds to an applied force producing an electrical output. It is used for dynamic pressure measurement such as combustion pressure in an engine cylinder.

Pig
(1) In the oil industry, a piece of equipment inserted in a pipeline and is carried along by the flow of oil or gas to clean or monitor the internal condition of the pipeline or to mark an interface between two products. (2) Lump of metal cast in a suitable shape and weight for storage or transportation.

Pig's ear
Funnel or tun-dish. A pipe system may include an open-ended pipe that discharges the fluid being carried into a pig's ear, providing a visual indication to the flow of the liquid in the pipe system.

Pile
Assembly of moderator material such as pure graphite in which there is a **neutron** source, such as pure uranium, together with neutron detectors and counting equipment. These assemblies were originally built up by stacking layers of this material leading to the phrase piles.

Pilferage
Petty theft.

Pilgrim nut
Patent design of nut for securing **propellers.** The design incorporates a **torus** ring of **elastomer** embedded in the face of the nut which can be expanded under hydraulic pressure to force the propeller boss on to the tapered **stern shaft** end, without the need of a key.

Pilgrim wire
Wire fixed at one end and passing over a pulley at the other with a weight hanging on the free end to maintain tension; used for checking the alignment of main bearings. The **catenary sag** of the wire is calculated and allowed for when measuring the position of each bearing.

Pillars
Vertical columns forming part of a ship's structure providing support for **deck** and deck beams.

Pilot exciter
Source of all or part of a field current for the excitation of another generator.

Pilot Valve
Small valve to admit fluid to one side of a piston operating a large valve.

Pilotage
The act, carried out by a qualified pilot, of assisting the **master** of a ship to navigate when entering or leaving a port.

Pinholes
Defect found in **castings** due to liberation of occluded gases causing minute cavities or pinholes throughout the casting.

Pinion
Small cog-wheel that engages with a larger one.

Pintles
Hinge pins on which certain types of **rudder** swing. *See* Figure 30.

Pipe-laying vessels
Ships designed to lay pipes on the seabed.

Piracy
Robbery on the high seas. Classic period was the late 17th and early 18th centuries, however, it has now re-appeared in Africa and the Far east.

Piston
A cylindrical metal object that reciprocates in a **cylinder**, either under combustion gas pressure, as in engines, or to displace or compress a fluid, as in pumps and compressors. In an engine it is connected directly or indirectly (crosshead) to the crankshaft.

Piston crown
Upper part of a piston which is exposed to the hot gases of combustion.

Piston end clearance
Minimum distance between piston and cylinder closure in a **reciprocating engine or pump.**

Piston ring
Spring tensioned rings set in grooves in the circumference of a piston that push out against the walls of the cylinder forming a gastight seal.

Piston rod
Rod connecting the piston to the **crosshead** in a large diesel engine.

Piston rod gland
In a large diesel engine, the **diaphragm** separating the crankcase from the cylinder through which the **piston rod** passes. *See* Figure 31.

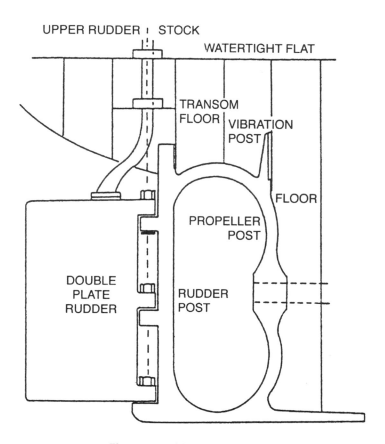

Figure 30 Rudder with pintles

Piston skirt

Cylindrical part of piston below the pressure rings keeping the piston in alignment with the cylinder. Can contain a scraper ring to prevent crankcase lubricant migrating and being combusted in the ring belt area.

Pit

A sump or tank with no roof holding liquids such as **drilling mud**.

Pitch

(1) Distance a specified point on the face of a **propeller blade** moves forward in one revolution. (2) The pitch of a screw thread is the amount of axial advance per revolution. When a nut is turned round on the bolt for one revolution, the nut travels a distance equal to the pitch of the screw thread on the bolt. (3) Black solid crude residue.

Pitch circle diameter(PCD)

In **gearing,** the diameter of an imaginary cylinder rolling without slip against an adjacent surface. In gears connecting parallel shafts the adjacent surface is also cylindrical. *See* Figure 1.

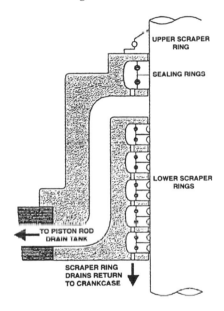

Figure 31 Piston Rod Gland
(Courtesy of Lloyd's Register)

Pitch ratio

Ratio of the **pitch** to diameter in a **propeller.**

Pitching

The action of a ship moving to the crest and descending to the trough of a wave; movement about transverse axis. *See* Figure 15.

Pitot tube
A tube inserted parallel to a flow stream. One orifice faces the flow to receive total pressure and the other registers the static pressure. It is connected to a differential pressure measuring device.

Pitot-static log
A log determining a vessel's speed by measuring the dynamic water pressure using a **pitot tube** projected outside the hull.

Pitting
(1) Small cavities caused by **erosion** or **corrosion.** (2) Corrosive action on steel plates making small surface indentations. (3) Surface indentations occuring on **gear teeth** usually in the region of the **pitch circle.**

Pivoting point
Point in a ship about which turning takes place when under helm.

Plain bearings
Type of **bearing** with a sliding motion, as distinct from rolling, such as **anti-friction bearings.**

Plan view
In a drawing, the representation of a structure or object viewed from above.

Plane sailing
Mathematical solution to problems of dead reckoning by considering the surface of the earth to be a plane.

Planetary gear
System of **epicyclic gears** with a fixed **annulus,** rotating sun wheel and planet carrier, and planet wheels rotating about their own axis.

Planets, navigational
Planets Jupiter, Mars, Saturn and Venus whose positions are tabulated for the use of navigation.

Planimeter
Machine for measuring the area within a closed plane figure.

Plankton
Drifting organisms on oceans and rivers consisting of minute animal and vegetable substances.

Planned maintenance
Organising the regular inspection of machinery in order to minimise any possible breakdown.

Plans
Drawings or diagrams of the entire ship or its individual systems, installations and equipment.

Plasma coating
Deposition of substances on to components by means of a plasma gun or torch. Ultra high temperatures can be reached in the gaseous stream emitted from the torch, so most materials introduced into the stream in powder form are volatilised. Coatings of a variety of substances, metals and **ceramics**, can be built-up by the process.

Plastic
Generic term for a range of high-molecular weight **polymers** that can be used to produce a variety of shapes.

Plasticity
Property of a body meaning it tends to retain its **deformation** after reduction of the deforming stress to its **yield stress.**

Plate clamp
Device fitted to the edge of a steel plate to prevent it from slipping when being lifted.

Plate type heat exchanger
Heat exchanger comprising a number of ribbed plates sealed together in a frame. The cooling medium travels down one side of the plate, the liquid to be cooled down the other side. Transfer of heat takes place across the plate material.

Plates
(1) Sheets of rolled steel making up a ship's hull. (2) **Electrodes** in a battery cell.

Plenum
Applied to a vessel under internal pressure, such as air pressure.

Pleuger system
As conventional **rudders** are of limited use at low speeds, a way of providing manoeuvring capability at low speed is to deflect the **propeller** race. This can be done by using deflector plates or by turning the propeller disc itself. The latter is the principle of the Pleuger active rudder which is a streamlined body mounted on a rudder containing an electric motor to drive a small propeller. To derive full advantage the rudder should be capable of angles greater than 35 degrees. With a ship's engines at stop, the system can turn a ship in its own length.

Plimsoll Line

More commonly known as the **load line** for British cargo ships that was laid down in the Merchant Shipping Act of 1875. An international load line was adopted by 54 nations in 1930 and amended in 1968 to include a new line permitting a smaller **freeboard** in new large ships. Samuel Plimsoll was the member of parliament and shipping reformer, who campaigned against the large number of ships that were lost each year at sea and he was responsible for passing the original bill through parliament. *See* Figure 19.

Plugging

A process whereby a well that is no longer (and never likely to be) needed is filled with concrete and abandoned.

Plummer block

Block containing bearings to support a revolving **propeller shaft (stern shaft)** with a removable cover for access to bearings.

Plunger

One part sliding in another, often cylindrical and sufficiently close fitting to retain fluid pressure as in a fuel pump plunger.

Pneumatic

Activating by means of compressed air. There are many types of both percussion and rotary tools operated by compressed air.

Pneumercator gauge

Remote reading instrument indicating the depth of liquid in a tank.

Point

Electrical term applied to any termination of fixed wiring intended for connecting a supply to a current consuming appliance.

Poise (Pc)

Unit of dynamic viscosity, usually quoted in centipoise.

Poisson's ratio

Ratio of transverse to longitudinal strain under tension or compression within the **elastic range.**

Polarity

Electric polarity is used to indicate which part of a conductor or circuit is anodic or positive and which cathodic or negative.

Polarisation

In a primary cell, the effect of the liberation of hydrogen at the surface of the copper electrode, leading to a loss of efficiency; avoided by the addition to of a depolarising agent such as copper sulphate to the **electrolyte.**

Pole
Part of a magnetic circuit, in an electrical rotating machine, that carries, or in which is embedded, an excitation winding or a permanent magnet.

Polishing
Highly polished **internal combustion engine** liner surface resulting in a reduction in ring sealing and excessive lubricating oil consumption.

Pollution
A modification of the environment caused by the release of noxious materials, rendering it harmful or unpleasant to life. The prevention and control of marine pollution from ships has been of concern to **IMO** since its inception. The first major step towards international control of marine pollution was taken by a Convention in 1954. The latest Convention covers pollution from ships by oil, noxious liquid substances, exhaust gases, noise, sewage and garbage. Oil carrying ships must be capable of operating with a method of retention on board in association with the load on top system. *See* **MEPC** and **MARPOL**.

Polyacrylamides
Class of resins that swell when water is added to them.

Polymer
Material composed of a series of small molecular units.

Polymerisation
Formation of a large molecule by chemically bonding two or more smaller molecules of the same species without the addition or loss of any atoms.

Polytetrafluoroethylene (PTFE)
A thermo-plastic polymer virtually immune to chemical attack and that can be used over a wide temperature range. Trade names are Teflon and Fluon.

Pontoon
Hollow buoyancy tank used to support a **semi-submersible rig,** barge or other structure.

Pontoon hatch cover
Hatch cover consisting of a removable single slab, for access to the hold. Typically found on cellular **container ships;** also fitted to multi-purpose and heavy lift ships. Sometimes named a lift-away hatch cover.

Poop
After superstructure on the upper deck.

Poppet valve
See **mushroom valve.**

Pore pressure
Natural internal pressure in a hydrocarbon containing rock formation.

Port
(1) Left side of a ship when facing forward. (2) Harbour designed to look after ships. (3) Opening in a ship's side for goods or personnel. (4) Opening in a pump or engine cylinder through which a gas or liquid enters or leaves.

Porthole
Circular opening in a ship's side to provide light, ventilation and if necessary a possible means of escape. Closed by a thick glass sidelight and equipped with a **deadlight** which can be closed in heavy weather providing additional security.

Port of refuge
A port outside the planned itinerary, called at due to some unforeseen hazard at sea. This could be for repairs, to refuel or resecure cargo.

Port of registry
Where a ship is registered shown on the stern of a vessel.

Position balance
The balancing of linkages and lever movements, usually in a pneumatic device, to achieve an **equilibrium condition.**

Position reference system
Fitted as part of a **dynamic positioning system,** to monitor any movement of the position of a vessel from a pre-set datum position. There are a wide variety of such systems, including micro-wave radio, mechanical, satellite, inertial navigation, laser, imaging camera and hydro-acoustic. As yet, no one system will operate independently and successfully in every part of the world, therefore, often three or more position reference systems are fitted to a dynamic positioning system.

Positive slip
When the distance travelled by a ship is less than that calculated from the propeller revolutions.

Possessory lien
The right of a **shipowner** to retain cargo until the freight or any general average contribution is paid.

Potential difference (PD)
The difference in electrical state between two points measured by the work done in the transfer of a unit charge from one point to another.

Potentiometer
Instrument for measuring or adjusting electrical potential.

Pounding
The heavy falling of the fore end of a ship into the sea after being lifted clear of the water by wave action. Also applies to a ship hitting the seabed due to wave action. Also known as **slamming.**

Pour point
The lowest temperature, expressed as a multiple of 3°C, at which oil ceases to flow when cooled under prescribed conditions. The pour point gives a rough indication of the oil's wax content. It is essential to maintain a temperature above the pour point for bunker fuel oil in storage, as once it solidifies it is extremely difficult to re-liquify.

Power (W)
The **SI unit** of power (watts).

Power factor (PF)
(1) In a single phase system, the ratio of W to VA, where W = Watts, V = Volts, and A = Amps. **(2)** In a symmetrical polyphase ac system with balanced load, it is the ratio of total W to total VA. **(3)** The PF of a motor or generator is the ratio of kW input (or output) to the kVA input (or output); usually expressed as a percentage.

Power take off (pto)
Relating to marine diesel engines, a set of gears working from the main engine crankshaft which may be connected to a shaft driven electric generator, a power turbine, or a combination of both. Power can be taken from or given to the main engine **crankshaft.**

Power turbine
Exhaust gas turbine driven by surplus exhaust gas energy from the diesel main propulsion unit. The power developed may be returned directly to the **crankshaft** via gearing or used to drive an electric **generator.**

Pratique
Certificate granted by a port authority stating the satisfactory health of those on board ship as well as confirming no contagious diseases exist.

Pre-arcing time
Time period between the incidence of a stated overcurrent and melting of the fuse element.

Precipitate

A solid substance separating from a liquid in which it was formerly dissolved, the separation resulting from chemical or physical change. This is distinct from a substance held only mechanically in suspension, which is called sediment.

Precipitation hardening

In a metal or alloy, precipitation of one phase in the lattice of another of different ionic diameter.This keys the structure against creep or slip under stress. Produced by precipitation during cooling of a super-saturated solution. The process may be carried out at room temperature (natural ageing) or at an elevated temperature and in some metals it is assisted by working (such as forging) at that temperature. Also known as age hardening.

Precipitation number

Number of millilitres of precipitate formed when 10 millilitres of oil are mixed with 90 millilitres of naptha of specified characteristics under certain prescribed conditions.

Precision

The accuracy of a measuring instrument.

Preferential trip

Automatic switch fitted in an electric circuit to protect the main switchboard from overload. When the load current reaches a specified amount the trip operates cutting off the supply of electricity to non-essential auxiliaries.

Pre-ignition

Uncontrolled burning of the combustible charge prior to designed ignition, sometimes caused by a hot surface such as an **exhaust valve**.

Pressure

Force applied to, or distributed over a surface; measured as force per unit area.

Pressure angle

In toothed gearing, the angle between the common tangent to the pitch circles of two teeth at the point of contact and the common normal point.

Pressure compounding

The use of a number of stages of nozzle and blade to progressively reduce steam pressure in an **impulse turbine** improving efficiency.

Pressure ring

Ring on a piston designed to prevent pressurised fluid leaking from one cylinder end to the other.

Pressure testing
Testing of tanks, compartments, and watertight bulkheads using water or air pressure.

Pressure/vacuum valve
Valve fitted to the **vapour** pipeline from a cargo tank. In the event of excess pressure it will permit safe venting of vapour and in the event of a partial vacuum it will allow air to be drawn into the tank.

Pre-tension
Amount of **tensile** load applied to a bolt or **tie rod** when it is installed but not subjected to in its working environment.

Preventers
Additional stays to support and relieve **strain** on the **mast**.

Primary recovery
Recovery of oil or gas from a **reservoir** using natural pressure in the reservoir to force oil or gas out.

Primary winding
Electrical **winding** on the energy input side; usually refers to the input winding of a **transformer**.

Prime mover
Engine or other primary source of power converting energy into mechanical or electrical power.

Priming
(1) In a boiler, the projection of minute particles of water into the steam, often due to impurities in feed water and incorrect water level in the boiler. (2) In a pump, the insertion of water to expel air and break air lock. (3) In painting, the first coat applied to a base surface assisting the adhesion of the final coating.

Principal dimensions
Dimensions by which the size of a ship is measured.

Prismatic coefficient
Ratio of the volume of water displaced by a ship to the volume represented by the length of a ship and the area of the immersed **midship section**.

Prismatic self supporting tanks
Tanks adopted in **liquefied natural gas** tankers. Tanks of the self-supporting type can be prismatic (single or double-walled), spherical or cylindrical.

Prize
Ship seized by force during hostilities.

Probe
(1) Instrument inserted into the interior of machinery or tubes for examination purposes. Electronic devices are available for drawing through a tube to indicate defects in, or the thickness of, the tube wall. (2) Exploratory bore made in a metal.

PROBO
*Pro*duct/*B*ulk/*O*re Carrier.

Process
Course of action designed to achieve an end result.

Processing plant
Plant installed on a **production platform** or pipeline terminal to separate gas, oil and water from a mixture containing all of these components.

Producer gas
Gas obtained by passing air and steam through incandescent materials such as coke or coal. Constituents are mainly carbon-monoxide, hydrogen and nitrogen.

Producing horizon
Rock from which oil or gas is produced.

Product carrier
A tanker designed to carry refined products such as gas oil, aviation fuel, and kerosene. Large numbers of tanks and several separate loading and discharge piping systems with suitably coated tank surfaces are particular features of this type of ship, ideal for discharging a number of separate parcels or types of products in any one voyage.

Production platform
Fixed or floating platform installed at a field for oil or gas production purposes, sometimes used for development drilling.

Production tubing
Pipe in a production well through which oil or gas flows from the **reservoir** to the surface. Also known as the production string.

Productivity
Efficiency of an industrial process and manpower involved.

Professional indemnity
Limited liability insurance for professional engineers. The assured are indemnified up to a certain sum for claims made against them. Most marine consultants use a scheme introduced by the **Engineering Council**.

Profile
Drawing showing the elevation of a ship, indicating the location of decks, bulkheads, and the like. *See also* **lines plan.**

Projected area
Area of the blades of a **propeller** when projected onto a plane perpendicular to the axis of rotation.

PROM
Programmable Read-Only Memory.

Proof load
Pre-determined load in excess of a normal load applied for testing purposes.

Proof stress
The stress necessary to produce a certain amount of permanent set in metals that do not exhibit a certain **yield point**. Generally, it is stress producing an extension of 0.1 or 0.5 per cent. In specifying proof stress in a **tensile** test, the amount of non-proportional **deformation** is expressed as a percentage of the elongation.

Propane (C_3H_8)
A petroleum gas obtained as a by-product in various oil refining processes. A colourless, easily liquefied product found in natural gas, it is an important raw material for the petrochemical industry. With a boiling point of 43.8°C, it is readily transported as liquid in tanks and bottles and is used as fuel for domestic and industrial purposes.

Propeller
An assembly of radially disposed blades of aerofoil shape that by reason of rotation in water and blade angle of attack, produces thrust or power. Force needed to propel a ship is obtained from a reaction against water causing a stream of water to move in the opposite direction. Of the devices used to propel ships, oars, paddle wheels, jets and the screw propeller, the screw propeller has almost exclusive application to ocean going craft. Fundamentally, the marine screw propeller can be regarded as a helicoidal surface which on rotation screws its way through the water. A screw propeller has two or more fixed blades projecting from a boss. The surface of each blade, when viewed from aft, is called the face and it is the driving surface when producing an ahead thrust. *See* Figure 9. Types of propeller are:

Fixed pitch propeller. Blades in the form of a screw have a fixed pitch.

Controllable pitch propeller. Blades can be controlled hydraulically to vary the pitch making it possible to provide astern thrust without reversing the direction of rotation.

Ducted propeller. Propeller surrounded by a duct which can be moved into the vertical plane to provide helm movement.

Bow thrust propeller. Propeller mounted in a tunnel athwart the hull at the forward end of a ship to provide athwartships movement.

Voith Schneider propeller. Patent design of propeller that rotates in a vertical plane. Vertical blades oscillate providing thrust to the horizontal plane.

Contra-rotating propeller. Two propellers mounted on concentric shafts rotating in opposite directions balancing the **torque** reaction generated by a single propeller.

Cupped propeller. Cupping consists of a slight turn in the trailing edges of the propeller blades producing greater thrust and reducing the onset of cavitation. They can be run higher on the transom, reducing the drag effect of the lower unit. Cupped propellers are usually only fitted to light, fast boats; their pitch should be about one inch less than normal propellers.

Propeller, cavitation
See **cavitation**.

Propeller efficiency
Ratio of thrust power over delivered power.

Propeller Efficiency = $\dfrac{PT}{PD}$

Thrust Power (PD). Product of thrust delivered to the propeller and its speed of advance.

Delivered Power (PD). Power delivered to the propeller

Propeller law
As with resistance experiments on model hulls, **Froude's Law of Comparison** may be used to predict the performance of geometrically similar propellers. The results are usually plotted in the form of non-dimensional coefficients.

Propeller, singing
Before the onset of **cavitation**, the blades of a propeller may give out a high pitched note or ring. Singing is due to the elastic vibration of the material excited by the resonant shedding of non-cavitating eddies from the trailing

edge of blades. Singing is a nuisance to a ship's crew and dangerous in warships as the high pitch can be picked up by enemy **sonar**. Sharpening the blade edge has been adopted as silent blades are essential at low speeds.

Proportional band
Range of values of deviation that result in the full operating range of output signal of the controlling unit as a result of proportional action only. Can be expressed as a percentage of the controller's scale range.

Proportional controller
Controller that provides proportional action only.

Propulsion
Method of propelling ship.

Propulsive efficiency
Ratio of the **effective power** to drive a ship at a particular speed to the **horse power** of the machinery.

Protection and Indemnity Club
P&I Club. Association of shipowners who by means of contributions known as calls, provide mutual protection against liabilities not covered by insurance, such as claims for injury to crew and loss or damage to cargo.

Protest
Declaration made by the master of a ship on arrival in port that circumstances beyond control have been encountered, such as heavy weather, that may have caused damage to a ship or its cargo. This declaration may be necessary to avoid liability for damage to cargo.

Proton
Nuclear particle of unit mass number having a charge equal and opposite to that of an **electron**; the **nucleus** of the lightest hydrogen isotope.

PRS
Polski Rejestr Statkow. Polish ship **classification society**.

PSI gauge
Pressure measurement taken with the gauge set to zero at standard **atmospheric pressure** (14.7 lbfin^{-2}).

PSI absolute
Actual pressure measurements with no allowance for **atmospheric pressure**.

Psophometer
Instrument measuring loudness of sound in relation to the sensitivity of the human ear.

PSTI
Petroleum Science and Technology Institute.

Psychrometer
Wet and dry bulb hygrometer.

Pteropod ooze
Deep sea deposit composed largely of small shells, generally found at depths of 500 to 1500 fathoms.

Pulley
Wheel with a flat or slightly convex rim to receive a flat belt, or grooved to receive a rope, chain or vee shaped belt. Used for transmitting power, raising weights or changing direction of pull.

Pulse
(1) Electrical disturbance whose duration is short in relation to a particular time scale and whose initial and final values are equal. (2) Radio signal of very short duration.

Pump
Machine, often electrically driven, producing a flow of fluid under pressure.

Pump room
Compartment in an oil tanker where cargo pumps and ancillary equipment are located. Enclosed within oil tight bulkheads, it is usually located between machinery spaces and cargo tanks.

Punkah Louvre
Ventilation system supplying fresh air at a given temperature to different compartments or cabins of a ship. Air is delivered from a spout (punkah louvre) working on a universal joint that can be rotated to direct the air to suit individual requirements.

Purchase
Raise or move with the assistance of leverage or **tackle**.

Purging system
System designed to free an enclosed space from **flammable** mixture by flushing it with an **inert gas** or liquid.

Purifier
Rotary machine for centrifuging contaminants from fuel or lubricating oil.

Purposes
Time allowed in a voyage **charter-party** for loading and discharging combined, expressed as a number of days or hours.

Push knees
Structures fitted to the hull of a tug allowing it to push barges with the minimum risk of damage to either craft.

Push rod
Rod working in compression to operate one machine part from another. Used for example between a cam follower and valve rocker in **mushroom** valve engines.

Pusher tug
Tug moving barges by pushing rather than towing.

Pyrometer
Instrument for measuring very high temperatures.

Pyrotechnic
Rockets and flares used for illumination, distress signals and target marking.

Pythagoras Theorem
The square on the hypotenuse of a right angled triangle is equal to the sum of the squares on the other two sides.

Q

QNCA
Qualifications and National Curriculum Authority. Authority bringing together the work of the SCAA (School Curriculum and Assessment Authority) and the NCVQ (National Council for Vocational Qualifications).

Quadrant
Fitting attached to **rudder stock,** connected by rack and pinion to the **steering gear.**

Quadruple expansion
Reciprocating steam engine where steam passes through four separate expansion in series.

Quadruple screw
Ship having four separate **propellers.**

Qualification
Document attesting a person has fulfilled certain conditions either academic, practical or both, and is capable of holding an appropriate position.

Qualitative analysis
Analytical breaking down of a substance to determine its constituents.

Quality assurance
Term meaning manufactured items are up to the required standards and have been checked at each stage of production to ensure that they conform with the specified requirements. Planning such a scheme is particularly important when large numbers of similar articles are being produced as it would be impractical to test each one individually. Also refers to checking the administration of any process to ensure it meets the requirements laid down.

Quality control
Inspection and testing of materials and components to ensure their uniformity and fitness for service. Also refers to checking that a process of any sort, including administration, meets requirements.

Quantitative analysis
Analytical breaking down process of a substance to determine the estimation of the quantity of each constituent.

Quantisation
Approximation process converting an **analogue** signal to a **digital** signal.

Quarantine
Isolation of a ship until **pratique** is granted. If an infectious disease is identified, a vessel can be placed in quarantine anchorage.

Quarl blocks
Refractory bricks of a special shape fitted round the burner openings of a boiler furnace.

Quarter Deck
(1) Refers to that part of the upper deck that is abaft the main mast. **(2)** In warships, the officers deck.

Quarters
Shipboard living **accommodation** spaces.

Quasi propulsive coefficient (QPC)
Ratio of the effective power necessary to drive a ship at a particular speed to the power which must be applied at the propeller. Calculated by the formula:

$$\frac{effective\ power\ (PE) + allowances\ for\ appendages\ and\ bad\ weather}{delivered\ power\ (PD)}$$

PE is the power required to tow a ship.
PD is the power delivered to the propeller.

Quenching
Rapid cooling of a metal by water or oil. In the case of heat treatable metals, quenching is carried out to change the structure prior to further heat treatment to enhance their properties.

Quick closing valve
Valve that has a collapsible bridge and can be shut quickly from a remote point.

Quill shaft
Shaft connecting two rotating components of a machine. Designed to provide torsional flexibility or to permit misalignment or **axial** movement.

Quoin
Wooden wedge for preventing the movement of casks and barrels.

R

Race
Inner or outer steel rings of a ball or **roller bearing.**

Rack
Straight bar with teeth suitable for engaging with a pinion to convert linear to rotary motion or rotary to linear motion.

Racking
Distortion of the hull structure caused by strain from a disturbed sea

R&D
*R*esearch *A*nd *D*evelopment.

Radar
*R*adio *D*etection *A*nd *R*anging. Navigational aid using radio waves of a very short wavelength sent out as a narrow beam by a highly directional aerial. The aerial rotates sending a beam out through a full 360 degrees. Any solid object of reasonable size will reflect the beam and be detected on the radar screen as a bright spot.

Radial flow
Fluid flow outwards towards the periphery of a circular body or from the periphery towards the centre.

Radian
(1) Unit of circular measure (rad). (2) Angle at the centre of a circle sub-
tended by an arc whose length is equal to the radius.

Radiant boiler
A **boiler** utilising the radiant heat of combustion to produce steam. This
radiant heat is transmitted by infra-red radiation within the furnace. Roof
firing and a very high boiler is required to ensure efficient operation.

Radiation
Emission and diffusion of rays, such as light, heat, **X-rays**, and radio.

Radio
Means of signalling through space using electromagnetic waves generated
by high frequency, alternating currents.

Radio direction finding (RDF)
Using the reception of radio waves to determine the direction of a station or
an object.

Radiographic flaw detection
Detection of flaws in materials by subjecting them to rays of very short
wave-length that penetrate the material and are exposed on a photographic
film placed on the opposite side. Flaws are detected on the film by the differences in density of the film in way of the flaws. **X-rays** emitted from an electrical apparatus can be used or **gamma rays** from radio-active materials such
as radium or **isotopes** of iridium, caesium or cobalt, which themselves have
been subjected to radio-activity.

Radius of gyration
Square root of the ratio of the moment of inertia of a body about a given axis
divided by its mass.

Rail
(1) Wooden or metal capping of **bulwarks**. (2) Pipeline, generally containing
fuel, maintained at a particular pressure to act as a distribution manifold. *See
also* **common rail.**

Raised forecastle
A **superstructure** at the extreme forward end of a ship.

Rake
Line inclined from the vertical or horizontal.

RAM
*R*andom *A*ccess *M*emory.

Ram
Thrusting motion, such as by a hydraulic ram.

Ramp
An inclined surface allowing access from one level to another, such as on **RO/RO** ferries, the success of which depends greatly on equipment used to move vehicles from shore to ship. The link is a ramp hinged at the ship end and supported at the outer end for flexibility to suit tide levels.

Rankine cycle
Thermal cycle used as a standard of efficiency for **heat engines** and **heat pumps** employing condensable vapour as working fluid.

Rapeseed oil
A type of **vegetable oil** used to manufacture **compound lubricants**. When mixed with water such lubricants form stable emulsions. Ideal for the lubrication of steam reciprocating engines and sterntubes where water is an ever present danger. If water gains access to a lubricant system it is preferable to have a stable emulsion than free water. Many of the vegetable and animal oils used for compounding have been replaced with additives performing the same duties.

Rapson's slide
Chain **steering gear** where mechanical advantage increases with the angle of helm. Chains are connected to a collar and are free to slide on the **tiller**.

Ratchet
Toothed wheel or rack capable of movement in one direction only. Movement in the other direction is prevented by a **pawl**.

Rate of penetration (ROP)
Depth of an oil hole drilled in a specified time; typically in feet per hour.

Rateau turbine
An **impulse turbine** employing a number of stages. Each stage has one row of nozzles and one row of blades, referred to as pressure compounded.

Rated output
In oil engines, the load in **brake horse power** which an engine can carry for a period of 12 hours at rated speed under the following conditions: mean barometric pressure 75 cm of mercury; atmospheric temperature 29.4°C (85°F); humidity 1.52 cm of mercury vapour pressure. The BSI issue two specifications about rating requirements. These are BS 649 oil engine types and BS 765 carburetted engines.

Ratline
Small lines fastened across the shrouds of a sailing ship used as ladder rungs.

Reactance (X)
Component of applied voltage in quadrature with current, divided by current. That component of **impedance** due to **inductance** and/or **capacitance**.

Reaction
Process involving chemical change forming new chemical products.

Reaction turbine
A **turbine** in which working gas expands through alternate rows of stator and rotor blades which absorb **kinetic energy** after each expansion through a set of stator blades. As the steam falls in pressure, it increases in volume so the casing and rotor become progressively larger in diameter.

Reaming
Enlarging a hole by the means of revolving in it a cylindrical slightly tapered tool with cutting edges running along its sides.

Receiver
Person or firm to whom cargo is consigned.

Reciprocate
Move towards and backwards **cyclically** over a fixed path.

Reciprocating engine
Engine with a piston **oscillating** in a cylinder under the periodic pressure of the working gas.

Reciprocating pumps
Pumps of the positive displacement type. A piston working in a cylinder displaces a given volume of fluid for each stroke. The amount delivered depends on piston area and speed. They are used for small quantity high pressure duties, with an efficiency of about 85 per cent and are self-priming.

Recirculating feed line
A pipeline allowing the recirculation of feed water back to a **condenser**. Used during reduced power operations to provide the cooling necessary for various steam returns; usually automatically controlled.

Rectifier
Static device for converting electrical power from ac to dc.

Redelivery
When the **charterer** returns a ship to the **shipowner** at the end of the period of charter.

Reducing valve
Valve arrangement designed to maintain constant fluid pressure at its downstream side irrespective of the inlet pressure.

Reduction gear
Machine with two or more **gear wheels** of different sizes that mesh together to reduce the output shaft rotational speed to less than the input shaft.

Redwood viscosity
Viscosity range originally used to measure bunker fuel and lubricants. Now **kinematic viscosity** is used for both applications.

Reef
Ridge of rocks near surface of the sea.

Reefer ship
Refrigerated ship specially engaged to carry perishable food products.

Reefer plug
Electrical power point on a cargo vessel where refrigerated **containers** are connected.

Reeve
Pass a rope through a **block**.

Reference circle
Circle of intersection of the reference cylinder of a **helical** or **spur gear** by a transverse plane.

Refining
Manufacture of **petroleum** products from **crude oil** by any of the various processes available. Commences with atmospheric distillation and can be followed by **vacuum distillation, thermal cracking, catalytic cracking** and various other processes to produce products ranging from gases to **bitumens.**

Refit
A ship's complete overhaul and refurbishment, including bringing all class items up-to-date.

Refractory
Material able to withstand high temperature conditions such as those experienced in boiler brickwork.

Refrigeration
Cooling and freezing on board ship is obtained by the vaporisation of liquid refrigerants. Installation consists of an evaporator, condenser and compressor. The main refrigerant used in marine installations has been R12, however

because this **chlorofluocarbon** *(CFC)* refrigerant damages the ozone layer there is a move towards more friendly products, notably R134A. Also making a comeback for the same reason is **ammonia** used in many early ships' refrigerant plants.

Register
Device regulating the draught to a **boiler.**

Register of Ships
Set of books or computer disks, continually updated, published by **Lloyd's Register.** Contains names and particulars of all known self propelled, seagoing merchant ships in the world with a gross tonnage of 100 or more. Also includes details of other marine craft and installations and provides a regular return of statistical information related to the shipping industry.

Registered length
Length of a ship measured from the foreside of the **stem** to the after side of the **stern post.** *See* Figure 2.

Registration
Recording the ownership of a ship with the authorities of a country. Details of the owners must be submitted with the plans and details of the ship, including measurements. The name of the ship and port of registry must then be clearly shown on the hull. Registration of a ship makes it subject to the laws of the country in which it is registered.

Registro Italiano Navale (RIN)
Italian ship **classification society.**

Reheat
Used with reference to high pressure main **boilers.** The superheated steam is returned to the boiler after doing work in the first part of the high pressure turbine. In the boiler the steam temperature is increased at constant pressure. The steam is then led back to the next stage of the turbine plant which improves the efficiency of the plant.

Reid vapour pressure (RVP)
Method of determining the **vapour pressure** of a particular **petroleum** liquid, usually expressed in bar; a measure of a liquids volatility. The RVP for propane is approximately 13.4 bar, for gas, oil and other marine fuels it is below 0.007 bar.

Relative humidity
Ratio of the amount of water **vapour** present in a given volume of air to the maximum amount of water vapour present before precipitation occurs.

Relay
Electrical switch that brings about a change in an independent circuit.

Relief valve
A spring loaded valve that releases fluid or gas from a system when the pressure reaches a preset level.

Reliquefication
Liquefying by refrigeration of cargo boil off from a liquefied gas carrier.

Reluctance (S)
Ratio of magnetomotive force to magnetic flux around a magnetic circuit.

Remanence
Remanent magnetic flux density obtained when initial magnetism reaches a saturation value of the material.

Render
To slacken a rope a little at a time to relieve it from excessive strain.

Repeatability
In a research project, the ability to exactly reproduce a set of conditions previously exhibited.

Replenishment at sea
Process or procedure of supplying fuel, stores, and personnel to a Navy ship at sea.

Reserve buoyancy
Spaces providing additional **buoyancy**.

Reserve factor
Ratio of the **stress** that would cause failure to the stress that is experienced in service. *See* **factor of safety**.

Reservoir
A **stratum** in which oil or gas is present.

Residual fuel
Residues from the various refinery processes. Sometimes heavy marine fuel is incorrectly referred to as residual fuel.

Residual magnetism
Magnetism retained by certain materials after the magnetising force has been removed.

Residual stress
The **stresses** present in a structure not due to externally applied loading.

Can be due to the method of working during manufacture, thermal effects, or as a result of welding operations.

Residuary resistance
Difference between the **total** and **frictional resistance** of a ship, largely made up of wave making resistance.

Residue
Waste or low value substance that remains following a process, such as the oil-water emulsion remaining after tank cleaning or residual product after refinery processing.

Resilience
Stored energy of a strained or elastic material, such as in a compressed spring or in rubber dampers.

Resilient mountings
Machine support fixing, embodying springs or elastomeric material permitting limited movement of the machine relative to its foundation to prevent the transmission of **vibration**.

Resin
A solid or semi-solid mixture of organic substances of complex composition, with no definite melting point. Added to **polymers** prior to curing and can be used for engine chocking or **resilient mountings.**

Resistance
Extent the flow of current in a body is restricted, represented by the quotient of a given direct voltage at the terminals of the body and the current passing through it. *See* **Ohm's Law.**

Resistance thermometer
Temperature measuring instrument using metals such as platinum or nickel in an electric circuit. An increase in temperature will cause an increase in resistance and a **Wheatstone bridge** will measure the **resistance** change and indicate the temperature. The measuring range is from -200°C to 600°C.

Resistor
An electrical component that introduces resistance into an electric circuit.

Resolution
(1) Quality of a visual image such as those produced on a computer screen. (2) Smallest change in output that can be detected by a measuring instrument.

Resonance
Condition associated with **vibration** or **oscillation** where the forcing impulses occur at the natural frequency of the component or structure. If sig-

nificant damping is not present the **amplitude** of the vibration or oscillation will increase continuously. Resonance can also occur in **acoustic** and electric systems.

Resonant frequency
In a particular circuit, the frequency where the inductive reactance equals the capacitive reactance.

Response time
In reference to a step function input signal, this is the time interval between the step in the input signal and the first coincidence of the output signal with the final steady value of the output signal.

Retraction
(1) Withdrawing or removing action. (2) Astern movement from a beach.

Reverse frame
Angle bar placed with its heel against another angle to give additional strength.

Reverse current protection
Type of protection for direct current only. A release permits a mechanical switching device to open with or without delay when current flows in the reverse direction exceeding a pre-determined value.

Reverse osmosis
Use of a high pressure pump to force liquid through a semi-**permeable** membrane, that will not pass salts or dissolved solids; a means of producing distilled water from sea water.

Reverse polarity
When a positive terminal is connected to the negative cable and a negative terminal connected to the positive cable, such as an incorrectly connected battery.

Reverse power protection
A relay monitoring the direction of power flow from a generator to the switchboard. In the event of reverse power flow it will trip and disconnect the main **circuit breaker.**

Reversing gear
Gear reversing the direction of motion in an engine, machine or mechanism.

Reynold's number (Re)
A constant governing the point at which laminar flow changes to turbulent flow shown by the equation:

$$\frac{VL}{Y}$$

Where V = speed relative to still water; L = length; Y = coefficient of kinematic viscosity of the fluid.

Rheology
Science dealing with the flow and deformation of matter.

Rheostat
Electrical resistor with means for readily varying the resistance in a circuit.

Rhombus
Oblique equilateral parallelogram, such as a diamond.

Rhumb
(1) A loxodromic curve, that makes a line on the surface of a sphere, making equal angles, other than 90 degrees, with all **meridians.** (2) Any point of the **compass** other than a **cardinal** point.

Rhumb-line
Curve on the surface of map or globe cutting all **meridians** at the same angle. Navigationally applied to the track of a ship sailing in a fixed direction.

Ride
Float easily and buoyantly, such as when anchored.

Rider
Turn of a cable on a **capstan** or winding drum which has jumped across another turn or turns, occasionally causing the cable to jam or hold.

Riding lights
Common term to denote the statutory anchor lights a ship must carry when riding at anchor.

Rig
Technical term for **derrick** and drilling equipment, commonly employed as the name for a complete unit.

Rigger
Person who attends to the wires and other rigging of a ship.

Rigging up
Operation where tools, machinery, fuel, water, and supplies get installed on a rig before drilling commences.

Righting lever
Length of lever arm between a vertical extended up from the **centre of gravity** to a vertical extended up from the **centre of buoyancy**. Referred to as GZ, it is the criterion used to determine stability at large angles of inclination. *See* Figure 12.

RINA
Royal Institution of Naval Architects. British association founded in 1860 to promote the Improvement of Ships and all that relates to them.

Ring bolt
Bolt carrying a loose ring to which a rope or tackle can be attached.

Ring main
(1) Electrical distribution system comprising a main circuit closed upon itself by bringing both ends back to a common busbar. (2) Arrangement of loading and discharge pipe lines in tankers embracing all cargo tanks.

Ring sticking
Freezing of a piston ring in its groove due to heavy deposits in the ring zone area leads to blowby, cylinder liner wear and increased lubricating oil consumption.

Rip
Turbulent water produced by conflicting currents.

Rise of floor
Height of the bottom shell plating above the base line. The rise of the floor is measured at the moulded beam line and this distance or height equates to a sloping of the hull intended to allow the drainage of liquids. *See also* **dead rise** and Figure 6.

Riser
A large diameter steel pipe running from the drilling floor of a floating rig to the wellhead through which the **drill string** and drilling tools pass and mud returning to a rig.

Riser tensioner
Support system for a drill rig riser pipe to maintain tension regardless of the heaving of the platform. A system of sheaves and pneumatic cylinders are used for each of the four or six tensioners installed.

Rising main
Pipe running vertically from a fire main to carry a water supply from pumps or to a hydrant.

Risk analysis
Method of hazard identification where all factors are considered.

Rivet
Straight shanked bolt without a screw thread used to fasten ships plating together. Secured by hammering over ends while rivet is hot.

RNLI
Royal National Life-boat Institute. British association founded in 1824 for the purpose of saving life at sea.

RO/LO
Roll On/Lift Off.

RO/RO
Roll On/Roll Off. In general such ships are designed for the carriage of motor cars, commercial motor vehicles and unitised cargo. Many ferries are designed in this mode.

Roaring Forties
Extraordinary gales in the South Pacific from 40–50 degrees latitudes.

Rock bit
Offshore drill bit for use in hard rock formations.

Rockershaft
Shaft carrying rockers to transmit the activating force from the **camshaft** to open valves in an **internal combustion engine.**

Rockwell hardness test
Indentation hardness test using a diamond cone or steel ball. A load is applied to the indenter to force it into the surface of the article to be tested. The depth to which the indenter travels into the surface is read on a clock gauge mounted on the machine and is a measure of the hardness of the material.

Roller bearings
Anti-friction bearings used for a variety of purposes aboard ship, such as in electric motors and turbo blowers. Rollers can be parallel, tapered or have long rollers of small diameter called **needle rollers;** able to carry heavier loads than standard roller bearings.

Rolling
Rotational motions about a longitudinal axis, for example the swaying motion from side to side in a seaway. *See* Figure 15.

Rolling hatch cover
Type of **hatch cover** typically found on the weather deck of **bulk** or **OBO** carriers. When opened to allow access to the hold, the cover can be stowed away sideways or longitudinally leaving a completely clear hatchway. *See* Figure 22.

Rolling keel
See **bilge keel**.

Roof fired boiler
Boiler in which burners project into the furnace from the roof.

Root angle
Angle between the axis and root cone generator of a **bevel gear.**

Root cone
Cone tangential to the bottom of the tooth spaces and co-axial with the gear. *See* Figure 1.

Root mean square (rms)
Applied to electrical quantities, such as amperes, volts and other recurring variable quantities; the square root of the mean value of the squares of the instantaneous values taken over one complete cycle.

Roots blower
A **compressor** for delivering large volumes of air at relatively low pressure ratios; consists of a pair of hour glass shaped members rotating within a casing with a small clearance so that no valves are required.

Rope guard
Shaped steel plate attached to the **stern tube** boss of a ship. They extend from the boss towards the **propeller** leaving a small enough gap between the two to prevent ropes from becoming wrapped round the shaft; usually made in two semi-circular halves and bolted or welded to the stern tube boss.

Rose box
Strainer at the end of a **bilge** suction pipe.

Rotameter
Instrument used to measure the flow rate of liquid or gas in a pipe.

Rotary burner
A **fuel oil burner** in which oil is fed to the inner portion of a revolving hollow cone, flying off the edge of the cone in small droplets. A blast of air round the cone further atomises the droplets.

Rotary convertor
Machine converting ac into dc by combining motor and generator action in a single armature winding connected to slip rings and a commutator. It is excited by a single magnetic field.

Rotary drilling
Offshore drilling in which the entire **drill string** and **bit** are rotated.

Rotary pumps
A type of pump, usually valveless, similar in principle to a gear pump in that two specially shaped members rotate in contact. They are true displacement pumps, yet differ from reciprocating pumps by having a higher rate of leakage.

Rotary table
Table on a rig **derrick** floor where the drill pipe is rotated. Also called **drilling table**. *See* Figure 8.

Rotary vane steering gear
Hydraulic **steering gear** in which a vaned rotor moves within a vaned stator. Chambers are formed between the vanes on the rotor and those on the stator. The rotor moves when oil is supplied to the appropriate chambers and removed from the others.

Rotating machine
Electric apparatus with components capable of relative rotary movement that depends on electro-magnetic induction for its operation; used for converting electrical energy into mechanical power, such as an electric motor.

Rotor
Revolving part of a rotary machine such as in a **turbine** or **alternator**.

Roughneck
An assistant to the driller on an oil rig; a worker whose duties are on the actual **derrick** floor.

Round of beam (ROB)
See **camber** and Figure 6.

Round trip
Process that occurs every time a drill bit has to be replaced. The entire drill **string** is removed from the hole in approximately 90 foot sections and then returned with a new **bit**.

Roustabout
General worker in an oil drilling or production operation.

ROV
Remotely Operated Vehicle.

Royal Fleet Auxiliary (RFA)
Service established in 1905 when the differences between commissioned ships flying the white ensign and fleet auxiliaries were defined. Primarily acts as a support for fighting ships supplying fuel, stores and ammunition at sea.

Royalty
Tax paid to the owner of mineral rights, often a share of the production or revenue. When offshore rights are involved payment generally goes to the government of that Country.

RPM
Revolutions Per Minute (revs/min); the rotational speed of machinery and shafts.

Rubbing strake
Longitudinal strake or stringer fixed outside a ship's skin plating positioned so as to make first contact with harbour walls or other vessels in event of impact or rubbing between them. Any resulting damage to the rubbing strake can be repaired without affecting a ship's main structure or plating.

Rudder
A means of directional control. The three main types adopted are: unbalanced; semi-balanced; balanced. *See* Figure 4.

Rudder bearing
The mass of the rudder can be carried by a lower pintle and partially by a rudder bearing within the steering gear compartment. In some designs the total mass is borne by the bearing. *See* Figure 30.

Rudder post
After part of **stern frame** containing bearings for the containment of rudder pintles. If a **balanced rudder** is fitted, the rudder post section of the stern frame is omitted so the unsupported sole piece is of more substantial construction. *See* Figure 30.

Rudder propeller
A conventional **propeller** steerable through 360 degrees, such as the **Schottel** type. These units can be mounted as a pair under the hull or at the stern.

Rudder stock
Vertical rudder shaft connected to the **steering gear**. *See* Figure 30.

Rudder stops

Projections provided with spring buffers to prevent the **rudder** from being angled more than about 38 degrees, typically located on the **tiller**.

Rudder trunk

The **rudder stock** passes through the rudder trunk, a space with a watertight gland at the top where the stock enters the intact hull.

Rules of practice

Rules used for the adjustment of the **particular average** and **general average**.

Run

Immersed body aft of the **parallel middle body**.

Run aground

Said of a ship that has touched bottom.

Runner

Rope in a single block with a round tackle block at one end and a hook at the other.

Running gear

Moving parts within an engine including crankshaft **crossheads, pistons** and other running parts.

Running in

Close attention to moving parts within a new or overhauled engine. Typically involves slow speed running for a period of time to allow the new parts to bed in and can initially require a better quality fuel.

Runout

Amount by which a rotating part is out of alignment.

Rupture

To fracture or break apart.

Rust (Fe_2O_3)

Normal corrosion product of iron or steel in an atmospheric or water environment. The red oxide of iron is referred to as white rust.

Rutile (TiO_2)

Titanium oxide ore containing about 60 per cent titanium. Refined rutile is used as a constituent for the coating of **arc welding** electrodes.

S

Sacrificial anode
Ring or slab of metal, often zinc, placed on a key part of an underwater structure to protect it from corrosion. The sea water attacks the **anode** rather than the structure.

Saddle tanks
Tanks, generally for water ballast, that saddle or are fitted over the upper sides of the main cargo tanks. They are triangular in longitudinal cross section, increasing in depth towards a ship's side, and are principally fitted on bulk carriers to provide a means of increasing a ship's **centre of gravity** when carrying light cargo.

SAE
Society of Automotive Engineers (USA). An organisation responsible for many internationally accepted standards in the automotive industry. Their procedures for the classification of crankcase and **transmission** oil by viscosity are used almost universally. For example, crankcase oils are classified in four grades (SAE 5W, 10W, 15W, 20W) according to viscosity at 0°F (17.8°C) and four grades (SAE 20, 30, 40, 50) at 210°F (98.9°C). Transmission oils have three grades (SAE 75W, 80W, 85W) at 0°F (17.8°C) and three grades (SAE 90, 140, 250) at 210°F (98.9°C). There is a viscous range common to both crankcase and transmission viscosities and an oil within this range can have 2 SAE numbers. **Multigrade** oils meet viscosity ranges covering viscosities at 0°F and 210°F, thus a multigrade crankcase oil could have the notation 15W/40. *See* Appendix 3.

SAFCON
Safety Construction Certificate.

Safe aground
Term in a **charter party** that allows the charterer to order a ship to port or a place where it can safely touch bottom.

Safe port
Port in which a ship and its cargo can remain safe without experiencing problems of a physical or political nature.

Safe working load (SWL)
Maximum working load that should not be exceeded. Ship **derricks** under Factory Act regulations are initially tested to a proof load in excess of the specified SWL.

Safety valve

A valve that opens automatically in the event of excess pressure in a container, such as a boiler steam drum. When fitted to high pressure systems, the valve is designed to open quickly then snap shut to avoid wire drawing and damage to the valve seat. A safety valve is normally fitted with easing gear and there are statutory and insurance company requirements that must be strictly observed. These demand that every **boiler** has two safety valves and that they are mounted directly on the shell or steam drum. *See* Figure 32.

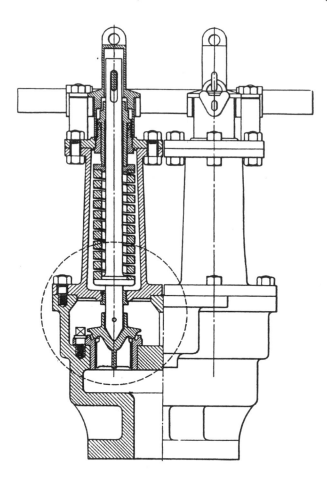

Figure 32 Boiler Safety Valve

Safety zone
Area around an offshore installation within a radius of 500 m.

Sagging
When a vessel drops at the middle of its length; opposite of **hogging.**

Saint Elmo's fire
Electrical discharges from the atmosphere that occur under certain climatic conditions and appear as blue lights or small flames on mastheads and yards.

Salient pole
Type of field pole protruding beyond the pheriphery of a circular yoke in the case of a stator field system, or the circular core in the case of a rotor field system.

Salinity
Degree of sodium chloride content in water.

Salinometer
Instrument indicating the proportion of salt in a given quantity of water. Usually measured in parts per 1000 as compared with fresh water. Sea water varies but is in the region of 1026.

SALM
Single Anchor Leg Mooring.

Salvage
Saving a ship or cargo from the danger of loss or destruction.

Salvage Association
Association founded in Great Britain in 1856 to protect the interests of the parties involved in maritime affairs. Its motto is Quaerite Vera, meaning seek the truth. With a worldwide network of representatives, often appointed to carry out surveys when loss or damage has occurred to ships or cargoes, the Association reports on the extent of the loss, the probable reasons for it and the likely cost of any repairs.

Salvor
Person or company performing a salvage operation.

Sampling
Process of obtaining a small quantity of material or liquid that is representative of the total volume.

Samson post
Rigid vertical post used instead of a **mast** to support **derricks.** *See* **king post.**

Sand blasting

Blast cleaning with dry sand. Wet sand blasting uses a sand and water mixture so it is not as severe as dry sand blasting. Great care must be taken to prevent sand entering and damaging machinery.

Sanitary pump

Sanitary system that supplies sea water for flushing toilets and urinals. A continuously operating pump is fitted to serve the system.

Saponification

When fat is converted into soap by the decomposing action of an **alkali**.

Sargasso sea

An area of the Atlantic Ocean between longitudes 20°–45°W and latitudes 20°–30°N. Notable for the weed floating on the surface known as Gulf Weed.

SARTOR

*S*tandards *A*nd *R*outes *TO* *R*egistration (UK Engineering Council). Assessment of the qualifications and experience required for registration to the UK National Register of Professional Engineers. Encompasses all three grades, CEng, IEng and Eng Tech.

Satellite link (SATCOM)

Communications system where a signal is passed between two points via an Earth satellite.

Saturated hydrocarbons

Hydrocarbons that are completely satisfied with respect to hydrogen. Paraffin and napthene hydrocarbons are saturated.

Saturated steam

The temperature at which water evaporates and becomes steam for any one pressure; varies according to pressure.

Saturation

(1) Condition of an electrical element where any further increase in the input signal produces negligible change in the output signal; can be applied to electronics, magnetic materials and electrical currents. **(2)** Steam at the same temperature as the water from which it was formed, as distinct from steam that was subsequently heated to become superheated steam.

Saturation diving

Technique whereby divers work and live under high pressure for long periods instead of undergoing decompression after every job.

Saturation Vapour Pressure (SVP)
Saturation Vapour Pressure. *See* **vapour pressure.**

Save all
A device that collects waste or spills under a machine or filter.

SBS
Single Buoy Storage.

SCAA
School Curriculum and Assessment Authority. Work to be merged with **NCVQ** to form the new body **QNCA.**

Scale
(1) Ratio between dimensions on a plan, chart or drawing, and actual dimensions. (2) Hard incrustation formed on wetted surfaces of boilers especially on heating surfaces such as furnaces and tubes. Mainly composed of sulphate of lime, carbonate of lime and chloride of magnesia. (3) Hard encrustation left on steel plates due to oxidation when hot-worked or exposed to high temperatures in the presence of air or steam.

Scantlings
Dimensions of structural items of a ship, such as frames, girders and plating.

Scarf
To bevel the edges of metal parts prior to **welding.**

Scavenging air
Fresh air introduced into the power cylinders of an **internal combustion engine** to displace exhaust gases and supply air for the next cycle.

Scavenge belt
Enclosed region around the air inlet ports of a **two stroke** slow speed diesel engine. Used to store pressurised air from turbo chargers prior to entry into the combustion space.

Scavenge fire
Fire in the scavenge space of an engine. Typically caused by an accumulation of cylinder and crankcase oil drainings, unburnt fuel and carbonaceous products ignited by hot gases blowing past the piston rings or by a hot spot within the moving parts of an engine.

SCC
Ship Control Centre. RN designation for the position from which all electrical and mechanical services are monitored.

Scending
Mixture of **rolling** and **pitching** that occurs when a ship is in a heavy seaway; gives rise to a cornerwise motion generally caused by a following sea.

Schottel rudder
Retractable **rudder propeller** powered by a diesel engine.

Sclerometer
Instrument for measuring **hardness** consisting of a diamond at one end of a lever attached to a vertical pillar. The diamond is loaded and the pillar rotated to make a scratch of standard depth. The weight in grams required to produce this depth gives a measure of the hardness.

Scleroscope hardness test
Instrument measuring **hardness** by dropping a diamond tipped hammer weighing about two grams from a given height. The distance of rebound is a measure of the hardness.

Scoop condenser
Type of **condenser** that receives cooling water from a scoop system.

Scoop
A spoonlike instrument for clearing out cavities.

Scoop cooling
A **scoop** that protrudes below the level of a ship's hull plating and faces forward. Forward motion forces water into the scoop and through the cooling water system. The arrangement reduces the power required for the main sea water circulating pump while a ship is moving ahead.

Scope
Length of cable a ship is free to **ride** when at **anchor.**

Scoring
Distress marks on sliding metallic surfaces in the form of long, distinct scratches in the direction of motion; advanced stage of **scuffing.**

Scotch boiler
Simple long established cylindrical **fire tube boiler.**

Scraper ring
Form of **piston ring** fitted to the crankcase end of the piston designed to remove excess lubricating oil from the cylinder walls and return it to the crankcase.

Scratching

Formation of fine scratches in the direction of sliding due to asperities on the harder surface or hard particles between or embedded in the surfaces. Scratching is less damaging than **scoring.**

Screen plate

Metal plate of heat resisting steel through which the **superheater** tubes of a **boiler** pass. It shield the headers from the direct heat of the furnace and also minimises the escape of gases into machinery spaces.

Screw aperture

Opening aft of the **stern frame propeller post** in which the propeller rotates. *See* Figure 30.

Screw displacement pump

Pump using the intermeshing of screw type rotors of screw inside a casing. Liquid or air is forced through the area between the casing and the space between the screws.

Screw down non-return valve

Valve where the disc is not attached to the spindle. The disc has **wings** or some other form of guide to ensure it will seat correctly when the valve is closed, and the disc will reseat automatically if a reverse flow of liquid occurs.

Screw effect

Sideways **thrust** resulting from **propeller** rotation that affects the steering of a ship. Most noticeable when near a quay or in a narrow channel.

Screw lift valve

Valve where the **lid** connects to the spindle and remains in the position set by the movement of the spindle.

Screw race

Turbulence in the water leaving the **propeller.**

Screw

See **propeller.**

Screw shaft

Aftermost shaft to which propeller is fastened. *See also* **stern shaft.**

Scrubber

Cleaning tower or column in an inert gas system. Sea water is sprayed into the gas path as it goes through the tower to remove soot and other contaminants before the **inert gas** is led from the tower to cargo tanks or the hold.

Scrubbing
Purification of gas or liquid by washing it in a tower.

Scuffing
Localised distress marks on sliding metallic surfaces appearing as a matt finished area rather than as an individual score mark.

Scum valve
Boiler valve is used to remove scum from the water surface. A shallow dish is positioned at the normal water level and connected to the valve.

Scuppers
Deck drains to remove sea water, rain water or condensation.

Scuttle
(1) Opening in ship's side that can be closed by a shutter. (2) Deliberate action to sink ship.

SD14
Replacement ships for the **Liberty** that appeared in the 1960s. The two most popular were the Japanese-built *Freedom* and the British SD14, designed and built by Austin & Pickersgill. Hugely successful, with over 200 built, the SD14 became a brand name in the world of shipping.

Sea anchor
Device for keeping the head of a small boat into the wind and sea. One type used consists of a cone shaped canvas tube open at both ends. A **hawser** or warp is fastened to ropes from the sea anchor enabling it to operate opened out as the sea enters the cone. A tripping line is fastened to the other end for hauling in. Also known as a drogue or drag anchor.

Sea cocks
Valves controlling the ingress of sea water from inlets in a ship's bottom or at any point below the waterline.

Sea inlet
Aperture in a ship's plating below the waterline that permits sea water to enter a pumping system for various purposes such as washing down decks and firefighting.

Sea trials
Testing a ship to ensure it will achieve the owners requirements for speed, power and other factors as specified in the contract. This includes its performance over a **measured mile** and only when all the owner's demands have been satisfied, or other arrangements made, will a ship be handed over.

Sea tube
Part of the inlet end of a ship's sea water circulating system attached to the hull.

Seaboard
Land bordering on the sea.

Seacat
Wave piercing **catamaran** for high speed sea service. *See* **HSSS**.

Seakeeping
Qualities that embrace the aspects of ship design affecting the ability to remain at sea in all conditions and carry out specified duties. These include strength, **stability** and endurance.

Sealant polymer
A **polymer** added to drilling mud to make a porous formation impermeable.

Seam
Lengthwise edge joint of any plating.

Seamless drawing
Method of producing seamless tubes from a solid billet pierced by rotary processes or a hollow press.

Seatings
Structural supports for main propelling machinery and auxiliary machinery, both in the engine room and on deck.

Seaworthy
Used to describe a ship with adequate strength, **freeboard** and **stability** to carry and deliver its cargo, crew and passengers to the port of destination in good condition.

Secchi disc
White, black or multicolored disc typically one metre in diameter used to measure water transparency.

Second (s)
Basic **SI unit** of time.

Secondary barrier
Structure capable of retaining the cargo of a liquefied gas tanker in the event of a main tank fracture.

Secondary recovery
Recovery of oil or gas from a **reservoir** by artificially maintaining or enhancing the reservoir pressure by injecting gas, water or other substances into the **reservoir rock.**

Secondary winding
The **winding** of a **transformer** that delivers energy to the load.

Second moment of area
Measure of the resistance of a loaded section to **bending.**

Section board
Grouping of electrical services fed from a main switchboard.

Section modulus
Ratio of the **second moment of area** to the distance measured from the neutral axis to the extreme edge of a section, such as the deck or bottom plating.

Sedimentary Rock
Rock laid down by the accumulation of sediments and organic matter from ancient seas and swamps. The organic matter is the source of **hydrocarbons.**

Sediments
Loose material lying on the bottom of a sea, lake, river or swamp.

Seel
To **heel** over suddenly.

Segregated ballast
Sea water used as **ballast** loaded into ballast only tanks, discharged through a separate piping and pumping system.

Segregation
Non-uniform distribution or concentration of impurities or alloying constituents arising during the solidification of an ingot or other casting.

Seismic
Relating to or caused by earthquakes or artificially produced tremors.

Seismic exploration
Oil and gas exploration technique involving the use of **seismic** methods. **Acoustic** shock waves are passed into the strata detecting and measuring the reflected signals.

Seismometer
Instrument used to record the reflected signals from a **seismic** survey.

Seizure
When relative motion ceases as the result of interfacial friction. Can be accompanied by gross surface welding. *See* **scuffing** and **scoring.**

Self polishing copolymer
Patent **anti-fouling paint.**

Self elevating rig
See **jack up rig.**

Self excited
Electrical machine supplying its own excitation.

Self inductance
Property of a circuit whereby self **inductance** occurs. Measured by the emf (in volts) induced in the coil or circuit when the current changes at a rate of one A/sec. The practical unit is the henry (H).

Self sustaining
Said of a nuclear reactor when it is producing enough power to run all associated auxiliaries to remove the load on a ship's auxiliary power equipment.

Self trimming
Vessel with large hatches and clear holds to permit coal, grain and similar cargoes to be trimmed into any part of the hold.

Semi balanced rudder
Design where part of the **rudder** is positioned forward of the turning axis as shown in Figure 4.

Semi conductor
Electronic conductor, usually solid, whose **resistivity** lies between that of metals and insulators. The concentration of electrical charge carriers increases with temperature over a certain range. Semi conductors, in contrast to metals, have a negative temperature coefficient of resistance over ordinary temperature rises. Commonly used semi conductors include germanium, silicon and selenium.

Semi diesel engine
Medium compression ignition engine where fuel is ignited by a **hot bulb** or plate located in the combustion chamber. The igniting surface is not water jacketed and is kept hot by the combustion process.

Semi membrane tank
Tank used to carry liquefied gas requiring insulation between the tank and the hull to be load bearing. It is almost rectangular in cross-section and unsupported at the corners.

Semi submersible rig
Floating **drilling platform** supported by underwater pontoons; generally used for exploration purposes.

Send
(1) Impulse given by a wave. **(2)** Plunge or pitch of a vessel caused by the impulse of a wave.

Senhouse slip
Quick-release mechanism. An example would be on lifeboat **gripes**. Slipping a ring will release a metal clip and the link of the chain it is holding.

Sensible heat
Amount of heat required to raise or lower the temperature of a substance without changing its state.

Sensors
(1) Method of securing stability control on **hydrofoil** vessels. Can be by **ultrasonic,** electro-magnetic or by using feeler arms; patent method is the Hydrofin. **(2)** Units for indicating pressures, temperatures and velocities.

Separator
Static or centrifugal. A centrifugal separator can be set up as a purifier or clarifier and can be manual or fully automatic; it is used for the treatment of fuel and lubricating oils.

Separator, oily water
Machinery used to remove oil from water to be pumped overboard; consists of a tank that can have filters and baffles, in which separation of the different liquids takes place utilising the effects of gravity. The oil is led to a dirty oil or **sludge** tank and the clean water is pumped overboard.

Series connection
A number of electrical components, such as batteries, **resistances** and **capacitors** are said to be connected in series when each positive terminal joins the corresponding negative of the next component so that current passes through them in succession, each component taking the full current. Can also apply to fuel oil and cooling systems.

Series wound
Denotes that a rotating electrical machine has excitation supplied from **windings**, connected in the primary series circuit, carrying either the whole or part of the load current.

Serve
To bind with a small cord to prevent fraying.

Service tanks

Oil fuel tanks situated within the oil fuel system containing fuel oil that has been treated and heated, ready for passing to the final viscosity temperature control prior to engine injection.

Servo motor

Final controlling element in a servo mechanism. The motor receives output from the amplifier elements and drives the load to produce a motion that can be rotary or rectilinear, as in the case of a hydraulic piston and cylinder. Hydraulic, electric or pneumatic power can operate the servo motor.

Set and drift

Direction and distance a ship is carried by a current within a set time.

Set

Direction a current flows in.

Setscrew

Screw threaded to the full length of the shank for locking a collar, sleeve or coupling to a shaft.

Setting

(1) Putting a ship on a specific course. (2) Determining the **compass** bearing of an object.

Settling tanks

Oil fuel must be provided to the **centrifuges** and the **service tanks** in reasonable condition, as free of water and sludge as possible. To facilitate this the fuel is first pumped into heated settling tanks with sloping bottoms that allow water and sludge to gravitate to the bottom where it can be drained regularly. The suction to the centrifuges should be clear of the tank bottom and in view of the time taken for settling to occur, consideration should be given to providing two settling tanks, one settling, while the other is in use.

Sewage treatment

The reduction of raw effluent into an inert sludge and water suitable for discharge overboard. The treatment can be chemical or natural. It is illegal to discharge untreated water overboard, therefore, inert sludge is retained on board for disposal ashore.

Sextant

Double reflecting instrument with an arc of sixty degrees used to measure **altitudes** and other angles up to 120 degrees to determine a ship's position.

Shackles
U-shaped steel forgings with a pin through an eye on each end of the U to serve as connecting links for rigging components. Used to anchor one end of a leaf spring to take up any length variation on deflection.

Shaft
Rod or bar for transmitting rotary motion, particularly in a **propeller shaft** or engine **crankshaft.**

Shaft alignment
Main propulsion shafting is checked for alignment during installation by the use of a taut wire, theodolite or laser measuring techniques. When in service the shafting can be checked for **static** and **dynamic alignment.** Static can be done by clock or strain gauges and dynamic alignment by measuring the **amplitude** of axial vibrations at various speeds when a ship is underway.

Shaft horse power (shp)
See **horse power.**

Shaft generator
A **generator** driven from the main engine or **intermediate shafting** by belt, gearing or other means when there is no individual prime mover.

Shaft tunnel
A watertight tunnel between the after end of machinery and the after peak bulkhead to protect the propeller shafting.

Shale oil
Oil distilled from oil-bearing shale-type geological formations of clay rock that can be split readily into thin laminae.

Shale shaker
Vibrating or rotating screen that removes the coarse drill cuttings from the drilling mud prior to its recirculation.

Shank
(1) Straight part of a bolt or rivet inserted into the parts to be connected. **(2)** Part of the drill held by a drilling machine. **(3)** Part of an anchor between the ring and arms. *See* Figure 3.

Shear
Stress or **strain** on the transverse planes of a loaded member that tends to cause parallel displacement in those planes.

Shear force
A force that tends to cause the sliding of adjacent layers, relative to each other, in a material.

Shear force diagram
A graphical representation of the shear force acting on every part of a body; values are given in **Newtons (N)**.

Shear modulus
With reference to the cross-section of a beam and either principal axis, the **moment of inertia** with respect to that axis divided by the distance from that axis of the most remote point on the cross-section.

Shear pin
Safety device in a power transmission system, strong enough to transmit the design loads but weak enough to fail under the **shear stress** induced by more severe loads.

Shear stability
Ability of a lubricant to withstand shearing without degradation. Particularly relevant in high viscosity index multigrade oils and hydraulic oils when high **shear stress** can reduce the performance of the **viscosity index** additive, resulting in a reduced viscosity index.

Shear stress
Stress that occurs across the section of a beam loaded transversely and also across the shaft sections subject to torque. The magnitude of the stress varies across the section depending on its geometric shape.

Sheave
Grooved pulley for use with vee-belts, ropes or round belts.

Sheave block
Blocks are classified according to the number of **sheaves** and are divided into two main groups, those for wire rope and those for manila rope.

Shedder plate
Sloping plate fitted within the trough of a corrugated bulkhead to allow a steady downward flow of bulk cargo during discharge as well as easier hold cleaning

Sheer
Longitudinal curvature of the deck between the ends of a ship. *See* Figure 2. It is the height of deck at the side above a line drawn parallel to the base, tangent to the deck line at amidships. Standard sheer is given by:

Sheer at After Perpendicular (cm) = 0.833 L (m) + 25.4

Sheer at Forward Perpendicular (cm) = 1.666 L (m) + 50.8

Sheer forward is twice sheer aft.

Sheer legs
Arrangement of three long poles or spars in the form of a tripod, for lifting heavy weights.

Sheer profile
Sections of a ship's profile obtained by the intersection of a series of vertical planes parallel to the centreline of a ship with the outside surface.

Sheer strake
Strake of shell plating at deck level.

Shell
Outside plating of a ship.

Shell bearing
Thin walled steel shell lined with anti-friction metal. Typically semi circular and used in pairs for main and big-end **bearings**.

Shell expansion
Plan showing disposition and thickness of all plates comprising the **shell plating**.

Shell plating
Plates forming the watertight skin of a ship.

Shelter deck
A **superstructure** deck, continuous from stem to stern.

Shelter decker
An added deck above the main deck of a ship. Originally enabled a ship to benefit from a lower registered tonnage as the shelter deck space would not be included providing there was a small opening known as the tonnage opening in this upper deck. Ships have now been assigned alternative tonnages with a tonnage mark painted on their sides. If this mark is submerged, a ship's higher tonnage is used for the purpose of determining port charges, if not submerged, the lower tonnage applies.

Sherardising
Patented process for coating small articles with zinc by placing the degreased articles in a drum containing zinc dust. The drum is then rotated in a furnace at a temperature of around 370°C to produce a matt grey coating on the surfaces.

Shifting boards
Portable bulkhead members fitted fore and aft in cargo holds when carrying cargo, such as grain, that might otherwise shift when a vessel is **rolling**.

Shim
Thin strips, typically brass, copper or steel, used to take up or to adjust clearances, endwise on shafts or diametrically on split journal bearings.

Ship's articles
Written agreement between the **master** of a ship and the crew concerning their employment; includes rates of pay, capacity of each member, leave entitlement, date of commencement, and the duration of a voyage.

Ship's head
Instantaneous forward direction along the longitudinal axis of a vessel.

Ship's official number
See **official number.**

Shipwrights
Worshipful Company of. A Guild in existence prior to 1199 that became a City of London Livery Company in 1782. Originally formed to regulate standards of workmanship and training in the shipbuilding industry, today's membership takes in men and women involved in all aspects of maritime activity.

Shock
Sudden application of load to a member or a sudden change of pressure.

Shock mounting
A mounting with **resilience** to reduce the harmful effects of shock.

Shock valve
A **relief valve** set to lift on the application of a sudden load. When fitted to hydraulic **steering gears** the valve will lift if the rudder is hit by heavy seas which allows the rudder to move to prevent damage. The **hunting gear** will return the rudder to its original position.

Shoe
(1) Friction member of a brake. (2) Base piece on which a **derrick** or **sheer leg** rests.

Shoot the Sun
Take the altitude of the Sun with a **sextant.**

Shortage
Goods shown on a ship's **manifest** that are missing when a ship discharges its cargo.

Short circuit
Faulty condition in an electrical system that causes the **impedance** of a circuit subjected to overcurrent to be considerably less than the rated value.

Short time current
Current an electrical device can carry for a stated short interval of time under prescribed conditions.

Short ton
Ton of 2000 lbs Imperial.

Shot
Small explosion used to produce shock waves during a **seismic** survey.

Shot blasting
Blast cleaning with steel or cast iron shot. Care must be taken to prevent abrasive dust entering and damaging adjacent machinery.

Shoulder
Curved part of a ship's side at the break of the **forecastle** head.

Show
Indication of oil or gas from an exploratory well.

Shrinkage
Temporary falling of water level in a boiler as the incoming cold feed water causes the collapse of steam bubbles. It is a phenomenon observed in **water tube boilers** as the control system corrects for an increase in load.

Shrouded propeller
See **nozzle propeller.**

Shrouding
Strip of metal to which each turbine blade is attached, typically by riveting a tenon at the tip of the blade to the strip.

Shrouds
Wire rope extending from the mast shroud to the side of a vessel to afford lateral support for the mast. Shrouds are often dispensed with and preventers adopted when heavy **derricks** are used. The mast has adequate **scantlings** to remain unstayed.

Shunt wound
Denotes a rotating dc machine with excitation supplied from **windings** connected across all or part of the primary series circuit.

Shuttle tanker
An **oil tanker** making regular round trips between a producing field and an onshore terminal or refinery.

Shuttle valve
The **valve** used to control the supply of steam to the cylinder of a double acting single cylinder reciprocating pump. Moves from one end of the valve chest to the other, generally in a horizontal direction. This motion is controlled by the action of an auxiliary valve.

SI units
Systeme International d'Unite's, the international system of units. A revision and expansion of the metric system with seven major base units which are:

Metre (m)   Length
Kilogram (kg) Mass
Second (s)   Time
Ampere (A)   Electric current
Kelvin (K)   Thermodynamic temperature
Candela (cd)   Luminous intensity
Mole (mol)   Amount of substance

There are two supplemental units which are:

Radian (rad)   Plane angle
Steradian (sr)   Solid angle

Side keels
See **keelson**.

Side loading
Loading cargo through a door in the side of a ship.

Side rods
Type of tension rod used in **opposed piston engines** to carry load from the upper pistons to the side crossheads through connecting rods to the crankshaft.

Side scuttles
Portholes or side lights in the sides of a ship or casing, to give light and air.

Side stringer
Fore and aft girder running along the inside of **shell** plating.

Side track drilling
Remedial operation that results in the creation of a new section of well bore to detour around junk, redrill a lost hole, or straighten key seats and holes.

Sidereal period
Interval between two successive positions of a celestial body in the same point with reference to the fixed stars; applied to the moon and planets to indicate their complete revolution relative to the line joining the earth and sun.

Sidewell cores
Cylindrical sections of rock or sediment obtained by shooting hollow cylinders of steel into the wall of a well bore. They are then recovered, together with their contents, for examination.

Siemens (S)
The **SI unit** of electrical **conductance,** a reciprocal of **resistance.**

Sight glass
A clear hollow pipe connected vertically to the side of a tank for visually measuring liquids. Also called **gauge glass.**

Signal
The transmission of information between one element of a control system and another.

Silent running
Quiet operation of machinery in a **submarine** to avoid detection by an enemy listening for noise.

Silica gel
An **amorphous** form of hydrated silica. Used in the form of hard granules it is chemically and physically virtually inert yet highly **hygroscopic,** therefore, very effective as an absorbent of fluids or vapours. Typically used for drying air, dehydrating gases or for filtration. After use, it can be regenerated by heating to drive off the absorbed matter; used with an inhibitor to dehumidify cargo holds.

Silicon (Si)
Brittle metalloid element (sp gr 2.4). **(1)** Used as an alloying element in cast iron, steel and some non-ferrous metals. **(2)** One of the main **catalysts** used in catalytic refining. Particles often find their way into **residual** type fuels and can abrade **fuel pumps,** and injectors.

Silicones
Compounds that can be likened in many respects to **hydrocarbons** except that the molecular chain is made up of silicon atoms bound to carbon atoms. Because of their unique temperature stability characteristics, silicones have found numerous applications, such as in components of hydraulic oils and speciality greases.

Sill
(1) Height of an opening above a deck. **(2)** Upper edge of the bottom of a dock entrance.

Simple harmonic motion (SHM)
Motion represented by projecting the uniform motion of a point round a circle onto a diameter.

Simpson's Rules
Arithmetical rules for the mensuration of areas, in which one boundary is parabolic, by the use of uniformly based ordinates.

Simulate
Imitate conditions of a process or situation for information or training.

Sine wave
Wave where the particles move in transverse vibrations of **simple harmonic motion.**

Singing propeller
Resonant vibration of **propeller blades** due to **wake** formation. Can cause a high pitched whine that can be heard in a ship. Silent **propellers** are essential in warships to avoid detection.

Single acting engine
An **internal combustion engine** where combustion takes place only on one side of each power piston; can be **two or four stroke.**

Single bottom structure
Construction method used in tankers and some small vessels where the bottom shell plating is stiffened by plate floors and longitudinal stiffeners.

Single buoy mooring (SBM)
(1) Mooring points at the end of a pipeline some distance from the shore in deep water. Primarily to discharge large tankers when draught or environmental conditions are a problem. **(2)** Floating chamber anchored near a production platform that serves as a flexible connection to a tanker taking on oil from a platform; such a system has no storage capacity itself. Also known as **single point mooring (SPM).**

Single decker
Vessel with no deck below the weather deck.

Single phase circuit
Circuit energised by a single alternating **electro motive force.**

Single phasing
Fault condition in an **induction motor** when one phase in a three phase circuit becomes open circuited. Excessive currents will occur in all **windings.**

Single point mooring (SPM)
See **single buoy mooring.**

Sintering
The **coalescing** of small particles or metal powders to form larger cakes or masses, without liquefying, by applying heat or heat and pressure together while under controlled conditions. Grains become bonded or fused together to form a homogeneous mass.

Sinusoidal
Trace of an alternating quantity plotted to a time base in as a **sine wave.**

Siphon
Pipe shaped in an inverted U, with unequal legs for conveying liquid over the edge of a container and delivering it at a lower level, utilising **atmospheric pressure.** Requires priming before flow can commence.

Sirocco
Warm Mediterranean wind blowing from south to south east.

SIRE
*S*hip *I*nspection *R*eport *P*rogramme.

Sisal
(1) Hygroscopic material that can absorb moisture and become very heavy; such materials can also swell and cause structural damage. **(2)** Describes sisal-hemp or agave fibre, used for ropes, matting, and fenders. Somewhat cheaper and less satisfactory than true hemp as it is less flexible and swells more when wet.

Sister beam
Steel section that stretches along the length of a hatchway on to which the centre portions of the hatch boards are placed to close the hatchway. This arrangement is mainly on older ships and has largely been replaced by the use of steel hatch covers.

Skeg
Finlike projection underneath a vessel to support the lower edge of the rudder.

Skew
Offset of **propeller blade** from the vertical in the plane of rotation. Always a distance in a direction opposite to rotation.

Skew gear
A **bevel gear** arrangement where the driven and driving shafts are at right angles yet different planes or skew. Also termed hypoid or skew bevel gear.

Skew lines
Two straight lines neither parallel nor intersecting, with one common perpendicular.

Skidding the rig
Moving a rig from the location of a lost or completed hole, preparatory to starting a new hole, with little or no dismantling of equipment.

Skids
Beams forming tracks on which lifeboats rest and are chocked into position.

Skimmer
Anti pollution device sucking oil from the surface of the sea.

Skin
Plating of a ship; the inside skin is often referred to as **ceiling** and the outside skin as the case.

Skin friction
Resistance or drag as a film of water is dwarf along by the surface of the hull and forms eddies in the adjacent water.

Skylight
Erection built on deck for the purpose of admitting light and/or air to the compartment below.

Slack water
Condition of the tide 20 minutes each side of high and low water when the rate of the flow slackens.

Slag
(1) Metal **arc welding** started as bare wire welding until it was found that by dipping the wire into lime or slag a more stable arc was obtained. Many forms of slag are now available for coating the wire or for deposition on the joint prior to welding. **(2)** Molten non-metallic layer floating on the surface of molten pig iron or on molten steel in a furnace.

Slamming
When the **bow** of a ship leaves the water and plunges back in again due to severe **pitching**. A large instantaneous force is generated near the bow that can damage the hull unless a ship's speed is reduced quickly.

Slave cylinder
In a hydraulic system, any cylinder containing a piston whose movement is controlled by the movement of a piston in a master cylinder.

Sleeve

Tubular piece, generally machined externally and internally, used to reduce another tube or cylinder and into which a shaft, piston or other tube can be inserted.

Slenderness ratio

Ratio of the length of a column to the **radius of gyration** of its section. An important factor when considering the resistance of structural members of a ship to **buckling**.

Slew

Swing about an axis in a horizontal plane.

Slewing

Rotary motion of the load about a vertical axis. Applied to **cranes** and **jibs.**

Slice

Long steel rod used to break up slag and stir up coal in a boiler furnace.

Slide valve

Valve that slides rather than rotates or lifts. Generally refers to the control valves of steam and gas engines.

Sliding foot

Supporting foot of a machine part that permits linear movement, generally to accommodate thermal expansion such as in a steam turbine.

Slime

Living fungus relying on the cool, dark and moist surroundings that exist wherever a supply of decaying organic matter is to be found. The main group is called myxomycetes.

Slimness

Indication of the form of a ship using the ratio of length divided by the cube root of the **volume** of **displacement.**

Sling

Apparatus used to support a hanging mass.

Slip

Difference between the theoretical movement of a **propeller** through water and the actual movement; can be positive or negative.

Slip coupling

Electromagnetic coupling with a permanent air gap between its two members. One member is associated with the driving shaft and the other with the driven. Power is transmitted across the air gap through electromagnetic interaction and used to couple diesel engines to gears for driving **propellers** as it damps out **torsional vibrations** arising from the engine crankshaft.

Slip-ring
Conducting ring on a shaft used to make an electrical connection between a moving and fixed conductor through one or more brushes.

Slips
Steel wedges forced into the tapered opening of a drilling table to hold the free end of the **drill pipe** in place.

Slipstream
Stream of water that leaves the **propeller** of a ship underway.

Slipway
Inclined support from which a ship is launched, usually lined with grease.

Slop tank
Tank (usually a pair) fitted on oil tankers at the after end of the cargo tank section. Provides a collecting place for oil and water mixtures that result from tank cleaning operations.

Slot
(1) Compartment in the hold of a **container ship** into which a container fits exactly. (2) Expression used by shippers to indicate the number of container spaces available for a particular voyage.

Slow speed diesel
Two stroke crosshead engine with a speed range of approximately 60–100 rpm. The direct coupled reversible engine is a favoured form of marine propulsion and the exhaust gases from two-stroke crosshead diesels are used in **waste heat boilers** and to drive **turbo blowers** and gas generators.

Slow steaming
Operating a ship below normal operating speed. Usually for economic reasons such as when awaiting a **charter** or when fuel is excessively expensive.

Sludge
Mud like mixture of oil, carbon, water and insolubles that can settle in **bunker tanks, settling tanks**, lubricating oil systems and elsewhere within the engine systems; can be separated by the use of **centrifuges** and clarifiers or manual cleaning.

Sluice valve
Shut-off valve with a closure controllable from above the load line. Fitted at the bottom of **watertight bulkheads** to control flow of the water from one compartment to another. Not permitted in a **collision bulkhead**.

Slurry
Watery mud or any material resembling it.

Smelting
Process where metals are separated from ore when they are present in a chemical combination. Involves fusion with suitable fluxes resulting in molten metal sinking to the bottom while slag floats at the top.

Smoke
Suspension of liquid and solid particles resulting from combustion, in a gaseous medium. In organic fuels, like those obtained from petroleum, smoke can form as a result of incomplete **combustion**.

Smoke detectors
Fire detection system enabling the presence of fire in inaccessible places on a **vessel** to be identified.

SNAME
Society of Naval Architects and Marine Engineers, USA. Founded in 1893.

Snatch block
Single **block** to alter the direction of pull on a rope. Has a hinged side to permit the fall to be put over the **sheave** without reeving the end through.

Snibs
Handles that can be operated from both sides of a watertight door.

Snifting valve
Valve to release gas from a liquid system.

Schnorkel
Device used by a **submarine** enabling to draw air from the surface while submerged.

Snotter
Type of sling made from rope or wire where an eye is formed at an end of a straight length to attach a hook for lifting.

Snub
(1) To turn a ship around by dropping an **anchor** under foot and utilising engine power. (2) Check **way** on a vessel with an anchor. (3) Check a rope or cable that is running.

Snubbing
Running pipe or casing into the well while the well is exerting pressure on surface equipment.

Soap
The salt of a fatty acid. Metal soaps are made by reacting a fatty material of animal or vegetable origin with a metal hydroxide such as barium or calcium hydroxide. Mixed with mineral oil and additives to manufacture greases.

Socket head screw
Screw with hexagonal socket for inserting an **allen** type key.

Softness
Opposite of **hardness,** contrasted with **brittleness.** A soft substance is easily deformed permanently without **fracture.** It is not necessarily identified with weakness and soft materials can possess considerable strength.

Soft nosed stem
Radiused plate above the waterline forming the upper part of the **stem.** In the event of a collision the plate will buckle under load, reducing impact damage.

Solar gear
System of **epicyclic** gears with a fixed sun wheel. The annulus and planet carrier rotate while the planet wheels rotate about their own axis.

SOLAS
Safety Of Life At Sea. A conference of **IMO,** responsible for factors relating to the safe operation of ships, in particular when human life is at stake.

Sole
Lower part of a launching cradle.

Sole plate
Bedplate of a marine engine.

Solenoid
Consists of a number of turns of wire wound in the same direction so that when the coil is carrying an electric current, all the turns are assisting one another in producing a **magnetic field.**

Solid
Substance that will continuously resist **deformation** provided that the **shearing stress** is below its **yield** value. The relative movement of the **molecules** is restricted and they tend to retain a definite fixed position relative to each other that gives rise to a crystal structure.

Solid injection
Process of injecting liquid fuel into the combustion chamber of a diesel engine without the assistance of air or gas.

Solid lubricant
Any solid used as a powder or thin film on a surface to provide protection from damage during relative movement, reducing friction and wear. Many solid lubricants have a layered **(lamella)** structure, such as graphite or molybdenum disulphide.

Solid solution
Two or more substances dissolved in one another in the liquid state that remain so upon solidification.

Solid state
Solid state device is one in which the electron flow takes place within solids such as a **transistor,** logic element or **integrated circuit.**

Solidus
Line on an **equilibrium** diagram indicating the temperature at which a metal or alloy becomes completely solid on cooling, or at which melting begins under equilibrium conditions. This line indicates the compositions of the phases that can co-exist in **equilibrium.**

Soluble
Capable of being dissolved, typically in water, unless another solvent is specified.

Solution gas drive
Primary recovery process in which the oil is driven out of a **reservoir** by the natural pressure exerted by dissolved gas.

Solvent refined
Refining technique in the manufacture of lubricant base oils using the selective extraction of undesirable components by means of a solvent.

Sonar
*So*und *na*vigation *a*nd *r*anging. Underwater acoustic detection system that transmits a pulse and receives a reflection from underwater objects. Also used to measure offshore pipeline wall thicknesses. *See* **asdic.**

Sonic
Pertaining to sound waves.

Soot blowers
Devices to blow off deposits in boiler furnaces using steam or compressed air. For high temperature zones they must be retractable.

Sound
Measure the depth of liquid in a tank or compartment.

Sounding pipe
Pipe leading to near the bottom of an oil or water tank used to guide a sounding tape or jointed rod to measure the depth of liquid.

Sour crude
Crude oil with a high sulphur content.

Source rock
Rock in which oil or natural gas originates.

Spalling
See **gear tooth damage.**

Span block
See **blocks.**

Spanish windlass
Means of exerting a powerful heaving action by bringing two parallel ropes together.

Spar
Floating on-field storage tank into which oil flows from a production platform prior to being transferred to a tanker for removal ashore.

Spark ignition engine
Relatively low compression engine where fuel is ignited by an electric spark. Fuel can be injected directly into the combustion chamber or carburetted and vaporised before entering the engine.

Special area
Area of the sea where extra care is required for recognised technical reasons in relation to oceanographical and ecological conditions and the nature of the shipping traffic therein, so that oil pollution can be minimised. Examples of such areas are the Mediterranean Sea, Baltic Sea, Black Sea, Red Sea and Gulf areas, as defined in Regulation 10 (1) of Annex 1 of the International Convention for the Prevention of Pollution from Ships.

Special survey
Classification Society surveys held at regular intervals for the renewal of classification. Requirements can differ depending on age and condition of a ship.

Specifications
Prescribed limits of control tests used to maintain the uniformity of a specific product, equipment or machine.

Specific energy
The energy content of a fuel expressed in megajoules per kilogram (MJ/kg). A typical value for a heavy marine grade is 43 MJ/kg and little variation in values occurs between heavy and intermediate grades. It is not controlled during manufacture.

Specific fuel oil consumption (SFOC)
Specific Fuel Oil Consumption. Varies with power output of the machinery. Usually measured in grams per bhp hour or grams per kW hour.

Specific gravity
Ratio of the mass of a given volume of product and an equivalent volume of distilled water. The standard reference temperature is 60°F. *See also* **density.**

Specific heat
Ratio of the quantity of heat required to raise the temperature of a substance one degree **Celsius** (or **fahrenheit**) and the heat required to raise an equal mass of water one degree. The **SI unit** for specific heat, and for specific **entropy** is the joule per kilogram **kelvin** (J/kgK).

Spectacle frame
Large casting that projects outboard from a ship to support the ends of the propeller shafts of a twin-screw ship. The **casting** is plated into the surrounding shell for streamlining. *See also* **A-frame.**

Spectrographic analysis
Electronic instrument for detecting metal elements in lubricating oil. An element's quality and quantity are detected.

Spectrum
Series of radiations produced by a prism. Components of a beam of radiant energy are segregated and focused in order of wave length.

Speed
Time rate of motion measured by the distance moved in unit time.

Speed/length ratio
Ratio to determine whether a ship is fast or slow when considering resistance.

Spelter
Brazing alloy consisting normally of 50 per cent copper and 50 per cent zinc.

Spheroidal graphite cast iron
Cast iron where graphite has been transformed from the long thin flakes typical of grey iron into discrete spheroids. This improves the mechanical properties, especially **ductility,** also known as nodular cast iron.

Spider
Rotating structure of an electrical machine on which armature core or field coils are mounted.

Spike
Short duration peak of current considerably exceeding normal levels.

Spiked cargo
When a certain amount of **liquefied natural gas** has been injected during loading. Should not be loaded into a normal tanker as boiling the gas will raise pressure in the cargo tank.

Spiling
Curve of a plate or **strake** as it narrows to a point.

Spillage
Accidental release of oil or other liquid.

Spindle
Pin on which something rotates; used to operate a device such as a valve spindle which opens or closes a valve when turned.

Spindrift
Spray blown from the crests of waves.

Spinning line
Wire rope or chain that is wrapped round a section of an offshore drill pipe and used to screw the section into another section.

Spiral
Curve whose radius vector increases or decreases progressively with the polar angle. The curve does not need to be in one plane.

Spiral gears
Teeth cut on a **helical** plan, designed to connect skew shafts. The theory is that they have point, instead of line, contact that causes a longitudinal sliding motion between the teeth.

Splash proof
Electrical equipment constructed so that liquid splashed from any direction has no harmful effect.

SPLASH
Self-Propelled vessels employed in feeder services for *LASH* vessels.

Splice
Joint in rope made by interweaving strands.

Spline shaft
Shaft having a number of longitudinal grooves giving in effect a series of narrow keys intregral with the shaft resembling long gear teeth (external splines). The shaft this engages with has its bore similarly grooved (internal splines) giving maximum strength and allowing relative axial movement to take place while maintaining the drive.

Split bearings
Bearings made in two or more pieces to permit dismantling without axial withdrawal.

Split windlass
Use of separate **windlass** for each anchor.

Sponson
Projections from each side of the hull to give maximum stability. One of the measures used to protect **roll-on roll-off (RO/RO)** ferries from **heeling.**

Spontaneous combustion
Fire caused by heat generated by chemical action within a substance, such as by slow **oxidation.** Common in coal bunkers on old coal burning steamers.

Spontaneous ignition
In air or oxygen, the lowest temperature at which heated oil will ignite automatically without the application of a test flame.

Spool valve
Valve arrangement where a number of spools or bobbins on a spindle slide in a cylinder to uncover various ports. Often used in hydraulic systems.

Spot
Ship available to load almost immediately.

Spreader
(1) Iron bar or wooden spar fastened to a mast to increase the angle at the head of the standing rigging and thus improve the staying. **(2)** Iron bar or framework used to separate the legs of wire slings when lifting a large load.

Springing
Continuous vibrating response, sometimes sustained over long periods. It is a Z-node vertical **vibration** which can occur with short wave lengths, augmenting the wave induced stresses considerably.

Springs
Lines keeping a ship from drifting fore and aft when moored.

Spring tide
High tides that occur when the moon is full producing a maximum tide.

Sprocket
Toothed wheel transmitting power by a link chain.

Spud
To move the drill stem up and down in the hole over a short distance without rotation. Careless execution of this operation creates pressure surges that can cause a formation to break down, resulting in lost circulation.

Spudding in
Process of starting to drill a well by making a hole in the sea bed using a large diameter bit.

Spume
Foam or scum on the surface of the sea.

Spur gear
Applies to **gears** where teeth are straight and parallel to the axis, similar in profile throughout their length. The gears are cylindrical in form and used to connect parallel shafts. Spur teeth can be cut externally on a cylindrical blank, as for an ordinary pinion internally, as for an annulus, or on a straight rack to form a rack-and-pinion mechanism. *See* Figure 1.

Spur line
Small diameter underwater pipeline connecting a production or drilling platform to a terminal platform, on-field storage facility, or main pipeline to the shore.

Spur wheel
Toothed wheel used for transmitting power between parallel rotating shafts. *See* Figure 1.

Spurling pipes
Port and starboard anchor cables are fed into the appropriate **chain locker** compartment through chain pipes or spurling pipes. These pipes are of tubular construction with castings as end mouldings to prevent chafing. *See also* **hawse pipe**.

Square propeller
Screw **propeller** where the **pitch** measurement equals the diameter.

Squat
Change of **trim** and overall lowering of a ship in the water at high speed. An important factor when there is insufficient difference between the draught of a ship and depth of water.

Squeeze

Operation where cement is injected under pressure between the casing and the well bore of an offshore rig at a particular depth.

Squirrel cage motor

Type of **induction motor** in which the rotor consists of bars permanently short-circuited through stout end rings. *See also* **motor.**

SSDC

*S*ingle *S*teel *D*rilling *C*aisson.

SSTH

*S*uper *S*lender *T*win *H*ull. *See also* **SWATH.**

Stabbing

Offshore expression for inserting the threaded end of a pipe or rod into the coupling at the end of another pipe or rod.

Stability

In relation to marine fuel oil, can be taken as a description of its ability to resist the precipitation of its **asphaltene** content, as and when blended, or subsequently with time or heat.

Stabiliser

(1) Used to reduce the rolling motion of a ship. The systems fall under two main headings, passive and active. Passive: **bilge keels**, fixed fins and **sponsons.** Active: Folding fin stabilisers, tank systems and moving weights. **(2)** Tower designed to separate high vapour pressure hydrocarbons from the crude oil so a good recovery of crude is realised and evaporation losses in storage minimised.

Stabilograph

Instrument used in inclining experiments to record the angle of heel to a base of time.

Stable

Act of being stable, tendency of a ship to remain upright or return to the upright position when inclined by a disturbing force. For stability to exist, the **centre of gravity (G)** must be below the **metacentre (M).** *See also* **GM, metacentric height** and Figure 12.

Stack factor

A **container ship** term relating to loading.

Stack

American term for a funnel.

Stainless iron
Corrosion resistant ferrous alloy containing less than 0.12 per cent carbon, less than 1 per cent silicon and manganese, and 11 to 14 per cent chromium. The term iron is used because of the low carbon content. The material cannot be hardened appreciably by heat treatment and is weldable.

Stainless steel
Covers a wide variety of alloy steels, generally more corrosion resistant than plain carbon steels. There are three main groups.

Ferritic. Containing less than 0.12 per cent carbon and 11 to 30 per cent chromium.

Martensitic. Containing more than 0.12 per cent carbon, 11 to 20 per cent chromium and up to 3 per cent nickel. These steels are hardenable.

Austenitic. Containing a minimum of 11 per cent chromium and 8 per cent nickel, the total of chromium and nickel together being not less than 23 per cent.

Stalling
Sudden stopping of an engine due to fuel starvation or mechanical failure.

Stanchion
Vertical column supporting deck.

Stand pipe
Rigid pipe conducting **drilling mud** up the **derrick** into the rotary hose.

Star connection
Method of connection in **three phase ac** working where three conductors or windings meet at a common point. Also known as a **Y connection**.

Starboard
Right hand side of a ship when facing forward.

Star delta starting
Means of reducing the starting current of an **induction motor** by initially connecting the **stator** windings in **star** (Y). Once the motor is running the **windings** are connected in **delta** (**mesh**).

Star gear
System of **epicyclic gears** in which the planet carrier is fixed, the **annulus** and sun wheels rotate and the planet wheels rotate about their own axis.

Starter motor
A motor with a small pinion mounted on than extension of its armature that engages with a gear ring on the periphery of a flywheel.

Starting air compressor
Main air compressors supplying compressed air at high pressure to start the main propulsion diesel machinery.

Starting air receiver
Storage vessel containing high pressure air for starting the main propulsion units.

Starting current
Current drawn by a motor when started and running up to speed.

Static
(1) In a state of **equilibrium**. (2) Electrical charges due to atmospheric effects or induced by **friction**.

Statics
The science of dealing with forces in equilibrium. It is typical to use a metal alloy equilibrium diagram that shows the limits within which an alloy is stable, with respect to temperature and combustion. By using this method, any change in the structure or limits can be established.

Static delivery head
Vertical distance from pump to delivery liquid level, or the highest point in the system.

Static excitation
Use of **transformers** or **rectifiers** to produce series and shunt components of an ac generator's field windings.

Static frequency convertor
Device used with shaft generator systems to provide a constant output voltage and frequency. The shaft generator voltage output is **rectified** into a variable dc voltage and then inverted into a three phase ac voltage. A feedback system within the oscillator invertor ensures a constant output voltage and frequency.

Static suction lift
Vertical distance a liquid must rise before it enters the pump.

Statical stability
See **stability**.

Stations
Ten equally spaced divisions along a ship's length between the **forward perpendicular**, numbered ten, and the **after perpendicular**, numbered zero.

Stator
(1) Fixed blades of aerofoil shape mounted on the casing of a turbine. (2) Part of an electrical machine including stationary magnetics and their associated windings. Usually applies to ac machines.

Stays
Wires or ropes from the deck to the head of **mast, samson post,** or **boom** to provide support or prevent movement.

STCW
Standards of Training, Certification and Watchkeeping for Seafarers. A convention of **IMO** that sets out the minimum standards to be aimed at for the certification of masters, deck and engineer officers, and ratings. In addition it provides broad guidance on the topics to be covered in the education and training of seagoing personnel.

Steadite
Micro-constituent of phosphate cast iron. A **eutectic** of ferrite saturated with phosphorus and iron phosphide (Fe_3P) with a melting point around 980°C. Steadite appears in the microstructure as a white finely dotted **eutectic.**

Stealer strake
Single wide plate that replaces two narrow plates in adjacent strakes.

Steam
Water converted to vapour by the application of sufficient heat energy to make the liquid change its state. It can be wet, dry saturated or superheated.

Steam atomisation
Breaking down fuel into very fine particles by mixing steam and oil in the burner nozzle. Improves fuel combustion and the efficiency of the plant.

Steam drum
Part of a **water-tube boiler** that receives the steam from generator tubes.

Steam engine
Prime mover where water converted to steam in a boiler exerts pressure against a piston within a cylinder to impart a reciprocating motion. The piston rod connects to a crankshaft changing the reciprocating motion to rotary motion. *See also* **steam turbine.**

Steam generator
(1) Piece of machinery using high pressure steam to produce steam from water. Used mainly in connection with lower pressure systems. (2) Package system of a **steam turbine** or steam engine connected to an electric generator.

Steam jacket
A jacket formed round a steam engine cylinder; supplied with live steam to maintain heat and prevent excessive condensation of working steam in the cylinder.

Steam trap
Device permitting discharge of the water contained in condensed steam, caused by pipelines and heat exchangers, without the loss of steam.

Steam turbine
Engine in which steam impinges on a series of blades on revolving discs converting the heat energy of steam into rotational energy.

Steaming
Originally referred to a **steam engine** powered vessel that was **underway**, it now refers to all vessels **underway** regardless of machinery type.

Steel
An **alloy** of iron and iron carbide. The carbon content is usually below one except for special steels. It is amenable to heat treatment and alloying with many other metals such as manganese and nickel and can be of various types such as **austenite, stainless,** and **cast** possessing a wide range of properties.

Steering gear
Complete machinery used to turn the rudder; includes wheelhouse signal equipment and auxiliary/hand operated gear, generally positioned aft. The main gear is usually electro-hydraulic and directly connected to the rudder stock.

Steering station
Place on the bridge outfitted with a steering mechanism and compass used by the helmsman to steer the vessel.

Stellite
Series of alloys used for services requiring hardness and wear resistance. They are alloys of cobalt and chromium with additions of tungsten and other elements.

Stem
Foremost part of a ship structure reaching from **keel** to top of **bow**.

Stemming
Maintaining sufficient propeller revolutions to overcome tidal currents, keeping a ship in approximately the same position.

Step down transformer
A **transformer** where secondary voltage is lower than primary voltage.

Step function response
Transient response that results from an input signal or disturbance in the form of a sudden occurrence or step function.

Step out well
Well drilled beyond the proven limits of a field to investigate a possible extension; occasionally called an out step well.

Step
Fitting into which the foot of a mast is placed.

Stepper motor
A dc motor used with a computer controlled servo-mechanism. An input pulse will cause rotation of the shaft through a fixed angle or step.

Stern
The after end of a ship.

Stern door
Door at the stern or rear of a **roll-on/roll-off** ship. Situated forward of the ramp, it is designed to provide a watertight barrier against sea water.

Stern frame
Large casting, forging or fabricated structure at the aft end of a ship that uses a vertical **rudder post, propeller post** and aperture for the **propeller;** attached to the side plating and **keel.** *See* Figure 30.

Stern ramp
Inclined plane connecting the after end of a **roll-on/roll-off** ship with the shore or quay where rolling cargo is wheeled on and off a ship. The ramp is often designed to make a **watertight door** to cover the opening in a ship.

Stern tube
Contains the after bearing for the propeller shaft and incorporates the watertight gland where the shaft passes through the intact hull. *See* Figure 28. The bearing can be manufactured from white metal in which case the shaft and bearing are oil lubricated, or from a composite such as Railko, Thordon, and Tufnol that can be oil or water lubricated.

Sternwheeler
Vessel with a wide paddle wheel at the stern for service in shallow waters such as the Nile and the Mississippi.

Stevedore
Person or firm contracted to load or discharge cargo.

Stiction
Tendency of two surfaces to adhere to one another unless kept in relative vibratory or rotary motion.

Stiff
A vessel with a large **metacentric height** that can have a short period of roll and thus roll uncomfortably. The opposite to **tender.**

Stiffener
Flat bar section or built up section used to stiffen plating.

Stiffness
Restoring force per unit displacement; the reciprocal of **compliance.**

Stiffness coefficient
In a **kinetic** control system, the **force** or **torque** per unit deviation.

Still water bending moment
The bending moment acting on a ship lying in still water due to uneven distribution of weight and **buoyancy** along a ship's length.

Stinger
Boom used to lower an underwater pipeline onto the sea bed from a lay barge.

Stirling cycle
Closed circuit external combustion engine cycle in which air is compressed, heated, allowed to expand, and then cooled before being compressed again. By using heat from the expanded air to preheat the external combustion air, high efficiency is obtained. Engines using this cycle are quiet and can burn low grade fuel, however, tend to be bulky.

Stirling engine
Engine where work is performed by the expansion of a gas at high temperature and supplied with heat through the cylinder wall.

Stirrup pump
Portable pump developed to meet the threat of fire. A simple double acting pump with only three moving parts: a plunger rod, ball acting as a foot valve, and ball forming a non-return valve in the piston at base of the plunger rod.

Stirrup
U shaped machine component with a shaft attached across the open end co-operating with a bearing in another component.

Stock
A cross piece just below the ring of an **anchor** at right angles to the line of **flukes.** By preventing an anchor from turning, it ensures the flukes enter and

maintain their hold in the sea bottom. Now replaced by a **stockless anchor.** *See* Figure 3.

Stockholm tar
Type of tar prepared from resinous pinewood, used to preserve ropes from the effects of water.

Stockless anchor
Type of anchor with no crosspiece on the shank and arms pivoted so both can engage at the same time. The shank can be drawn into the **hawse pipe** of a ship. *See* Figure 3.

Stoichiometric mixture
Chemically correct mixture of substances bringing about a **reaction** or creating an **alloy.**

Stokehold
Compartment containing steam boilers. In coal burning days, it was the area used by stokers/firemen to manually feed the boilers with coal, hence the name stokehold. Today most boilers are oil burning so these compartments are normally called boiler rooms.

Stoke's Law
Law of physical chemistry dealing with small spherical particles that move freely in a liquid.

Stokes (St)
Unit of kinematic viscosity, 1 St = 100 cSt. The most commonly used viscosity unit for marine fuels and lubricants is the centistoke (cSt).

Stopper
Short length of rope used to secure a larger rope under **tension,** such as a mooring rope, while it is being transferred from a **winch** or **capstan** onto **bitts.** One end of the stopper is firmly secured to a ring bolt or to bitts, the other to the larger rope which it securing.

Stop valve
A valve that can be closed to shut off a supply.

Stowage factor
Volumetric capacity of a commodity. Includes, packing, dunnage and unavoidable vacant spaces.

Stowage plan
An outline of a ship's holds showing the disposition of cargo.

Stowage
(1) Place where goods can be stowed. (2) Act of stowing.

Straight mineral oil
Mineral oil free of compounds or additives.

Straight run
Products produced by simple refinery distillation without cracking or any alteration to the structure of the constituent **hydrocarbons.**

Strain
Extension or contraction per unit length produced by **tensile** or **compressive** loads respectively.

Strain gauge
Instrument for measuring the amount of **deformation** in a material when subjected to mechanical **stress.** The most commonly used is the electric resistance strain gauge in which fine platinum wire is bonded to the component. When the component deforms due to applied stress, the wire is stretched altering its resistance to the passage of an electric current through it. The change of resistance is proportional to the amount of change in the length of wire.

Strain hardening
An increase in resistance to **deformation** caused by previous deformation.

Strainer
Coarse filter to remove large particles.

Strake
Continuous horizontal line of plating from stem to stern on shell, decks and bulkheads.

Stranded
Said of a ship that has ceased to move as a result of touching the bottom.

Strata
Set of successive layers of any deposited substance. Sampling the strata or stratum of a prospective oil field gives an indication of its likely oil and gas bearing potential.

Stratum
Layers of deposited substances.

Streamlined
Smoothing and shaping of surfaces so a fluid flowing over them experiences reduced resistance.

Strength
Maximum **stress** required to overcome the cohesion of a material. Strength involves the idea of resistance to **rupture,** hardness involves resistance to **deformation.**

Strength calculation
Determination of the structural strength of a ship when considering both **static** and **dynamic** loading.

Strength deck
Deck designed as the uppermost part of the main hull longitudinal strength **girder.**

Strengthened hold
Hold of a ship with a tank top reinforced to carry dense cargoes such as ore.

Stress
Mutual actions taking place across any section of a body to which a system of forces is applied. Stresses are described as **tensile, compressive** and **shear.** Defined as force per unit area.

Stress corrosion
Accelerated tendency of steel to corrode when it is stressed, often leading to cracking.

Stress ratio
Ratio of maximum to minimum stress in **fatigue**.

Stress relieving
Removing residual stresses in steel or non-ferrous metal structures by heating to suitable temperatures, such as 600-650°C for steel, and maintaining that temperature for a time sufficient for the stresses to be released.

Stress/Strain relationship
The effect of increasing **stress** on a material and its corresponding increase in **strain** will vary with a selected material. For stresses up to the elastic limit a material will return to its original length upon the removal of stress. Over this length the ratio of stress over strain is a constant known as **Young's Modulus** and the material is obeying **Hooke's Law.** If the load induces stress above the **elastic limit,** the material will pass through the plasticity state and then fracture.

Stress, yield
Lowest stress resulting in an extension of a tensile test piece without an increase in load.

Strike
When a drilling operation produces oil or gas. Also known as show.

Stringer
The **strake** of deck plating at the ship's side.

Stripping pump
Pump in a tanker brought into use towards the completion of discharge to drain the remaining cargo tanks.

Stroboscope
Instrument used to measure the rotational speed, detection of wear and distortion and chatter of moving parts and mechanisms. Used for high speed objects as it synchronises frequencies with the aid of a flashing light.

Stroke
Distance travelled by the piston of a reciprocating engine or a ram, in moving from one end of the cylinder to the other.

Strongback
A beam that is longitudinally over a lifeboat to support the canvas covers and give them a pronounced slope to shed water.

Strop
Length of rope with ends spliced to make a loop.

Structural failure
Said to occur when all the materials of a bending structure have reached their **yield stress.**

Strum box
Perforated plate box welded to the open end of bilge suctions in holds and other compartments; prevents debris being taken up by the bilge pump.

Strut
Structural member designed to take **compression** loads.

Stud welding
Shielded arc process. The stud is inserted in a gun chuck and a **ceramic** ferrule slipped over before the stud is placed against the plate surface. When the arcing period is complete the stud is driven into a molten pool of weld metal attaching it to the plate.

Stud
(1) Projecting boss or stem usually screwed to take a nut. **(2)** Screwed rod to create permanent screw positions. **(3)** Strengthening cross piece in centre of a chain link.

Stuffing box

Gland space surrounding a shaft that is filled with packing to make a pressure tight and leakproof joint. The packing is compressed by a gland. *See also* **piston rod gland and** Figure 31.

Sub division

Sub division of ship into compartments by means of **watertight bulkheads,** with or without **watertight doors** and hatches. This to localise damage and safeguard stability in the event of a collision or other ship accident.

Sub sea wellhead

Offshore well head installed on the sea floor that is remotely controlled from a platform or floating production facility, or from land.

Sublimation

Vaporisation of a solid without the intermediate formation of a liquid.

Submarine

Vessel designed to operate below the surface of the sea. Used by the world's navies as an attacking force. Conventional submarines are usually diesel driven with **schnorkel** breathing and the world's superpowers have **nuclear power** driven submarines, able to stay long periods underwater.

Submersible

(1) Refers to electrical equipment that is constructed so that it will operate successfully when submerged in water under specified conditions of pressure and time. (2) Vehicle suitable for deep diving applications such as repair work on undersea cables and for exploring wrecks. (3) A drilling platform that can be ballasted to sit on the sea bed.

Suction

To draw or suck in fluid by reducing pressure, such as to suck in sea water for engine cooling, condensers, and sanitary purposes.

Suction pressure decay

Fall off or reduction in the **net positive suction head (npsh)** of a pump with an increasing flow rate.

Suezmax

Term given to a vessel of the maximum dimensions that allow it to transit the Suez Canal.

Sulfinuz process

Also known as the **Cassel** process, consists of the treatment of steel articles in a salt bath containing cyanide and sulphur compounds at a temperature ranging from 500–600°C; claimed to produce an anti-scuffing surface.

Sullage stripping
To remove residues, emulsified mixtures and sludge.

Sulphate reducing bacteria (SRB)
Bacteria that thrive in the absence of oxygen and are highly corrosive, often attacking metal parts and penetrating steel plate. Common in bilge pipes and the section of the inside hull that coincides with the level of bilge water.

Sulphur
Element occurring naturally in petroleum products as an impurity, in the form of its various compounds (**mercaptans**); often used as a specification limit in the quality control of critical fuels, solvents and lubricating oils.

Sulphur content
In marine fuel oil, refers to the amount of sulphur present. Sulphur contributes to engine corrosive wear and also reduces the **calorific value/specific energy** of the fuel. Specifications such as ISO 8217 and the **CIMAC** residual fuel specifications stipulate maximum quantities of sulphur for each grade of product. High fuel oil sulphur contents require commensurate increases in the alkaline content of cylinder lubricating oils. *See also* **low sulphur fuels.**

Summer draught
Depth of water to which a ship's hull can be immersed in a summer zone at all times, or in a seasonal zone at certain times of the year. The depth is indicated by the summer **load line** painted on the ship's side. See Figure 19.

Summer tanks
In early tankers, the expansion tanks reserve spaces that could be filled with oil to bring a vessel to the loading mark in summer.

Sump
(1) Pit or well receiving liquids such as oil and water. (2) Oil reservoir at the bottom (wet sump) or below (dry sump) the crankcase of an **internal combustion engine.**

Sun and planet wheels
Gear wheel (sun) around which one or more wheels (planets) rotate in mesh. *See also* **epicylcic gears** and Figure 16.

Supercargo
Name often given to persons in merchant ship management when travelling on board a managed ship.

Supercharging
To raise the density of the charge air in the cylinder at the end of the suction stroke so a greater weight of mixture or air is trapped in the cylinder. This

allows a greater weight of fuel to be burned. Most diesel engines are super-charged by means of their own exhaust gas driven turbo blowers.

Superconducting machines

The electrical resistance of a metallic material decreases as the temperature decreases, approaching zero at absolute zero temperature (0°K or -273°C). A current induced by a **magnetic field** in a ring of superconducting material at such a low temperature will continue to circulate after the magnetic field has been removed. This phenomenon can be used to drive an electric motor with the minimum of electrical energy supplied to it.

Superheated steam

Steam heated at constant pressure out of contact with the water from which it was formed, i.e. at a higher temperature than that of saturation. If heat is sup-plied at a constant rate to ice at, say, - 20°C and no heat is lost by conduction, convection or radiation then the temperature at first will increase uniformly from - 20°C to 0°C as indicated by line AB in Figure 33. It remains constant at 0oC for time BC to melt into water. Further heat raises the temperature uni-formly to 100°C as shown by CD. If the pressure on the water surface is atmo-spheric the water boils and the temperature remains constant at 100°C until all the water is evaporated. If the heat supply is maintained after all the water has been evaporated, the temperature and volume of the steam will increase above their saturation values and the steam will become superheated as shown by EF. Superheating also occurs if steam is compressed without any loss of heat or if steam is throttled to a lower pressure. See Figure 33.

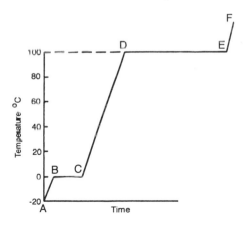

Figure 33 Steam Temperatures

Superheater

Bank of tubes in the exhaust gas path from a boiler furnace. Steam from the boiler steam drum passes through tubes where its temperature is raised, at constant pressure, above **saturation** temperature.

Superstructure

Decked structure above the upper deck, the outboard sides of which are formed by **shell** plating.

Superstructure efficiency

Ability of a superstructure to diffuse or accept forces associated with the longitudinal bending of a ship. It is largely dependent upon the ratio of the superstructure length to its transverse dimensions.

Supply ship

Vessel carrying equipment, stores and other supplies from shore base to off-shore structures, occasionally doubling as an **anchor handling vessel** or **tug.**

Surface coefficient

Thermal transfer of heat per unit area, caused by **convection** and **radiation** and divided by the temperature difference between the surface and neighbouring air or fluid.

Surface condenser

Steam **condenser** that consists of a shell containing a large number of tubes through which cooling water is circulated. Exhaust steam enters the shell and condenses once coming into contact with the cold tubes.

Surface tension

Cohesive action of the particles composing a fluid act in all directions below the surface. As no force counteracts above the surface, this unbalanced condition produces a tenseness at the surface known as surface tension.

Surfactant

Compound able to reduce surface tension; commonly used to achieve **emulsification,** wetting or **detergency.**

Surge

(1) In still water at constant power a ship will move at constant speed. On encountering waves there will be a mean reduction in speed due to the increased resistance. The speed is no longer constant and the term surge defines the variation in speed about the new mean value. **(2)** A transient and abnormal rush of electrical current. **(3)** Alternate slackening and holding of a rope on a **capstan.**

Surging
(1) Severe fluctuation or abrupt decrease in delivery pressure of a supercharger. (2) Fore and aft linear movement of a ship. *See* swaying and Figure 15.

Survey
Detailed examination of a ship or its machinery to verify its standard of fitness for continued service.

Surveyor
Person employed or engaged by a Government, classification society, shipping association or consultancy to inspect cargoes, ships or ships machinery. Can inspect and report on a damaged ship or ship for purchase or delivery.

Survival/storm draught
Depth of water a semi-submersible floats in during heavy weather to maintain a sufficient air gap.

Susceptance (B)
Component of admittance due to inductance and or capacitance. The reciprocal of reactance.

Swaging
Process of forging metals to reduce the cross-section of a piece. The piece is held between dies that are hammered so the piece takes the required form. Used for reducing the diameter or tapering of rods and tubes and for forging stock to shapes having the opposite sides concentric.

Swamp
Overwhelm with water, although not necessarily in sufficient quantities necessary to sink a vessel

Swarf
Metal grindings, filings, or lathe turnings, generally iron or steel, produced during manufacturing operations. Extremely dangerous if left in machinery particularly within a lubricating oil system.

Swash plate
(1) Longitudinal or transverse non-watertight plate fitted in a tank to reduce the swashing action of liquid contents. It functions best when the tank is partially full. (2) Disc set obliquely on a shaft so that it wobbles as the shaft rotates. Axially arranged pistons and cylinders can be operated by the swash action and this mechanism is commonly used in hydraulic pumps to control delivery.

Swashplate pump
Axial cylinder variable delivery pump used in hydraulic systems. The driving shaft rotates the cylinder barrel, swash plate and pistons. An external

trunnion allows the swash plate to be moved about its axis which varies the stroke of the pistons in the barrel.

SWATH
Small Waterplane Area Twin Hull. Term given to a vessel with two slim hulls that supports the main structure of the vessel holding it clear of the water.

Swaying
A ship moving in a wave system has six degrees of freedom, three linear and three rotational: **heaving, surging, swaying, rolling, pitching** and **yawing**. The transverse linear movement is called swaying. See Figure 15.

Sweat
To join two metals by partial fusion, as in solder.

Swedged plating
Corrugated plating that gives rigidity to the plating without the use of stiffeners. Used for bulkheads, storage tanks and boiler casings.

Sweet crude
Crude oil with a low sulphur content. See also **sour crude.**

Swell
Undulating movement of the surface of the sea in fine weather, typically an after effect of winds in that area that have died down, or winds prevailing in the distance.

Swept volume
The volume of a cylinder displaced by a piston in one complete stroke.

Swim
Projecting part of **bow** or **stern** structure below **load line**. As this projection sinks deeper a ship's **buoyancy** increases.

Swing
(1) Turn a ship in several directions to record **compass** errors in all directions.
(2) Move round a fixed point, such as swinging to an anchor.

Switch
Mechanical device for making and breaking a circuit carrying a current not greatly in excess of its rated normal current.

Switchboard
General term applicable to an assembly of apparatus for the operation, metering, regulation and control of an electrical installation.

Switchgear
Apparatus protecting and controlling the distribution of electrical energy.

Swivel
Rotating coupling connecting an offshore rig rotary hose to a **drill string.**

SWOPS
Single Well Oil Production System.

Synchronising
Process where the voltage, **frequency** and **phase angle** of an incoming alternator are adjusted to be as close as possible to those of the machine or system with which it is to operate in parallel; carried out after the incoming machine has been run up to speed yet before it is connected to the system.

Synchronous
Occurring at the same time; acting simultaneously; in step.

Synchronous vibrations
Vibrations that correspond exactly in **period** and **phase.**

Synchroscope
Instrument indicating when two electrical supplies are **synchronous** and can be paralleled.

Syneresis
Weeping or bleeding of greases.

Synthetic lubricant
Non petroleum lubricant produced by synthesis. Particularly valuable when a high viscosity index product is required, such as in hydraulic fluids. It is expensive to produce compared to mineral oil based products, therefore, are only used when sufficient advantage is obtained to offset the higher cost.

Synthetic rubber
Rubber manufactured from chemicals rather than obtained naturally from rubber trees.

T

Tabernacle
Three sided socket permitting the lowering of a hinged mast to allow a vessel to pass under bridges or other obstacles.

Table
Thwartship platform on each side of mast to take heels or bottoms of cargo derricks.

Tachogenerator
An ac or dc generator that provides an output voltage proportional to its rotational speed. Can be used to measure speed or as part of an automatic control mechanism to regulate speed.

Tachometer
(1) Instrument for measuring **velocity** (usually of rotation). (2) Name given to the counter indicating the number of engine or propeller revolutions per minute.

Tackle
Collection of wires and ropes used with a ship's **derrick.**

Tacky
Sticky or adhesive substances, i.e. certain greases.

Taffrail
Rail over **bulwarks** round **stern.**

Tailshaft
Shaft passing through the **stern tube** to take the propeller. Generally a short section of shafting with a tapered outer end onto which the propeller is locked. Also known as **propeller shaft, screw shaft** and **stern shaft.** *See* Figure 28.

Taint
Trace of a substance found contaminating a cargo making it unfit for the original purpose. Some cargoes, like citrus fruits, have a tendency to taint, others like tea are more susceptible to being tainted themselves.

Taken charge
Object that breaks away and rolls out of control from side to side.

Tally clerk
Those who keep an account of intake and outurn of cargo.

TAN
Abbreviation for *T*otal *A*cid *N*umber, also known as **neutralisation number.** Most often used to measure the acidity of a turbine lubricating oil.

Tandem
Two cranes employed together to combine their lifting capacity.

Tangent point
Point on a sphere or circle where the tangent touches it.

Tangent tube
Form of furnace wall construction in a boiler. The various waterwall tubes are fitted close together and backed by refractory insulation and boiler casing.

Tangentially fired boiler
A boiler with burners fitted at each corner of the furnace aligned in order to fire tangentially to a circle. This arrangement is thought to improve **turbulence** and, therefore, the mixing of air and fuel.

Tank
Reservoir or cistern that contains liquid. In relation to ships, they are tanks built into the ships structure for carrying liquid cargoes such as crude oil products or bunker fuel. Other tanks not necessarily built into the structure carry lubricating oil and fresh water.

Tank cleaning
Cleaning out and clearing gases from the cargo tanks on board a **tanker.** Automatic mechanical tank washing machinery is used to jet high pressure hot or cold water around the tank. Portable or fixed machines can also be used that enter the tank through circular apertures in the deck.

Tank farm
Collection of petroleum storage tanks.

Tank heating coils
Fitted in bunker tanks, settling tanks, and service tanks. Used to raise and maintain the liquid temperature.

Tank tests
(1) Tank tests of a model hull are generally specified. These provide the designer with a range of speeds and corresponding powers for the hull form. Due to the considerable costs involved in conducting full scale experiments on the resistance of ships, a great deal of attention has been given to experiments on models. The **resistance** of a ship and the power required to drive it can be estimated from the model. *See* **Froude's Law of Comparison. (2)** Pressure tests on tanks to ensure fitness for service.

Tank top
Plating that forms the top of the **double bottom.**

Tanker
A ship constructed to carry liquid cargoes in bulk. They come in various sizes, including **VLCC** and **ULCC,** with various designs to cover a multitude of purposes, i.e. **product tanker,** chemical tanker, or crude carrier.

Tappet
Sliding piston-like cam follower that moves within a guide, with a flat end or an end affixed to a roller bearing on the cam.

Tar
Dark viscous substance obtained by distilling coal, oil, or natural **bitumen.**

Tare
Weight of a container, packing case or other wrappings deducted from the gross weight to determine the net weight of goods.

Tarpaulin
Tough canvas treated with a waterproofing substance to cover non-watertight **hatch covers.**

Taut
Tightly drawn.

TBN
Total Base Number. Prescribed test applicable to lubricating oils indicating the amount of alkali (base) available to neutralise acids. Particularly useful for alkaline diesel engine cylinder and crankcase oils as one of the main measurements of oil condition. Has now been shortened to **base number.**

TBT coatings
Tributyltin hull paint. Declared dangerous to the environment (poisoning the water and damaging sea life) and **IMO**'s **MEPC** recommends a phase out to be followed by a complete ban. TBT free paints such as low surface energy coatings (teflon, silicon) have been developed as replacements for the environmentally undesirable TBT coatings.

Tchebycheff's Rules
Used to determine the area of a figure bounded by straight lines and a curve. The ordinates do not require internal multiples as in **Simpson's Rules.**

TDC
Top Dead Centre. Point of highest travel of a piston in its cylinder.

Teak
Hard, durable wood suited to marine conditions, i.e. handrails and decking.

Teeth
Tooth shaped projections on equipment such as cog wheels, gear wheels, and ratchets. *See* **gears** and Figure 1.

Telegraph
Device operated from the bridge for transmitting changes in engine speed while manoeuvring.

Telemetry
Science involving the taking of measurements and their transmission to detached stations where they can be displayed, interpreted and recorded.

Telemotor system
Generally an arrangement of hydraulic pipes for controlling a ship's rudder. As the helmsman on the bridge rotates the wheel, a plunger is moved that applies pressure to the steering gear control valve via hydraulic pipes. This in turn moves the rudder. Some ships are fitted with electronic rather than hydraulic control systems.

Tell tale
(1) Index adjacent to the steering wheel that indicates the rudder position. (2) Instrument in Master's cabin for checking ship's course. (3) Method of indicating engine orders to/from the **bridge**.

Temper
Condition of **hardness** and **toughness** in steel obtained by heat treatment and cold working.

Temperature
Relative condition of heat or cold recorded by a sensation produced, or a thermometer or pyrometer. The **SI unit** of temperature is the kelvin (K). Units of measurement in common use are degrees Celsius (°C) and degrees Fahrenheit (°F). The kelvin as a unit of temperature difference is exactly equal to the degree Celsius. To convert Celsius to kelvin add 273.15. Absolute zero is 0°K or -273.15°C.

Temperature compensation
Automatic adjustment of the reading of an instrument to allow for changes in the ambient temperature.

Temperature detector
Thermometer element of resistance or thermocouple, or apparatus built into a machine to indicate temperature at an inaccessible point, particularly while a machine is in service.

Temper carbon
Small particles of graphite resulting from the decomposition of iron carbide during the annealing of iron castings.

Temper colours
Heating bright steel in the range of 200–350°C produces a surface oxide of certain colours depending on the temperature and time. This phenomenon is sometimes used as an indication of temperature, particularly when temper-

ing tool steel. Time is important and if the operation is prolonged the colour will correspond with that normally associated with a higher temperature. For plain carbon steels the usual colours for normal tempering are:

Light Straw	210°C	Straw	225°C
Dark Straw	240°C	Yellow-Brown	255°C
Red-Brown	265°C	Purple	275°C
Violet	285°C	Dark Blue	295°C
Pale Blue	310°C	Grey	330°C

To produce the same colours in stainless or heat resisting steels would require higher temperatures.

Tempering
Treatment process usually carried out after quenching to impart **ductility** to metals which become **brittle** on quenching; heating steels to a suitable temperature less than the transformation range.

Template
Mould or pattern.

Temporary hardness
The bicarbonates of calcium and magnesium, in boiler feed water, decomposed by heat that come out of a solution as scale forming carbonates.

Tender
(1) Small vessel attending a larger one to take persons or goods to or from.
(2) An unstable ship with a tendency to roll slowly, due to having a small **metacentric height;** often caused by stowing dense cargoes high in the ship.

Tenacity
See **ultimate tensile stress.**

Tenon
Protrusion at the end of a component that fits into a socket (mortice) in another component for attachment. Tenons are provided at the tops of turbine blades to attach them to **shrouding**.

Tensile
Related to pulling or stretching.

Tensile strength
Force required to break a bar of unit cross-section under tension. The tensile strength depends on the cohesion of the material, its consistency and also to some extent upon the rate of application of the load.

Tensile test
Test in which a specimen of known area of cross-section is subjected to increasing **stress** in tension until it fractures. Measurements taken are: stress to **fracture** (ultimate tensile stress), **yield point** or **elastic limit, elongation** at fracture (measured between gauge marks), and the reduction of area (the difference between the cross-sectional area of the specimen before testing and the area at the fracture).

Tension leg platform (TLP)
Floating concrete or steel platform anchored to caissons on the sea bed by numerous wires. The tension in these wires creates a stable platform from which to operate in deep water.

Tera (T)
The **SI** prefix for a multiplication factor of 10^{12}.

Terotechnology
Name given to the process of coordinating and controlling the various techniques and practices that influence efficiency and profitability of capital plant, equipment and engineering installations, the technology of installation, commissioning, maintenance, replacement and removal of plant, machinery and equipment, a feedback of information to design and operation, and related subjects and practices.

Terrestrial
Earthly or pertaining to Earth.

TEU
Twenty-foot Equivalent Units. Measurement of standard containers in international shipping.

Therm
Unit of heat applied to gas equalling 10^5 **Btu** or 105.5 MJ.

Thermal
Pertaining to heat.

Thermal conductivity
Measure of heat flow through a material. It is given as the quantity of heat flowing through a unit area of unit thickness in one second when the temperature difference between the faces equals one degree.

Thermal cracking
Oil refinery secondary process that breaks down heavy **hydrocarbon** molecules into lighter molecules by raising them to a high temperature.

Thermal efficiency
Ratio of the amount of work achieved by an engine to the mechanical equivalent of the heat content of the fuel.

Thermal loading
Stress level resulting from heat flow into the walls surrounding a hot zone in a machine such as a heat engine.

Thermal shock
Property of a material to withstand rapid changes in temperature without fracture.

Thermal trap
Device operated by temperature variation for releasing water from a steam system.

Thermal trip
Device operated by a rise in temperature; used on **circuit breakers** and **relays,** often a bimetal strip that deflects when heated.

Thermionic
Emitting of charged particles, such as **ions** or **electrons,** from a heated body. A thermionic valve is a vacuum tube in which a heated filament emits electrons carrying current in one direction. Used as a rectifier of ac and in radio equipment for detecting and amplifying radio waves.

Thermistor
A **resistor,** typically with a large non-linear negative temperature **coefficient** of resistance. Frequently inserted between the **windings** of rotating machines to form an embedded temperature detector or safety indicator.

Thermit
Mixture of iron oxides, finely divided aluminium, steel and de-oxidisers. On ignition of the mixture a reaction takes place that produces molten metal which acts as a source of heat. It is used in certain welding processes as a source of heat obtaining temperatures of around 3000°C.

Thermocouple
When certain metals are joined and the junction heated, an electric current is generated. The potential can be measured away from the heat source by a millivoltmeter (the cold junction). This potential is related to the difference in temperature between hot and cold junctions.

Thermometer
Instrument for measuring temperature.

Thermometer pocket
Recess in a machine or pipe that takes a thermometer. To ensure accurate readings the recess must be kept full of oil to act as a medium for heat conduction.

Thermophile
A number of **thermocouples** connected together in series or parallel. The series arrangement has all hot junctions at the same temperature and all cold junctions at the same temperature, therefore, very sensitive measurements are possible. The parallel arrangement has the hot junctions at different temperatures and the cold junctions all at the same temperature, therefore, an average reading is obtained.

Thermoplastic
Plastic material that softens under the action of heat and then hardens when cooled without any change of properties, i.e. **polyvinyl chloride.**

Thermosetting
Plastic material that can be moulded when heated, will undergo a chemical change on further heating and then set hard, i.e. **epoxy resin.**

Thermostat
Device for maintaining or adjusting temperature. Often an expandable element can be used to either cut off heat supply or start the flow of cooling medium when temperature exceeds the required value.

Thickeners
Solid particles, usually metal soaps, dispersed in **mineral** or **synthetic** oils to produce a **grease.**

Thief
Equipment for sampling the contents of a tank or drum at any desired depth.

Thimble
Metal ring with concave sides into which a rope can be spliced to prevent it fraying or weaving.

Thin shell bearing
Bearing in which anti friction metal is bonded to a thin shell of stronger material, enclosed in and supported by a heavier and stronger housing.

Thixotropy
Tendency of a substance like grease to soften or flow when subjected to **shearing** action.

Thole
Pegs of wood or metal inserted in the gunwhale of a rowboat to take the place of a crutch or rowlock.

Three island ship
Ship with a **poop, bridge** and **forecastle**.

Three phase supply
Combination of three circuits supplied by **electro motive forces,** different in **phase** by one third of a cycle.

Three term controller
Controller providing proportional, integral and derivative actions.

Threshold
Value of input to a measuring instrument, or any system, below which no output change can be detected.

Throttle valve
(1) Valve to reduce the pressure of a fluid, such as in a steam system; can be used to reduce the pressure of steam before it is used for auxiliaries. (2) Valve to control the admission of fuel to an internal combustion engine.

Throughput
Total amount of raw material processed by a plant such as an oil refinery in a given period.

Throw
Distance between the centre of an engine crankshaft and the centre of the crank pin. In an **eccentric engine** it is the distance between the centre of the shaft and the centre of the eccentric sheave, i.e. the amount of eccentricity.

Throwing chain
Employing a spinning line to make a connection between two sections of pipe on an oil platform.

Thrust
The **compressive** force in a member or structure of an engine or mechanism.

Thrust bearing
Bearings that reduce **friction** through axial loading on rotating components.

Thrust block
Unit taking the propeller thrust. As the thrust is of a pulsating nature, the block foundation must be rigid. Thrust is usually taken by pads of anti-friction metal each side of a collar that are slightly inclined to maintain a hydrodynamic oil film. *See* Figure 25.

Thrust power
Product of propeller thrust and speed of ship's advance.

Thrust shaft
Section of intermediate shafting that passes through the thrust block to sustain propeller thrust. Has a large collar running between the thrust block anti-friction pads. Must have anti-friction pads each side of the collar to take care of ahead and astern movements. *See* Figure 25.

Thrusters
Manoeuvring **propellers** originally developed for passenger liners, ferries and bulk carriers to assist docking without tugs. Now frequently utilised in offshore vessels and **semi-submersibles** for manoeuvering, position-keeping and propulsion. There are a wide variety of thrusters, such as tunnel, azimuthing, retractable, and pump jet. The propeller in the thruster can be fixed pitch, uni-directional, reversible or controllable pitch. There are also a variety of types of power drives, including electric motor (ac or dc), geared diesel and hydraulic motor. Multiple thruster installations on drill rigs, can contain four, eight or even sixteen thrusters, usually as part of a **dynamic positioning system.** On some offshore support vessels, three azimuthing thrusters, fitted in line athwartships at the stern, have replaced conventional main propeller and stern shafting arrangements.

Thyristor
Transistor in which one of the three electrodes (the control electrode) initiates the main current flow between the other two without limiting it. The device is used as an electronic switch. The terms silicon controlled rectifier and thyristor are synonymous.

Tide
Flow of sea normally occurring twice each lunar day. Flood tide is rising and ebb tide falling. Geographical considerations sometimes engender one tide per day (diurnal) or four tides per day (double).

Tie rods
Long bolts used to hold together the bedplate, **A-frames** and cylinder blocks of a slow speed, two stroke diesel engine.

Tiller
Casting or forging keyed to the **rudder stock** used to turn the rudder.

Time lag
Device for retarding operation of an electrical **circuit breaker** or relay.

Time zone
Time of day adopted locally in a particular geographical zone.

Timing

Point or time in a cycle when a particular operation takes place, such as a valve opening or closing or fuel being ignited by a spark.

Tin (Sn)

Ductile, malleable metal resistant to corrosion and widely used in the marine world, especially in **anti-friction bearing** alloys.

Titanium (Ti)

Ductile metal element (sp gr 4.5) that, when alloyed with small amounts of other elements, has a high strength to weight ratio. It is practically corrosion resistant in sea water.

Toggle

Arrangement consisting of two links hinged at the centre. A force applied at the centre point transmits a force at right angles.

Tolerances

Amount of variation permitted in an object determined by quality requirements and dimensions.

Tom

To exert pressure in a downward direction.

Ton

Imperial measure of mass. One ton equals 2240 lbs or 1016.047 kgs in **SI units.**

Tongs

Hydraulically operated grabs used to hold sections of pipe during screwing or unscrewing operations on an oil rig.

Tonnage

See **deadweight, gross, light displacement, loaded displacement, net** and **registered tonnage.**

Tonnage opening

Permanent opening in the shelter deck of a ship designed so the registered tonnage does not include the shelter deck space. *See* **shelter decker.**

Tonne

Measure of mass in **SI units** (1000kg). Equivalent to 2204 imperial lbs.

Tonnes per centimetre (TPC)

Number of tonnes to be added or deducted from a ship to change the mean draught by one centimetre.

Tons per inch (TPI)
Number of tons to be added or deducted from a ship to change the mean draught by one inch.

Tool joint
Joint or coupling in an offshore drill string.

Tooth
See **teeth, gears** and Figure 1.

Top dead centre (TDC)
Piston position when nearest the cylinder head at the top of its stroke. The crank of the crankshaft for that unit will then be vertical.

Topping wire
Wire rope used to support, raise, lower or fix the position of a boom.

Topside
Portion of the hull above the designed waterline.

Toroid, torus
Magnetic component made in the shape of an anchor ring. Adopted because, with this construction, most of the magnetic field is contained within the core and leakage is minimal, therefore, there is little or no interaction with adjacent components and circuits.

Toroidal winding
Winding formed by coils wound on a magnetic core of annular form so one side of each coil is looped through the ring.

Torque
Product of a turning force. The radius at which it acts is the torque about the axis of rotation, in Nm.

Torque convertor
Device in a drive line providing more or less torque in the driven shaft than in the driving shaft at correspondingly lower or higher rotational speed. The most common types are hydraulically operated.

Torque meter
Test equipment attached to a rotating shaft measuring the angle of twist of a known length of shaft between two gauge points; enables transmitted power to be calculated.

Torque motor
A motor, usually ac, that does not rotate continuously as it is arranged to exert a torque opposing, for example, that of a spring or gyroscope.

Torque tightening
Tightening of screws and nuts to a predetermined torque value to produce the desired **pre-tension** in a machinery assembly.

Torr
The international unit of vacuum measurement. One standard **atmosphere** = 760 torr.

Torsion
State of **strain** caused by twisting. The external twisting effort is opposed by the **shear stresses** induced in the material.

Torsion test
Test where a specimen is fixed at one end and torque load applied axially at the other. The load required to fracture the specimen and the angle of twist can be measured. It is most commonly used for testing bar or wire material for the subsequent manufacture of springs.

Torsional vibration
Cyclical twisting and untwisting of a shaft due to variation in applied **torque.** When the frequency of torque variation coincides with the natural frequency of the shaft system resonance occurs and the **vibration amplitude** builds up to a higher than normal level. This condition is known as **critical speed.**

Torsionmeter
Instrument that measures the power being transmitted by a shaft. With a ship in service it is typically based on using the torque transmitted by a calibrated length of the propeller shaft.

Total energy
Total heat energy available from the combustion of fuel used in an engine. A total energy system is one which attempts to use all waste heat such as that in exhaust gas or cooling water.

Total head
Difference in pressure between the suction and discharge branches of a pumping system, required to produce a flow of liquid. It is expressed as the height of a column of liquid.

Total loss
See **constructive total loss.**

Total resistance
A ship moving in a calm water surface has a number of component resistances collectively forming the total resistance: wavemaking; frictional; form

drag; eddy-making; air and appendage. Skin friction is the resistance due to roughness of the hull or surface of a body in a gas or liquid.

Total static head
Vertical height of a stationary column of liquid produced by a pump, measured from the suction level.

Toughness
Property of a material that combines its **strength** and ability to absorb energy; a quality between **brittleness** and **softness**.

TOVALOP
Tanker Owners Voluntary Agreement Concerning Liability for Oil Pollution.

Towage
Action of a ship being hauled in a seaway by a tug or salvage vessel.

Toxic
Name given to a poisonous substance.

Tracking
Formation of a carbonised conducting path across the surface of an insulated material between electrodes maintained at a **potential difference**. Tracking can be caused by the effect of a high voltage current discharge across the surface, by impingement of a relatively low voltage arc on the surface, or by action of minute leakage currents initiated by the presence of excessive surface moisture or foreign matter.

Tractor tug
Tug with the propellers or propulsion units located beneath the hull, forward of amidships, to pull rather than push the vessel along. Usually propelled by **Voith Schneider** or azimuth units.

Trade winds
Winds that blow steadily towards the equator and are deflected westward by the rotation of the earth. Fairly constant and reliable for long periods.

Tramp ship
A cargo ship not on regular liner trade voyages, scheduled runs or time schedules and not limited to any particular type of cargo other than by the construction of a ship.

Transducer
(1) Electrical device for converting mechanical or thermal stress into an electrical signal to operate a warning lamp indicator or to measure a load/stress.
(2) Part of a **sonar** set or **echo sounder** which transmits or receives the sound signal into or from the sea.

Transductor

Device consisting of one or more ferro-magnetic cores with **windings** by which an alternating voltage or current can be varied by an independent voltage or current that utilises the saturation phenomena in the **magnetic circuit** or circuits. In its usual form, independent (control) windings are energised by dc which, at each half cycle of the ac supply, either assists or opposes the ac. Magnetomotive force and the sum of the two when assisting cause saturation. Device becomes an **amplifier** since a small change in the dc control current can bring about a relatively large change in the output current or voltage. Device is also known as a saturable reactor.

Transfer function

Equation, expressed as a Laplace transform, representing the relationship between output and input for an element or system.

Transformation temperature

In steel heat treatment, the temperature at which a change of phase occurs. Depending on the temperature and its rate of change, different properties can be obtained.

Transformer

Static electromagnetic unit consisting of two **windings** magnetically linked by an iron core so that alternating **electro-motive force (emf)** applied to one of the windings will produce a corresponding **emf** in the other winding; used to convert energy supplied at one voltage into energy supplied at a different voltage. *See* Figure 34.

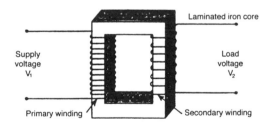

Figure 34 Simple Transformer

Transhipment

Transfer of a cargo from one ship (or means of transport) to another.

Transient

Term applied to the phenomena that takes place in an electrical system due to a sudden changes in conditions persisting for a relatively short time, after the change has occurred, such as transient voltage and transient resistance.

Transient response

Time variation of the output signal that results when an input signal or disturbance of some specific nature has been applied.

Transistor

Semiconductor device capable of providing **amplification** with three or more **electrodes**. Consists of a thin slice of P type or N type semiconductor between two slices of N type or P type semiconductor. The first combination is referred to as an N-P-N device and the second a P-N-P device. The terms P type and N type describe how the charge carriers flow in a semiconductor material; in P type material the hole density exceeds the conduction electron density, whereas in N type material the conduction electron density exceeds the hole density. A non-vacuum electronic device that can replace the thermionic valve.

Transition temperature

Temperature of steel at which a change from **ductile** to **brittle** fracture occurs. Usually determined by taking **charpy** impact tests at different temperatures. Can also be found using **bend tests**.

Transmission

Mechanism for transmitting power from a prime mover to the drive shaft.

Transmission efficiency

Ratio of **delivered power** to shaft power (**horse power**).

Transmitter

Device designed for mounting at or near the point of measurement, to receive the primary measurement signal and generate a related output signal suitable for transmission. Some examples are: **(a)** Electrical component for transmitting the state of a measuring device, such as a fuel gauge, to a suitably scaled indicator. **(b)** Apparatus necessary for producing and modulating radio-frequency current. Includes associated antenna system. **(c)** Cylinder and piston unit in ship's steering gear **telemotor** system which transmits helmsman's wheel orders to rudder.

Transom stern

The **stern** of flat athwartship plates, offering increased deck area in comparison with the cruiser stern.

Transom
After part of a square sterned boat.

Transponder
Small electronic instrument with many uses in the field of offshore drilling such as tracking down divers on the seabed.

Transporting line
Rope from ship to shore **for warping** a ship to change its position.

Transverse
Direction at right-angles to the **centreline** of a ship or an item of structure in this position.

Transverse framing
Stiffening member of a ship's hull, disposed transversely to the logitudinal axis. In **double bottom** construction it is that portion above the tank margin.

Transverse metacentre
See **metacentre** and Figure 12.

Transverse pitch
Distance between the traces of adjacent teeth of a **gear** measured around the reference circle.

Transverse thrust
A thrust at right angles to the motion of a ship. Can refer to the side thrust created by a single propeller when moving a ship forward.

Trap
Geological structure in which **hydrocarbons** build to form an oil or gas field.

Trapezoidal rule
Method of determining the area under a curve by approximating it to a straight line. A number of equally spaced ordinates are then used to form a trapezoid whose area can be found.

TRAPR
*T*ethered *R*emote *A*utomatic *P*ipeline *R*epairs.

Travel
Maximum linear movement of a reciprocating part such as a piston.

Travelling block
Moving pulley system used in conjunction with the (fixed) crown **block** for raising and lowering machinery on a drilling platform, such as the **drill string** and **casing**. *See* Figure 8.

Trawling
Catching fish by dragging a trawl net along the sea bed.

Tread
Length of **keel**.

Trend
Angle between the anchor cable and fore and aft line of a ship.

Triac
Semiconductor device made up of two silicon controlled **rectifiers** connected back to back on a single piece of silicon.

Tri-metal bearings
Steel bearing, such as a diesel engine **crosshead bearing**, to which a tri-metal lining is bonded. Generally comprises a tin (40 per cent), aluminium (60 per cent) main bearing material within the range 0.5 to 1.0 mm thickness, a thin nickel layer (to improve bonding), and a lead (90 per cent), tin (10 per cent), soft overlay, approximately 0.03 mm in thickness. The soft overlay is to assist the initial running in process and plays an important role in determining the formation of an effective oil film thickness. It is important that the overlay is not worn down to the nickel bonding which is hard and can damage the crosshead pin.

Trial condition
Loaded condition specified for a vessel when on sea trials.

Trial trip
Short voyage of newly completed ship to test engines, steering, and deck machinery to verify compliance with specifications. Typically includes speed trials, compass swinging and anchor trials and will be attended by builders, owners, government, and classification surveyors. A more restricted trial can be taken after an extensive refit.

Trial trip rating
Short time rating for an engine when on sea trials.

Triatic stay
Horizontal stay between the caps of two masts or the top of the funnel and the mast. Previously known as a **jumper stay** because of its use when jumping cargo. Blocks on it are used for signal halyards hoisted from the bridge.

Tribology
The study of what happens when surfaces rub together, embracing friction and wear in all their aspects including lubrication, bearing design, and selec-

tion of materials. The term was introduced because other terms already in use only refer to part of the technology of interacting surfaces.

Trickle charge
Steady, low-current charge sufficient to maintain a battery in a fully charged condition.

Trigger pulse generator
Circuit configuration designed to produce pulses of current, such as would change a **thyristor** from the off to on state.

Trim
Inclination of the **keel** in a fore and aft direction. When floating with the keel horizontal a ship is said to be on even keel. When trimmed by the **stern,** a ship is deeper aft and when trimmed by the head it is deeper forward.

Trim indicator
Instrument for measuring and indicating **trim.**

Trimmer
In a coal fired ship, the person who shovels coal from the bunker tanks into a position in the stokehold convenient for the stoker.

Trimming tank
Watertight compartment that can be filled with water ballast to change the trim of a ship.

Trinity House
Institution founded by King Henry VIII and whose powers and privileges are derived from various Acts of Parliament. Concerned with navigational aids, such as lighthouses, lightships, and buoys.

Trip free
Electric **circuit breakers** that are free to open immediately. Tripping power is applied during the period of closing.

Triple expansion engine
Reciprocating steam engine in which three separate expansions, high pressure, medium pressure and low pressure take place.

Triple point of water
Temperature at which ice, water and water vapour are all in **equilibrium** at a pressure of one standard atmosphere in a sealed vacuum flask (triple point cell). *See* **kelvin.**

Triple screw
Ship propelled by three propellers such as the Titanic which had two quadruple expansion steam engines and an exhaust steam turbine each driving their own propeller.

Tripping bracket
Flat bar or plate fitted to a deck girder, stiffener, or beam to reinforce the free edge.

Tripping
(1) Breaking and heaving an **anchor** out of the ground. (2) Opening of an electrical switch.

Troichoid
Curve traced out by a point on the radius of a circle as the circle is rolled along in a straight line.

Tropical draught
Depth of water to which a ship can be immersed in a tropical zone as indicated by the tropical **load line** painted on the side of a ship. *See* Figure 19.

Truck to keel
Mast top to **keel**.

True
(1) The direction of the North Pole where all lines of longitude converge, opposed to the magnetic pole where the compass needle points. (2) Value after errors and adjustments that have been accounted for.

Trundle head
Circular top of **capstan**, with sockets to insert capstan bars.

Trunk
Passage extending through one or more decks to provide access or ventilation to a space.

Trunk piston engine
When the pistons in a reciprocating engine are connected directly to the crankshaft through a connecting rod without a piston rod or crosshead. In this type of engine, the side thrust caused by the angularity of the connecting rod is taken by the piston bearing against the cylinder wall.

Tube expander
Boilermaker's tool consisting of a central tapered mandrel with rollers progressively screwed in and rotated to increase the end diameter of a boiler tube, securing and effectively sealing it in the tube plate.

Tube heat exchanger
Heat exchanger with a tube nest enclosed in a shell. The end plates are sealed at either end with entries made for cooling the water inlet and outlet. Liquid to be cooled is circulated around the tubes.

Tufnol
Synthetic plastic material sometimes used for bearings such as **rudder pintles** and **stern tube bearings.**

Tuftriding
Process of forming a thin hard case on steel by immersion in a liquid salt bath containing cyanides at a temperature of approximately 800°C.

Tug
Vessel designed for towing purposes that is easily manoeuverable with ample engine power. Vary greatly in size from low powered small harbour tug to massive **horse power** deep sea salvage tug.

Tumblehome
Inward curvature of the midship side shell in the region of the upper deck. *See* Figure 6.

Tun
A 225 gallon cask used for the shipment of wine, although there are specialised bulk wine carriers.

Tungsten (W)
Heavy metal element (sp gr 19.3). One of the chief uses is as an alloying addition to steel (12 to 18 per cent) producing high speed steel for cutting tools.

Tuning
Adjustments of the **capacitive** or **inductive resistances** of an electric circuit to values at near **resonance,** giving the required current or voltage in that circuit.

Tunnel
See **shaft tunnel.**

Turbid
Condition of a liquid that is normally clear when a foreign matter becomes suspended in it giving a cloudy appearance.

Turbine
Machine in which rotary motion is obtained by steam, gas or water impinging on a vaned wheel.

Turbine blading, end tight
Method of keeping steam leakage to a tight minimum between the pressure stages of a **turbine.** The shrouding is ground to a knife edge allowing a small axial clearance between the fixed and moving blades. This clearance can be varied, in some cases while manoeuvring, to prevent damage to the blades. The clearance will be adjusted to a minimum after full away to obtain maximum efficiency from the turbine. Movement of the rotor is achieved by means of an adjustable thrust housing.

Turbine drilling
Drilling in which the **drill string** remains stationary, the **bit** being rotated by a down-hole multi-stage turbine powered by the **drilling mud.**

Turbo blower
Multi-stage rotary air compressor; can be powered by electricity.

Turbo charger
Turbine driven air compressor powered by exhaust gases from the parent internal combustion engine. The higher pressure of this air dramatically increases the volume of oxygen available during the engine compression stroke allowing a larger amount of fuel to be ignited and economically combusted increasing the power output of the engine.

Turbo feed pump
Steam turbine driven boiler feed water pump.

Turbometer
Instrument for indicating main engine revolutions. Fitted in an engine room.

Turbulence
Disturbed and irregular movement of a fluid, liquid or gaseous.

Turbulence stimulator
Device fitted to a ship model being tested to ensure that **laminar** flow does not occur on the hull surface. A trip wire or small projecting studs can be fitted at the forward end.

Turbulent flow
Movement of water inside the wake can follow two patterns, **laminar** and turbulent. **Reynolds** investigated the flow of water in pipes, and demonstrated that there are two distinct types of flow. With laminar flow in a straight tube, the particles of fluid move in straight lines parallel to the axis of the tube. In turbulent flow, the motions of the particles are in the form of spiral eddies.

Turn down ratio
Ratio of maximum to minimum flow through a device such as a **fuel burner.**

Turn of the bilge
Curved section between the bottom and side of a ship. *See* Figure 6.

Turnbuckle
Sleeve or link with right and left-handed screw threads at opposite ends fitted with corresponding eye bolts so rotation of the body or sleeve either draws together or separates the eye bolts; used for setting up and retaining tension in shrouds, stays or other rigging.

Turning circle
Standard manoeuvre carried out as a measure of the efficiency of the **rudder;** the circle described by a ship when the **helm** is put hard over, with its diameter the distance from the point at which the turn was initiated and where direction has changed by 180 degrees.

Turning gear
Mechanism for turning the shaft of a machine for overhaul or **setting.**

Tuyere
Nozzle through which air is blown into a furnace, cupola or producer gas generator. Generally cooled by circulating water through passages created for that purpose.

Twaddel hydrometer
Used in testing the strength of tanning extract and density of brine in refrigeration systems, distillers and boilers.

Tween decker
Popular type of general cargo ship with holds divided horizontally by one or more decks, known as **tween decks.** This arrangement allows a wide range of commodities to be carried effectively and safely, normally by stowing heavier, denser cargoes in the lower hold and light cargoes in the upper part of the hold or tween deck. The tween decks have **hatch covers** in the same way as the main deck but very often these are flush with the deck to enable vehicles and fork lift trucks to move easily across them. *See* Figure 13.

Twin screw
Twin propellers, one each side of the centre line aft. Typically, each propeller turns outward. From aft, the port propeller turns counter-clockwise and the starboard propeller clockwise when steaming ahead.

Two step controller
Controller whose output signal changes from one predetermined value to another as a result of the **deviation** changing sign.

Two stroke engine
An **internal combustion engine** where the cycle of operation is completed in one revolution of the crankshaft. Compression takes place soon after the upward stroke of the piston begins when the scavenge and exhaust ports are covered or the exhaust valve closed. At the end of the stroke fuel is injected which then fires. Expansion takes place on the downward stroke until the exhaust ports are uncovered, or the exhaust valve opens, when scavenge air under pressure is admitted. This clears out the burnt gases and leaves clean air ready for the next compression stroke.

Two term controller
Controller providing proportional and either integral or **derivative** action.

U

UHF
*U*ltra *H*igh *F*requency.

ULCC
*U*ltra *L*arge *C*rude *C*arrier. Crude oil tankers above approximately 330 000 Dwt tonnes.

Ullage
Amount of unoccupied space above the contents of a tank or compartment.

Ullage plug
Point where ullage volume is assessed.

Ultimate load
(1) Maximum load a structure is designed to withstand without failure. (2) Product of the limit load and ultimate **factor of safety**.

Ultimate tensile strength (UTS)
Load applied to break a tensile test piece divided by the original cross-sectional area of that test piece.

Ultimate tensile stress
Ratio of the highest load applied to a piece of metal during a tensile test divided by the original cross-sectional area. Also called **tenacity**.

Ultrasonic
Those **frequencies** above the upper limit of normal hearing, at or about 20 k Hz. Low ultrasonic waves at high frequency are used in non-destructive testing to locate defects and cracks in metal.

Ultra violet crack detection
Detection of cracks in metal by coating the metal with a penetrating oil carrying a fluorescent substance that shows up under ultra-violet illumination.

Ultra violet light fluorescence
Emission of light from a **molecule** that has absorbed light. During the interval between absorption and emission, energy is lost and light of a longer wave length is emitted. Oil fluoresces more than water and this becomes a means of detecting it.

Umbilical
Flexible cable or pipe connecting equipment or a diver to a control position in a ship or rig that supplies power, life support or other such services.

Umpire
Person deciding a dispute on a subject of arbitration involving two arbitrators who are unable to agree.

UMS
*U*nattended *M*achinery *S*paces. **Classification society** notation indicating that certain essential operational and safety requirements have been met. The ship may operate for agreed periods with unattended machinery.

Unbalanced rudder
A **rudder** design with no area forward of the turning axis. *See* Figure 4.

UNCLOS
*U*nited *N*ations *C*onference on the *L*aw *O*f the *S*ea

UNCTAD
*U*nited *N*ations *C*onference on *T*rade *A*nd *D*evelopment. Agency of the United Nations whose work in shipping includes the liner code which refers to the sharing of cargoes between the shipping lines of importing and exporting countries.

Unctuousness
Slipperiness of solids which determines the **friction** between them. Depends on the chemical nature of the substances.

Undamped natural frequency
The natural **frequency of oscillation** of a system that would occur if **damping** were reduced to zero.

Under consumption
Amount of fuel used by a ship when it is less than the amount expected or agreed between **shipowner** and **charterer.**

Under cooled graphite
Very fine form of flake graphite in cast irons. Its production is dependent upon metal composition, melting treatment and cooling rate.

Under cooling
Reducing the condensate temperature below that of the steam temperature in a **condenser.**

Under deck tonnage
Volume of a ship between the under surface of the tonnage deck to the top of her **double bottom.** Measured in 100 cu ft per ton.

Under foot
When an anchor cable is approximately vertical under a ship's stern.

Under keel clearance
Minimum distance between the bottom of a ship and a river or sea bed. Required by some authorities as a safety margin due to unseen hazards, climatic changes in water depth or ship **squat.** Also known as **keel** clearance.

Under voltage release
Device causing a **circuit breaker** to open if voltage falls below a predetermined value. The preferred term for no volt release or low volt release.

Underway
Describes a vessel travelling through water that is not anchored, attached to the shore, or aground.

Undercurrent
Current below sea surface that differs in rate or direction from the surface.

Undercut
Groove or channel along toe of **weld** caused by wastage of the parent metal.

Underwriter
One who insures the whole or a percentage of the ship and its cargo against marine risks.

Undulating
Moving or **vibrating** in a wave-like manner.

Uniflow scavenge
Relating to a **two stroke** internal combustion engine. Describes the introduction of pressurised charge air through ports around the bottom of the cylinder

to push the combustion gases straight up the cylinder through the exhaust valve at the top, leaving a charge of fresh compressed air ready for ignition.

Union purchase
A common method of combining two **derricks** for the purpose of loading or discharging cargo from a ship. One derrick is positioned over the hatch, the other over the quay. The two falls are connected together with a cargo hook and once the cargo has been lifted to the necessary height, it is swung by pulling on the ropes of one derrick while releasing the ropes of the other.

Unit
(1) Quantity or value used as a basis for measurement. (2) Equipment assembly such as a fuel oil treatment plant or ship section.

Universal joint
Allows the transmission of power by a shaft at any selected angle. *See* **Hooke's Joint.**

Unmoor (to)
Remove or cast off moorings which attach a ship to the shore.

Unsaturated hydrocarbons
Occurring in **cracked** products, they are **hydrocarbons** that are not satisfied with respect to hydrogen. *See* **cracking.**

Unship
Remove articles or goods from a ship.

Unstable equilibrium
Condition where any change from an existing state of **equilibrium** can result in a loss of control.

Unsymmetrical flooding
When water enters a compartment on one side of a ship causing **heeling** in addition to the effects of **flooding.**

Unworked penetration
Measure of the hardness or consistency of a grease before it has been subjected to **shear** by **working.**

Up and down
Position when an anchor is about to break bottom; information would be passed to the bridge at this stage of weighing the anchor.

Upper critical point
Temperature reached when a microstructure becomes fully **austenitic** when carbon steel is heated above the **lower critical point.** This temperature

depends on the carbon content and ranges from 900–930°C for pure iron and from 695–730°C for steel having a carbon content of 0.85 per cent.

Upper deck
Uppermost continuous deck.

Upper works
All structures above the **freeboard** deck.

Uptake
Metal casing taking **exhaust gases** from the boiler or engine to the funnel and then the atmosphere.

USCG
United States Coast Guard. In addition to traditional coastguard duties, they are responsible for ship safety, including inspections in US waters.

Utilisation factor
Ratio of in-service **stress** to ultimate **stress**. If stress is proportional to load for the material considered, then this factor is the reciprocal of the **reserve factor.**

V

Vac strip pumping
Use of a separator tank, vacuum pump, centrifugal pump and associated equipment to strip the oil from **oil tanker** cargo tanks. Non liquid elements are separated from the oil before they reach pump suction and the pump discharge rate is adjusted to match oil flow to pump suction.

Vacuum
Difference between **atmospheric pressure** and a lower pressure, generally measured in inches or millimetres of mercury (Hg). The **SI unit** is the **pascal (Pa)** and 1 mm Hg = 133.3224 Pa; in practical terms vacuum is the space from which air has been almost exhausted.

Vacuum circuit breaker
When the main current carrying contacts of a **circuit breaker** are enclosed within a highly evacuated envelope.

Vacuum contactor
When the main current carrying contacts of a **contactor** are enclosed in a highly evacuated envelope.

Vacuum distillation
Refinery process carried out under reduced pressure.

Vacuum residue
Residue from refinery vacuum distillation tower enriched in **aromatic** compounds. Often used in fuel oil blending.

Valence
Combining or replacing the power of an **atom** in comparison with standard hydrogen atoms.

Valency
Unit of combining capacity.

$$\text{Chemical equivalent mass} = \frac{relative\ atomic\ mass}{valency}$$

Value analysis
Minimising cost without impairing function by carrying out a systematic examination of products, component by component.

Value engineering
Approach to component design seeking the required quality of work at minimum cost by taking simplicity into account, avoiding unnecessary functions and implementing design and manufacturing techniques to the best advantage.

Valve
(1) In electronics, a glass or metal tube containing a vacuum allowing electric currents to flow between installed **electrodes** without gaseous influence. (2) Device for controlling liquid flow.

Valve bridge
Part of a mechanical valve through which the male threaded valve spindle fits. As the spindle is rotated the valve is raised or lowered via a female thread in bridge. *See also* **male and female.**

Valve, by-pass
Device allowing fluid to bypass a normal path for an alternative route when a preset differential pressure is reached or when actuated manually.

Valve cage
Cylinder fitted with ports in which a **valve disc** moves. Port openings are shaped to produce various flow characteristics for different valves, such as linear or equal percentage.

Valve characteristics
Relationship between valve lift and flow, particularly important when dealing with control valves. The common characteristics are quick opening, linear and equal percentage.

Valve distribution chest
Suction connections are led to each hold or compartment from the main line. Valves are introduced to prevent one compartment being in direct communication with another. Screw-down, **non return valves** are provided.

Valve clearance
Gap between valve stem and rocker arm when valve is fully closed.

Valve disc
Moveable disc reducing or stopping liquid flow by closing on the valve seat. Also known as valve lid and valve plug.

Valve rotator
Device rotating the valve stem of a four stroke diesel engine exhaust valve.

Valve seat
Area inside a valve on which a valve disc or plug sits.

Vanadium (V)
Metal element (sp gr 6.0) added in small quantities to many high strength steels and present in crude oils in various amounts depending on the origin of the crude. Also found in residual fuel oils in various quantities depending on the origin of the crude and the severity of the refinery processing. Combustion appears as vanadium pentoxide V_2O_5 that produces a corrosive slag in boilers and, in association with sodium, may cause corrosion of diesel engine exhaust valves known as hot corrosion.

Vane
(1) One of the elements that variably divides fluid space in a **vane pump**. (2) Another name for blades in turbines, flow metres and other rotary devices.

Vane pump
Assembly in which a **rotor** runs eccentrically within a casing. Several vanes are located in slots within the rotor, free to slide radially. As the rotor turns the vanes move against the casing and pump liquid.

Vapour
Substance in a gaseous state.

Vapour compression cycle
Form of reversed **Carnot cycle** used in refrigeration systems. Refrigerant gas is compressed and condensed then passed through an expansion valve and evaporated before re-entering the compressor.

Vapour lines
Vent pipes from cargo oil tanks leading to pressure/vacuum valves, usually mounted on stand pipes some distance above the deck.

Vapour lock
Condition arising when a gas or vapour is present in the fuel line or fuel pump in sufficient volume to interfere with or prevent the flow of fuel to the engine.

Vapour pressure
Pressure exerted by the vapour from liquid in an enclosed space above the liquid. Vapour pressure, or more precisely the **saturation vapour pressure (SVP)** varies with temperature.

Variable area flow meter
Instrument measuring volume flow rate by reference to area of constriction in a pipeline, when pressure differential is held constant.

Variable fuel injection
Method of varying fuel injection timing when an engine is operating under part load conditions to effect savings in **specific fuel oil consumption (sfoc).**

Variable stroke pump
A **swashplate** hydraulic pump in which the crank throw or swash angle respectively can be varied, allowing the amount of fluid delivered per revolution of the pump to be varied. *See also* **heleshaw.**

Variation
Angle at any position between magnetic north and the true **meridian.**

Variometer
Device for varying **inductance** in an electric circuit composed of two or more coils where the relative position of the coils vary to each other.

Varnish
Thin lacquer found on engine parts, particularly liner surfaces. Composed primarily of organic residues and can increase lubricating oil consumption if not removed.

Vector
Directed line segment that has both **magnitude** and direction.

Veer and haul
To pay or ease out cable and then immediately haul it in. This allows the **windlass** or **winch** to pick up speed.

Veering
Clockwise change in the direction of the wind.

Vegetable oil
Used to blend a special range of lubricating oils because of their ability to form strong emulsion when mixed with water. Ideal for open steam engines and sterntube applications. Most common in the marine industry is rapeseed. *See also* **fatty oils**.

Velocity
Rate of motion in a given direction. **SI unit** is metres per second (m/s).

Velocity ratio
Ratio of the distance moved through by the point of application to the corresponding distance moved by the load.

Velocity compounding
Use of a single nozzle in an **impulse turbine** with an arrangement of several moving blades on a single disc. Between the moving blades are guide blades fastened to the casing so that steam velocity through the turbine is progressively reduced.

Vena contracta
Position where liquid flowing through an orifice contracts to a minimum area downstream; the minimum static pressure position and also the maximum velocity point.

Ventilation
Circulation and refreshing of air in a space while maintaining temperature.

Ventilator cowl
Hood-shaped top to a ventilator, turned into the wind to gather the maximum cooling effect.

Venturi
Restriction or choke in a tube or pipe producing a change in **velocity** and pressure. Technique used in carburetors and **ejectors** to suck out liquids and to measure fluid flows in instruments.

Venturi meter
Instrument for measuring the **velocity** of flow of a liquid.

Vernier
Pair of adjacent scales for determining very small measurements or making adjustments as in a micrometer or timing shaft.

Vertex
(1) Point furthest from base. (2) Meeting point of lines bounding an angle.

Vertical
Perpendicular to the horizontal.

Vertical lift control
Use of **foils** to raise a vessel out of the water, as in **hydrofoil** craft.

Vessel
(1) Refers to any ship larger than a sailboat, rowing boat or similar small craft. (2) Container for holding liquid.

Vessel bridge
Superstructure on upper deck with a clear view forward and to either side from which a ship is conned and navigated. In the three island ship the bridge is amidship and extends out to the ship's side, the side being a continuation of the side shell of the ship. In bulk carriers and oil tankers the bridge is aft. In some special ship types such as drilling and supply vessels, the bridge and control station are forward.

VHF
*V*ery *H*igh *F*requency radio telephony.

Vibrating reed tachometer
Instrument to measure vibrations using a set of thin reeds, each with a different natural **frequency**, fixed at one end. When placed in contact with a rotating machine one reed will vibrate and the speed is read from a scale.

Vibration damper
Device fitted to an engine **crankshaft** to suppress or reduce the stresses resulting from **torsional vibration.**

Vibration measurement
Determination of the **frequency** and **amplitude** of vibration, usually as a means of diagnosing a vibration problem with rotating machinery before damage occurs.

Vibration whipping
Ship struck by a **slamming** force will vibrate in its natural **frequency** and eventually come to rest. High stresses can result from this whipping action, frequently referred to as **whipping** stresses.

Vibrometer
Instrument for indicating variations from the correct balancing of revolving machinery.

Vickers hardness test
Indentation hardness test using a diamond square pyramid indenter which is forced into the prepared surface of an article under a standard load. The load is applied automatically by the machine and the diagonal width of the impression is measured by a microscope attached to the machine. The hardness number may be calculated by dividing the load by the area of the impression or, in practice, by reference to tables.

Victory ship
Prefabricated American built cargo ship of World War II. *See* **Liberty ships.**

Vigia
A danger to navigation that has been notified but not yet charted or confirmed by survey.

Virtual inertia factor
In ship vibration, the total mass being vibrated equals the displacement of the ship plus the mass of surrounding water. The ship displacement may thus be considered to be multiplied by the virtual inertia factor which takes into account the surrounding or entrained water giving the total or virtual mass.

Visbreaking
Thermal cracking process generally following vacuum distillation in oil refining. Significantly reduces the viscosities of vacuum residues by reducing molecular size. Temperature and time are vital process variables.

Viscometer
Instrument to measure the viscosity of oils.

Viscosity
Internal resistance of a fluid to relative movement. Viscosity units commonly used include Redwood, Saybolt Universal, Saybolt Furol and Engler. The most commonly used for fuels and lubricants is kinematic cSt. For fuels, distillates are usually quoted at 40°C and heavier fuels at 50°C. For lubricants the chosen temperature is 40°C.

Viscosity index (VI)
Empirical number indicating the degree of change in an oil's viscosity as temperature changes. The higher the index, the smaller the relative change in viscosity with temperature. A typical diesel engine crankcase oil would have a VI of 98 and an all weather hydraulic oil a VI of 140. Synthetic oils may have a viscosity index well in excess of 140, making them widely used

in the hydraulic systems of ships exposed to worldwide, all season, ambient temperatures.

Viscosity improver

An **additive,** generally a **polymer,** that reduces the variation of viscosity with temperature, increasing the viscosity index of an oil. Susceptible to a reduction in its properties due to **extreme pressure** or **shear.**

Viscous

Possessing viscosity. Frequently used to imply high viscosity.

Visibility

Distance at which an object or light can be seen on a clear dark night with the human eye from 15 ft above the high water level.

VLCC

Very Large Crude Carrier. Refers to crude tankers of 210 000 to approximately 330 000 tonnes. The leap in size from 45 000–70 000 tonne tankers into the VLCC class started when European oil consumption increased eight-fold between 1950 and 1968. New technology involved the introduction of high tensile steel plates and improved corrosion control systems to save weight, large cargo tanks, development of single-screw 27 500 HP turbines with large single boilers, and later, high powered large bore diesel engines.

Voith Schneider Propeller

Form of vertical axis propeller that can provide a variable directional thrust to enable steering. The propeller blades are vertical and of aerofoil shape as shown in Figure 35. *See also* **tractor tug.**

Volatility

Tendency of a liquid to evaporate. High volatility is required in **hydrocarbon** fuels and low volatility is required in lubricating oils.

Volt (V)

Practical unit of **electro-motive force** and **potential difference.** One volt applied steadily to a conductor with a resistance of one **ohm** will produce a current of one **ampere.**

Volt-ampere (VA)

Apparent power in an electrical circuit equal to the product of **root mean square** current and voltage.

Voltage dip

Dip or instantaneous reduction of voltage occurring in an ac generator when a large load current is suddenly applied, such as a large **induction** motor being switched direct-on-line.

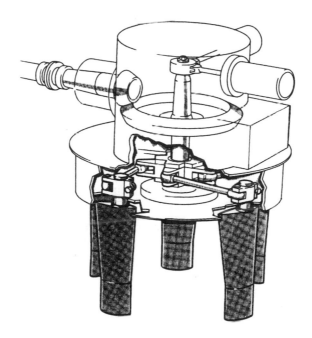

Figure 35 Voth Schneider Propeller
(Courtesy of MJ Gaston, Tugs Today)

Voltage drop
Drop in voltage from source to equipment caused by the **resistance** of cable runs and badly connected cable terminations.

Voltage ratio
In a power transformer, the ratio between the voltage applied at the terminals spanned by higher voltage windings to that between terminals spanned by lower voltage windings at no load.

Voltage regulator
Means for automatically stabilising supply voltage in an ac or dc **generator**.

Voltage striking
Minimum voltage in **arc welding** at which an arc may be struck.

Voltage transformer
A **transformer** that reduces the value of high mains voltage prior to measurement.

Voltmeter
Instrument for measuring voltage.

Volume
Amount of space occupied by a body, measured in cubic metres (m^3).

Volute
(1) Term most commonly applied to springs where successive coils are of progressively increasing or decreasing diameter arranged with some spacing axially. The resulting geometrical arrangement may be described as a conical spiral, or conical helix. It is a spring configuration which results in a spring having a progressively increasing rate with increasing deflection and also facilitates having a large number of coils within a moderate overall length, successive coils being able to enter each other as compression proceeds. (2) Spiral shape; the internal casing shape of a centrifugal pump.

Vulcan clutch
Hydraulic unit for connecting an engine to the propeller shaft. Consists of an outward flow water turbine driving an inward flow turbine fitted in a common casing, similar to a fluid clutch in a motor car.

Vulcanite
Hard vulcanised rubber.

Volumetric efficiency
Efficiency with which a 4-cycle diesel engine replaces the spent gases of combustion with fresh air.

Voyage charter
Contract of carriage. The **charterer** pays for the use of a ship's cargo space for one or more voyage. Under this type of charter, the **shipowner** pays all the operating costs of the ship while port and cargo handling charges are the subject of agreement between the parties.

W

Waist
Upper deck between **forecastle** and **poop**.

Wake
Mass of water carried by a ship in motion with a forward velocity in which the propeller operates, therefore, the speed of the propeller through the wake water is less than the speed of the ship.

Wake friction
Ratio of wake speed to ship speed.

Walking beam
Equipment imparting a vertical, reciprocal motion to the cable tools used in petroleum drilling.

Wall sided formula
Formula relating to the righting lever, **metacentric height,** and the angle of inclination for a vessel of rectangular cross-section when inclined up to approximately 10 degrees.

Wall sided ship
Vessel with vertical sides in the vicinity of the waterline.

Wankel engine
Rotary engine of the **eccentric rotor** type. Only two primary moving parts are present, the rotor and **eccentric shaft.** The rotor moves in one direction around a **trochoidal** chamber which contains intake and exhaust ports.

Ward-Leonard system
Method of regulating the speed and direction of rotation of a dc motor by connecting it to a dc generator and varying, or reversing, the dc motor armature voltage by control of the field current of the dc generator. Widely used in electric **steering gears** and deck machinery.

Warps
Ropes extending from ship to shore to haul a ship into position when docking or changing position without using the engine.

Wash
Waves caused by the passage of a vessel.

Wash bulkhead
Perforated bulkhead fitted into a cargo or deep tank to reduce the sloshing movement of liquid through the tank.

Waste heat
Heat arising from the combustion of fuel in a heat engine that is dissipated without doing useful work. Heat passing out with exhaust gas and cooling water are examples.

Waste heat boiler
Boiler in which steam is raised using the heat of the engine exhaust gases which might otherwise be lost to the atmosphere, usually associated with the diesel engine. *See also* **composite boiler.**

WASP
Wind Assisted Ship Propulsion.

Watches
Periods into which a ship's day is divided for watch keeping duties. Normally of four hour duration, occasionally the 4–8 pm watch may be divided into two periods known as dog watches to allow crew to have a change of watch.

Water ballast
Weight of water carried in **ballast tanks** for stability when a ship is without cargo or carrying reduced cargo.

Water drive
Recovery process where oil or gas is driven out of a **reservoir** by the pressure of the underlying water.

Water gauge glass
Glass tube connected to the outside of a receptacle containing fluid that indicates the fluid level within that vessel.

Water guard
Member of Customs and Excise marine anti-smuggling service.

Water hammer
Percussion in water pipe when tap is turned off suddenly. The velocity of water suddenly retarded can produce enormous pressure. Remedies include air chambers, relief valves or surge tanks in line. A similar effect may become apparent in a steam pipe when live steam is admitted.

Water injection
Process where treated water gets pumped into **reservoir** rock to maintain reservoir pressure.

Water jet propulsion
Where the main engine drives a seawater pump instead of a **propeller,** ejecting a jet of water astern. This form of propulsion is less susceptible to underwater damage, particularly for inshore operation, and is safer if divers or swimmers are involved. Many of the latest fast, gas turbine driven ferries use water jet propulsion.

Waterline
Line on ship's side corresponding to surface of water at a specific draught. *See* Figure 19.

Waterlogged
Ship full of water but still afloat.

Water pocket
(1) Collecting place for water from which it can be drained, such as an air compressor intercooler. (2) Collecting place for water as a result of bad design, which will lead to subsequent corrosion.

Waterplane area
Horizontal section of hull at **waterline** at any particular plane.

Waterplane area coefficient (Cw)
Ratio of the area of waterplane to that of the circumscribing rectangle having a length and breadth equal to that of the ship.

Water pressure test
(1) Testing of a tank or bulkhead by filling it to the maximum working head with water. No leaks must occur, although **deformation** is permitted depending upon the classification of the tank or bulkhead. (2) Testing of a pressure vessel or pipe system using hydraulic pressure to the test pressure laid down by the regulations, which may be several times the working pressure.

Water ring primer
Air pump used to prime **centrifugal pumps**. Can be mounted on top of the pump or stand alone as a separate motor driven unit.

Watertight
(1) Structure that will not admit water from its exterior or permit water which it contains to escape. (2) Applied to electrical apparatus, means that an enclosure is so constructed that water projected from a nozzle in any direction, under specified conditions, will have no harmful effect.

Watertight doors
Doors below the waterline, either vertical or horizontal sliding types, strengthened to withstand full hydraulic pressure when one of the adjoining compartments is completely flooded. Can be operated by power and actuated locally or by remote control.

Watertight subdivision
Dividing up of a ship's hull into a series of watertight compartments by means of watertight bulkheads. *See* **floodable length**.

Water tolerance
Water separation and alkalinity retention characteristics of a lubricating oil. In a marine oil, water tolerance is generally determined in a centrifuge test.

Water treatment
Testing of either drinking or boiler water to determine the amount of chemicals needed to maintain the water at the required level of purity.

Watertube boiler

Steam boiler in which the heating surface consists almost entirely of an array of tubes connecting a steam drum at the top with one or more water drums or headers at the bottom. The arrangement promotes circulation of the cooler water downwards so the hottest water and steam go upwards through the relevant tube stacks.

Waterwall

Sides forming the walls of modern **water tube boilers** consisting of a bank of tubes encased in refractory material. The tubes are part of the boiler water circulating system acting as downcomers.

Water washing

Spraying gas turbine blades with fresh water to remove any combustion deposits.

Watt (W)

An **SI unit** of power and standard unit of measurement of electrical power. Amperes multiplied by volts of a dc circuit form the calculation to determine the power used by the circuit in watts.

1 hp = 746 watts   1 kW = 1.34 hp

Wattmeter

Instrument for measuring the power in watts of an electrical circuit. In one form it works on the principle of the Siemens' **dynamometer,** consisting of a fixed coil of fine wire and a moving coil of thick wire. The two coils, at right angles to each other and connected in **series,** develop a **torque** between them when either direct or alternating current is passed through them. This is measured by the **torsion** of a spring, the **torque** being directly proportional to the watts (product of amperes and volts) in the circuit.

Wave spectra

The energy content of waves in a sea is shown in the wave spectra. The energy content of a wave is proportional to the height squared. Wave height is in turn dependent upon wind speed, the direction of the wind and the distance over which the wind has been blowing. Several formulae exist for the determination of wave spectra each taking into account the above factors in various different ways. Typical wave heights using a similar scale to the Beaufort scale for wind are as follows:

Code	Description	Max Height in feet
0	Glassy Calm	0
5	Rough	8-13
9	Phenomenal	Over 45

Wave Resistance

As a ship moves through water it creates a wave system or resistance around itself that is the complex result of varying pressures below the surface of the water. It commences with a heaping up of water ahead and to each side of the bows followed by alternate crests and troughs along the sides, and finally leaves an area of eddies behind the stern. The total wave resistance is a combination of skin friction and the speed of a ship through water. As speed increases the waves become higher, therefore, a greater part of the resistance is accounted for by the speed.

Wave winding

Distributed winding of a rotating electrical machine with a sequence of connections causing it to progress in one direction around a machine by passing successively under each main pole of the machine. Generally used for **series** or series **parallel** windings.

Wax

Solid **hydrocarbon** present in some crude oils, especially in paraffinic crudes. Wax deposits itself in pipelines and equipment which can cause mechanical problems.

Wear

Progressive loss of substance from the operating surfaces of a body occurring as the result of relative motion at the surface. Wear is usually detrimental, however, can be beneficial under certain circumstances such as running in. Includes mechanical, chemical and thermal effects.

Wear debris

Particles becoming detached in the wear process.

Weardown

Wear to the main bearings of an engine allowing the shaft to drop below its design level.

Weardown gauge

Instrument used to measure the weardown of a bearing.

Wear test

Specimens may be rubbed together under a given load to measure the amount of material removed from the surfaces in contact after a given time. It is an empirical test which varies in type for specific conditions.

Weather bound

Confined to port or harbour due to the weather.

Weather deck
Uppermost continuous deck.

Weather routing
Use of meteorological and oceanographical information to determine the most favourable route, in terms of good weather, for ocean crossings by ships or valuable tows.

Weather side
Side of the ship to **windward**.

Weather window
Estimate of the number of days when the weather should be good enough to perform a critical offshore task such as installing a production platform.

Weathertight
Means of closure that will stop the penetration of water regardless of the sea conditions.

Weathertight door
Door fitted in a structure above the **freeboard** deck. It must be of adequate strength to maintain the **watertight** integrity of the structure.

Web
To provide extra strength to a hull or engine structure using a plate, flanged or otherwise stiffened on its edge.

Web frame
Deep-section built-up **frame** providing additional strength to the structure.

Weigh anchor
To lift **anchor** off the sea bed.

Weight
Resultant force of attraction on the mass of a body when subjected to the gravitational field of another body.

Weld decay
Term for a defect that may occur as a result of welding **austenitic** chromium steels. In the region of the parent metal adjacent to the actual welds, the temperature attained may favour the formation of chromum carbide at grain boundaries. This can only occur by the removal of chromium from the adjacent crystal zones, and those areas lose their corrosion resistance.

Welding
(1) Joining two metals by the application of heat and/or pressure.

Arc welding. Melting the metals by heat from an electric arc.

Gas welding. Melting by heat from a gas burning torch.

Resistance welding. Passing electric current between metals to generate heat by the resistance of the junction.

Friction welding. Generating heat by rotating one metal and pressing it against the other.

Plasma welding. Volatilisation of the depositing metal in a plasma arc.

Electron beam welding. Melting the metals in a vacuum by focusing a beam of electrons at the joint.

(2) In tribology, adhesion that occurs between solid surfaces in direct contact at any temperature.

Well
(1) Open deck space between **erections**. (2) Space into which bilge water drains. (3) Offshore borehole that is producing or expected to produce oil or gas.

Well bore
Hole in the rock made by the drill bit.

Well deck ship
See **Three Island Ship.**

Well head
Control equipment fitted to the top of a well casing, incorporating outlets, valves, and blowout preventers.

Well logging
Comprehensive record of all data collected during the drilling of a well, allowing a highly detailed picture of the **strata** to be built up.

WEMT
West European Confederation of Maritime Technology Societies.

Wet bulb temperature
Temperature measured by a thermometer; the bulb is kept moist by a water soaked wick.

Wet liner
Removable cylinder barrel, sealed at both ends against surrounding coolant, in a cylinder block. The centre section has water circulating round it.

Wet natural gas
Natural gas containing large amounts of associated liquids.

Wet steam
Steam containing fine particles of water in suspension, not heated enough to convert to dry steam.

Wet sump
Lower half of an engine crankcase into which the lubricant drains and is then re-circulated.

Wet weight
Weight of a bulk cargo including its moisture content.

Wetted surface
The part of the external hull in contact with water.

Wet tree
Subsea wellhead where the equipment is exposed to the sea.

Whaleback
Vessel where the deck of the **poop** has a pronounced **camber** to the ship's side.

Wharf
Building constructed along the shore for loading and unloading ships. Also for fitting out and repairs.

Wheatstone bridge (l)
(1) Instrument measuring electrical resistances. A network of resistances connected as shown in Figure 36. When the **galvanometer (G)** shows no deflection, the current in the four arms is balanced and R1/R2 = R3/R4. Rl and R2 are resistances of known value, R3 is a variable resistance, and R4 is an unknown resistance. If R3 is adjusted until the galvanometer shows no resistance, the value of R4 can be calculated using the above formula. **(2)** Technique used for monitoring flammable compounds in the atmosphere. The resistance of an active element on which controlled combustion takes place is compared with an inactive element, the pair being part of a Wheatstone bridge.

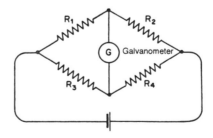

Figure 36 Wheatstone Bridge

Wheel house
Erection on navigating bridge deck containing steering wheel. Also the centre for other purposes connected with the navigation and control of the ship.

Wheft
Any flag tied half way along the fly, or with the fly tied to the staff.

Whelps
Projections on the warping ends (drums) of **windlasses** or **capstans** to prevent heaving ropes from slipping.

Whip
Rope and pulley hoisting apparatus.

Whipstock
Wedge shaped piece of equipment placed at the bottom of a well forcing the **bit** and **drill pipe** to deviate from their original direction when drilling is resumed.

Whirling
Resonant transverse **vibration** of a rotating shaft.

Whipping
(1) Transient response caused primarily by wave impact. Fast ships having small **block co-efficients** and large bow flare are particularly susceptible to this type of wave induced stress. Even in the case of a **hogging** ship, compressive bending moments can be induced in the deck. (2) Twine or similar material passed round the end of a rope to prevent it unlaying.

Whistle
Ship's audible indicator, usually affixed to the forward funnel. It can produce short or long blasts and is a requirement of international regulations.

White Ensign
Ensign flown by all British Royal Navy ships and establishments. Red Ensign is flown by British merchant ships and Blue Ensign by the **Royal Fleet Auxiliary** and certain merchant ships commanded by Royal Navy Reserve officers.

White horses
Waves with white foam or **spindrift** at their crests.

White layer
(1) Comparatively soft layer under 25 microns thick present on nitrided components. (2) Term applied to a hard layer formed by scuffing on cast iron.

White metal

Alloy used as anti friction lining for bearings. Consists of tin, copper, antimony, and lead.

WIG

Wing-In-Ground effect craft. Form of high speed (500 km/h) conveyance combining sea and air technology. **WIG** craft fly just above sea level generating their lift from an air cushion created by the ground effect; described as an increase in the lift-to-drag ratio of a lifting system at small relative distances from an underlying surface. First introduced by Russia. **IMO** is devising a code for such craft. *See also* **Ekranoplans.**

Wildcat well

Exploration well drilled with little knowledge of the contents of the underlying rock structure.

Winch

Machine using the winding or unwinding of rope or wire around a barrel for various cargo and mooring duties.

Windage loss

Power loss in a **steam turbine** due to the astern turbine blading churning steam within the casing.

Winding

Wires around the stators and rotors of electric motors forming the circuits and magnetic fields through which the electrical current flows. Can be **shunt, series** or compound wound in dc motors. In an ac alternator it can be star or delta wound. *See* Figure 34.

Windlass

Machine used to hoist and lower the **anchor.**

Windsail

(1) Canvas funnel conveying air to lower parts of a ship. It is fitted with hoops to maintain its shape and can be used to blow out gas fumes. **(2)** Name sometimes given to a modern passenger or cargo combined powered/sailing ship, where the sails are canvas or plastic or metal framed, moved by a hydraulic mechanism controlled by computer.

Windward

Towards the direction from which the wind is blowing.

Winter draught

Depth of water a ship's hull may be immersed in a winter zone at certain times of the year. The depth is indicated by the **winter load line** painted on the ship's side as shown in Figure 19.

Wire drawing

Effect produced when steam is throttled by valves or in engine cylinders. Takes place when passages are contracted so that the rate of the entering steam is less than that required by a piston towards the end of its stroke.

Wireline

Wire or cable used when drilling an offshore **borehole**.

Wiring diagram

Drawing showing detailed wiring and connections between items of electrical equipment. Can also show the routing of connections.

Work

A form of **energy**. The **SI unit** is the joule (J), 1 Joule = 1 Newton metre (Nm).

Worked penetration

Measure of the hardness or consistency of a **grease** after having been worked a specified amount.

Work hardening

Improving the **hardness** and strength of steel by mechanical working in a cold state.

Working

(1) In reference to materials, an implied movement leading to opening of joints or fatigue failure of metals. (2) In reference to machinery or manpower, some productive useful operation. (3) Subjecting a lubricating grease to any form of agitation or shearing action.

Working pressure

The normal working pressure of a machine, as distinct from its test or maximum working pressure.

Workover

When a completed production well is subsequently re-entered and any necessary cleaning, repair and maintenance work carried out.

Worldscale

Widely used scale to quote tanker freight rates enabling shipowners to easily compare returns on like voyages. The figure 100 is prefixed by W and allocated to a hypothetical return per ton of cargo using a ship of 75 000 tonnes deadweight as a base on each of a number of standard routes, allocating a return in U.S. dollars on each route. For example, if the W100 chosen is $10 a tonne and a shipowner negotiates for $11, the rate quoted is W110. Similarly, if a rate of $9 is obtained, W90 will be quoted. The W100 is variable dependent on time, size of ship, bunker price, and other such considerations.

Worm gear
Toothed wheel worked by revolving spiral. Single or multi-start threads on the worm engage with shaped teeth on the periphery of the worm wheel, the axes of worm and wheel generally being at right angles. Rotation of the worm pulls or pushes the teeth of the wheel causing rotation. A useful form of gearing where large reduction ratios are required in a single stage, also when non-reversibility is important, such as when a gun mounting fires.

Woodruff key
Semi-circular key for connecting coupling to shaft. Keyway in shaft is milled by cutter of same radius as key with normal keyway in coupling or hub.

WOW
Waiting On Weather.

Wrought iron
Iron produced by a variety of methods, characterised by the use of temperatures which are too low to result in melting, the metal being sufficiently hot to be soft and plastic.

X

X-ray
Electromagnetic radiation with wavelengths between **ultraviolet** and **gamma** radiation. X-ray equipment can be used to check the quality of welds.

Y

Yard
(1) Cylindrical spar tapering at each end. (2) Enclosed site used for ship-building.

Yaw
Said of a ship that fails to steer a straight course.

Yawing
Term used to describe the rotation about a vertical axis. One of the six degrees of freedom. *See* Figure 15.

Y connection
See **star connection**.

Yield value
Minimum shearing stress required to produce continuous **deformation** in a solid, measured in dynes per square centimetre.

Yield point
Minimum stress required to produce **strain** or flow in a plastic material. In a tensile test the stress level at which **deformation** of the test piece first occurs without increasing the load is known as the **yield point** or yield stress. Not all materials exhibit a **yield point** in tensile testing.

Yoke
(1) Crossbar of rudder on a pulling boat. (2) Coupling piece of two pipes discharging into one. (3) Main frame of an electric motor made of cast or rolled steel, to which field coils and motor feet are attached.

Young's Modulus (E)
The **modulus of elasticity**. Ratio of **stress(σ)** to **strain(ε)**. The amount of elastic stress produced in a material by a given load can be calculated if the **modulus of elasticity** is known.

$$E = \frac{direct\ stress\ (\sigma)}{direct\ strain\ (\varepsilon)} = \frac{load/area}{extension/original\ length}$$

Z

ZDDP
Zinc DialkylDithioPhosphate or Zinc DiarylDithioPhosphate. Widely used as an anti-wear agent in marine lubricants.

Zechstein
Geological formations containing salt laid down in the second part of the **Permian** period which has risen up under or through the overlying formations producing a salt pillow and/or salt dome traps.

Zener diode
A **diode** across which the voltage drop is constant over a range of current. Used to provide a stabilised voltage in some circuits.

Zenith
Point in the heavens vertically above an observer.

Zero
Starting point in scales from which positive and negative quantities are measured.

Zig zag
Short alternate turns to the right and left. A ship might steer a **zig zag** course in wartime to deter submarine attacks.

Zinc (Zn)
Hard white metallic element with good resistance to atmospheric corrosion. Used as a coating for steel in **galvanising** and is contained in many alloys.

Zinc chromate
Certain pigments in paints confer protection from corrosion on steel. Red lead and Zinc chromate, a cathodic inhibitor, are good examples of this.

Zirconium (Zr)
High melting point metal element (sp gr 6.5) used in some light alloys. The oxide, zirconia (ZrO_2) is extremely hard and refractory.

Zone
Division or area on a surface, especially on the surface of a sphere. The earth is divided into five zones; arctic, antarctic, temperate north, temperate south, and tropics.

Zones
Sections into which the hull, superstructure and deck houses are divided, for fire resisting purposes, by **bulkheads** and decks capable of preventing the passage of smoke and flame for a specified period under a standard fire test.

ILLUSTRATIONS

APPENDIX 1 - Elemental Symbols and Weights

Element	Symbol	Atomic Weight	Element	Symbol	Atomic Weight
Aluminium	Al	27.1	Manganese	Mn	54.9
Antimony	Sb	120.2	Mercury	Hg	200.6
Barium	Ba	137.3	Molybdenum	Mo	95.9
Bismuth	Bi	208.0	Nickel	Ni	58.7
Boron	B	10.8	Nitrogen	N	14.0
Cadmium	Cd	112.4	Oxygen	O	16.0
Calcium	Ca	40.1	Phosphorus	P	31.0
Carbon	C	12.0	Platinum	Pt	195.2
Chlorine	Cl	35.5	Potassium	K	39.1
Chromium	Cr	52.0	Silicon	Si	28.3
Cobalt	Co	58.9	Silver	Ag	107.8
Copper	Cu	63.5	Sodium	Na	23.0
Helium	He	4.0	Sulphur	S	32.0
Hydrogen	H	1.0	Tin	Sn	118.7
Iron	Fe	55.8	Titanium	Ti	47.9
Lead	Pb	207.2	Tungsten	W	184.0
Lithium	Li	6.9	Vanadium	V	50.9
Magnesium	Mg	24.3	Zinc	Zn	65.3

APPENDIX 2 – Conversion Factors

Length
1 km = 0.53961 U.K. nautical mile
1 km = 0.53996 International nautical mile
1 m = 0.54681 fathom
1 m = 3.2808 ft
1 mm = 0.039370 in
1 mm = 0.039370 mil

Area
1 m2 = 10.764 ft2
1 mm2 = 0.0015500 in2

Volume
1 m3 = 35.315 ft3
1 l = 0.21998 gal

Section Modulus
1 m cm2 = 0.50853 in2 ft
1 cm3 = 0.061024 in3

Second moment of area
1 m2 cm2 = 1.6684 in2 ft2
1 cm4 = 0.024025 in4

Frequency
1Hz = 1 c/s

Speed
1 km/h = 0.53961 U.K. knot
1 km/h = 0.53996 International knot
1 m/s = 3.2808 ft/s

Acceleration
1 m/s2 = 3.2808 ft/s2

Mass
1 tonne = 0.984207 ton
1 kg = 2.2046 lb

Specific volume
1 m3/tonne = 35.881 ft3/ton
1 l/kg = 0.016018 ft3/lb

Mass flow
1 tonne/h = 0.98421 ton/h
1 kg/h = 2.2046 lb/h

Volume flow
1 m3/min = 35.315 ft3/min
1 m3/h = 3.6662 gal/min
1 l/h = 0.21998 gal/h

Density
1 g/cm3 = 0.036127 lb/in3
1 g/l = 0.062428 lb/ft3

Moment of inertia
1 kg m2 = 23.730 lb ft2
1 kg cm2 = 0.34172 lb in2

Momentum
1 kg m/s = 7.2330 lb ft/s

Moment of momentum and angular momentum
1 kg m2/s = 23.730 lb ft2/s

Force
1 kN = 0.10036 tonf
1N = 0.22481 lbf

Moment of force
1 kN m = 0.32927 tonf ft
1 N m = 0.73756 lbf ft

Pressure
1 MN/m2 = 9.8693 atm
1 MN/m2 = 145.04 lbf/in2
1 kN/m2= 0.29530 in Hg
1 kN/m2 = 4.0147 in w.g.
1 N/m2 = 10 dyne/cm2
1 bar = 105 N/m2 = 14.504 lbf/in2

Stress
1 N/mm2 = 0.064749 tonf/in2
1 N/mm2 = 145.04 lbf/in2

Absolute or dynamic viscosity
1 cP = 10 -3 N s/m2
1 kg/m s = 0.67197 lb/ft s

Kinematic Viscosity*
1 cSt = 10-6 m2/s
1 m2/s - 10.764 ft2/s

Energy (work, heat)
1 kWh = 1.3410 hp h
1kJ = 0.94782 Btu
1 J = 0.73756 ft lbf

Power
1 kW = 1.3410 hp
1 W = 0.73756 ft lbf/s
1W = 3.4121 Btu/h

Fuel Consumption Rate
1 kg/kWh = 1.6440 lb/hp h

Absolute temperature
oF = 9/5 K – 459.7
oR = 9/5 K

Celsius temperature
oF = 9/5 oC + 32

Temperature interval (oC)
1oC = 9/5oF

Linear expansion coefficient
1 oC -1 = 5/9 oF-1

Heat flow rate
1 kW = 0.94782 Btu/s

Specific energy, calorific value, specific latent heat
1 kJ/kg = 0.42992 Btu/lb

Specific Heat Capacity
1 kJ/kg oC = 0.23885 Btu/lb oF

Specific entrophy
1 kJ/kg K = 0.23885 Btu/lb oR

Density of heat flow rate
1 W/m2 = 0.31700 Btu/ft2 h

Volumetric heat release rate
1 W/m3 = 0.096622 Btu/ft3 h

Coeficient of heat transfer
1 W/m2 oC = 0.17611 Btu/ft2 h oF

Thermal Conductivity
1 W/m oC = 6.9335 Btu in/ft2 h oF

Prefixes (in order of magnitude)

tera	T	=1012
giga	G	=109
mega	M	=106
kilo	k	=103
hecto	h	=102
deca	da	=10
deci	d	=10-1
centi	c	=10-2
Milli	m	=10-3
Micro	m	=10-6
Nano	n	=10-9

Unchanged factors
Plane angle
Angular velocity
Time
Angular acceleration.
Rotational speed.

*Diagrams for converting Redwood and Saybolt seconds, Engler degrees, and Barber Fluidity are given in standard textbooks, e.g. H.M. Spiers' *Technical Data on Fuel*.

APPENDIX 3

1. ISO & SAE Lubricant Viscosity Classifications

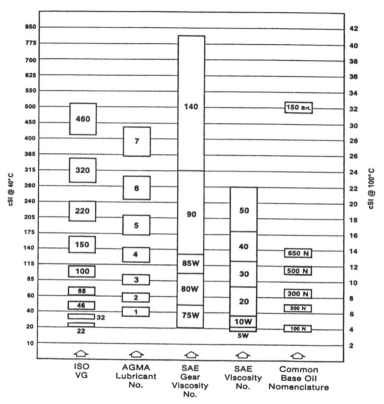

2. NLGI Grease Classifications

NLGI Number	Worked Penetration at 25°C
000	445 – 475
00	400 – 430
0	355 – 385
1	310 – 340
2	265 – 295
3	220 – 250
4	175 – 205
5	130 – 160
6	85 – 115

To receive a copy of our latest Publications Catalogue
containing details of all publications available from
The Institute of Marine Engineers, please contact:

Publication Sales Administrator
The Institute of Marine Engineers
The Memorial Building
76 Mark Lane
London, EC3R 7JN

Publications
from the
Institute of
Marine
Engineers

• Books covering a
wide range of subjects
relating to maritime &
offshore engineering
• IMarE Conference
proceedings

• Journals, namely MER
& The Journal of
Offshore Technology
• Electronic Publications
on CD-ROM
• Transactions (the
above four items by
subscription only).

Notes

Notes

Notes

Notes

Notes